GEOPOLITICS

PAST, PRESENT AND FUTURE

GEOFFREY PARKER

PINTER
London and Washington

PINTER
A Cassell Imprint
Wellington House, 125 Strand, London WC2R 0BB, England
PO Box 605, Herndon, Virginia 20172, USA

First published 1998

British Library Cataloguing in Publication Data
A catalogue record for this book is available from the British Library
ISBN 1 85567 398 3 (Hardback)
     1 85567 397 5 (Paperback)

Library of Congress Cataloging-in-Publication Data
Parker, Geoffrey, 1933–
     Geopolitics : past, present and future / Geoffrey Parker
       p.   cm
     Includes bibliographical references and index.
     ISBN 1-85567-398-3 (hardcover). – ISBN 1-85567-397-5 (pbk.)
     1. Geopolitics.   I. Title.
JC319.P268   1997
320. 1 ' 2–dc21   97-13907
                                                                        CIP

Typeset by BookEns Ltd, Royston, Herts.
Printed and bound in Great Britain by
Biddles Ltd, Guildford and King's Lynn.

CONTENTS

FIGURES

TABLES

PREFACE

A British geographer once commented that French geography textbooks appeared to have little knowledge or concern with what happened to the Rhine above Basle or below Lauterbach, that is to say when it was no longer a part of the French hexagon. No doubt this same comment could be made about the 'nationalisation' of geography in many other countries. It applied most of all in the field of geopolitics, which has been that branch of the subject most closely associated with politics and political decision-making. Indeed, during the first half of the twentieth century geopolitics came to be regarded by many geographers and political scientists as being far too closely involved with policy to be considered to be a really objective discipline in its own right. Matters to do with the interface of geography and politics were therefore grouped together under the safer umbrella of political geography.

In recent years there has been a greatly renewed interest in geopolitics in many Western countries and — together with its associated adjective 'geopolitical' — it has come to be used in discussions on a wide range of contemporary issues. While there are many reasons for this new interest, underlying it has been a growing concern with the earth as a whole. Since the 1970s there has been an increased consciousness both of the unity and the fragility of the planet which is the home of mankind, and political decision-making has been an important aspect of this.

Holistic thinking has thus come to be seen as being not only desirable but essential if the human race is to survive at all. While such thinking has been widely spread across the disciplines, geography, equipped as it is to deal with the interactions of terrestrial phenomena, has been a particularly important vehicle for it. Holistic thinking has also entered the realm of international politics, replacing those national and nationalist perspectives which saw the earth as being little more than the theatre in which the all-important states played out their various destinies. The new geopolitics represents the application of geography and the geographical method to international questions. However, it has its being less in the *Realpolitik* of the past than in the environmentalism which is concerned with understanding the earth as a totality and the provider of humankind with its sustenance. It is particularly concerned with such issues as the use of physical resources, the impact of political decision-making on the environment and the organisation and apportionment of geographical space. It is also concerned with the relationship of the political organisation of the earth to its human and cultural diversity.

The basic purpose of the book is to examine the origins of geopolitics, to trace its development and, finally, to consider its future role. The conceptual basis of geopolitical thinking is always kept in mind and is explained using appropriate terminology. A wealth of useful information on terms, concepts and the major geopolitical thinkers themselves is to be found in the *Dictionary of Geopolitics*, edited by John O'Loughlin (Greenwood Press, 1994).

I wish to thank all those who have given me such valuable support and advice during the writing of this book. My thanks go particularly to those who have given permission for their maps and diagrams to be reproduced. All are specified in the Acknowledgements. I also wish to express my thanks to my publishers for the help and support which they have accorded to me during the writing of the book.

Most of all I wish to record my indebtedness to my wife Brenda, who, despite having so many other commitments of her own, has made time to give me invaluable advice and assistance with the manuscript and is responsible for preparing the index.

Geoffrey Parker
Lichfield, 1997

ACKNOWLEDGEMENTS

Grateful thanks is given to the following for permission
to reproduce the material below:

The Geographical Association   Figure 7.2

Dr Arno Peters   Figure 8.3b

Professor Saul B. Cohen   Figure 8.5

CHAPTER 1

TERMS IN THEIR TIMES: POLITICAL GEOGRAPHY AND GEOPOLITICS

'Geopolitics is *à la mode*,' wrote Paul Claval in 1994, whereas the great ideologies had become *'passées de mode'*. The wind had changed: after having been virtually banned from intellectual life for decades following World War II, geopolitics had returned (Claval, 1994: 3). Claval attributes this reversal of fortune to the changing world situation as the Cold War moved towards its conclusion and the outlines of the new global scenario began to take shape. The collapse of the Eastern bloc followed by the end of superpower confrontation had created a climate in which, Claval asserted, 'reflection on geopolitical and geostrategic problems [became] more than ever essential' (*ibid.*).

The term 'geopolitics' was coined in the late nineteenth century, and from the outset it attracted considerable controversy. This was caused by its supposed involvement in actual matters of national policy, something which caused particular concern to academics. After World War I, in Germany geopolitics became very involved in national policy and subsequently in the rationalisation and planning of the policy of territorial expansion and the justification of Nazi claims to a position of dominance in Europe. As a result of this, after the end of World War II German *Geopolitik* was lumped together with the rest of the ideological baggage of Nazism and the whole lot was banished. This inevitably had adverse repercussions on the subject elsewhere, and these were to last for a generation.

The return of geopolitics took place during the 1970s, the 'new geopolitics' being pioneered in the United States and France. In the former it was particularly associated with American Secretary of State Henry Kissinger, who introduced it into his foreign policy discourse (O'Loughlin and Nijman, 1994: 137–8). With Kissinger's seal of approval, geopolitics, together with its associated adjective 'geopolitical', then rapidly entered the established vocabulary of politics and international relations in the United States. In France at around the same time it was being reintroduced by a new school of political geographers led by Yves Lacoste. This centred on the journal *Hérodote*, and it was only after geopolitics had regained its academic credentials that it entered the general political vocabulary in France (Parker, 1994d: 146).[1]

The reasons for the return of geopolitics at this particular time can be traced to a certain serendipidity in the convergence of political semantics and international relations. Semantically, it is a term which expresses a particular relationship between political activity and the terrestrial environment in which this activity is taking place. It might be speculated that, as with Voltaire's God, had there been no geopolitics in the 1970s, it would have been necessary to invent it or something very similar to it. By the 1980s politicians, journalists, businesspeople and academics of all descriptions in the francophone and anglophone worlds were slipping it into speeches, articles and books on subjects ranging from global warming to multinational firms. In such a variety of contexts its precise meaning or, indeed, its relevance to particular situations, was often far from clear. However, in the conditions of rapid international change, this lack of precision may have been one of its particular attractions. Its precise meaning in any particular situation has often appeared to matter less than the fact that it is one of those terms which is instinctively felt to have a relevance to the times; it is a term which sets the scene, as it were, for the tone of contemporary discourse. It is a term which fits its time.

While the fact that geopolitics has become *à la mode* can in part be explained by the complete alteration in the international situation, even more significant have been the dramatic changes which have taken place in the perception of the overall relationship of humanity to its geographical environment. This change has been so all-embracing that it has virtually been on the scale of a holistic paradigm shift. Since the 1970s the idea of mankind as 'master' capable of transforming nature has been increasingly replaced by that of humankind as a 'participant' in an environmental totality, and as such having to treat nature with care and respect. The realisation dawned that the global ecosystem is a fragile and finely balanced structure susceptible to irreparable damage. The industrial developments which took place during the period from the 1950s to the early 1970s, especially those associated with the supply of energy and the related expansion in the mass use of the internal combustion engine, demonstrated all too clearly that a radically changed approach was needed in order to stop the environmental degradation which was demonstrably taking place at an accelerating pace. Put at its starkest, the switch which has taken place in thinking, particularly in the West, since the 1970s has been from the idea that humankind is capable of everything to the idea that, in the longer term, humankind may be capable of very little except the destruction of the planet. This was the essence of the situation identified by Johnson and Taylor as indicating 'a world in crisis' (Johnson and Taylor, 1989).

A consequence of these new perceptions is that the environmental politics of control have increasingly been giving place to those of concern. While this represents a revolutionary change from the triumphalist humanism of the earlier twentieth century, it is less revolutionary in terms of geographical philosophy. The effects of the holistic paradigm shift have been to bring geographical thinking on the relationship of humanity and environment to the fore. It has been increasingly realised that to be successful humanity must act within the constraints of the environment and be aware both of its limitations and of its possibilities. Such environmental awareness was inherent in that 'possibilism' which was developed and refined by the French *vidalien* school of geographers in the first half of the century. This was founded on the proposition that collective human action is circumscribed by the possibilities afforded by the environment and that success can be achieved only by making the right choices from among these possibilities rather than by attempting to ignore them.[2] As Francis Bacon put it, in order to conquer nature it is first necessary to obey her (Bacon, 1924). This is was something which was forgotten, or ignored, throughout most of the twentieth century by those who saw 'development' as being all and 'nature' as being something which was waiting to be 'altered' so as to make it more useful for the Lords of Creation.

The new earth consciousness has increased considerably since the end of the Cold War and has manifested itself both in direct environmental concerns and in the awareness of the significant role which political decision-making needs to play. The obvious devastation caused by much of that human activity which for half a century has been given the overall collective label of 'development', together with such associated events as the Chernobyl nuclear disaster of 1986, have had the effect of reinforcing the unease about the general direction in which humankind is moving. Environmental degradation, much of it clearly attributable to human activity, has increased a consciousness of the essential unity of the planet and the dangers of what Bunge referred to collectively as 'the destruction of human space' (Bunge, 1989: 355–7). In this view destruction can be prevented only by collective action, and in today's world this of necessity means action on a global scale. Bunge concluded that 'this planet is not too small for peace but it is too small for war' (*ibid.*).

Thus a major feature of the holistic paradigm shift is that the earth sciences have moved to the fore, and this has inculcated that intellectual climate in which 'geo' has become an in-word. As a prefix it emphasises the consciousness of the environment present in a particular discourse and as a prefix to politics it implies the necessity for political action to take the global dimension into account.

The widespread revival in the fortunes of geopolitics stands in marked contrast to the situation in the recent past. 'Of all the topics of study in political geography,' asserted Brunn and Mingst, 'probably none has attracted as much controversy as geopolitics' (Brunn and Mingst, 1985: 41). The reasons for this they attributed, in the way which had become accepted since the 1940s, to its manipulation during World War II. This had certainly been the case, but it was only part of the story. While the immediate cause of the banning of geopolitics from intellectual life was without doubt to be found principally in its Nazi associations, there were longer-term causes for the doubts which it raised. In order to appreciate how such a situation had come about it is necessary to understand the subject's unusual academic lineage. Geopolitics had a divided parentage – political science and geography – and from the outset both disciplines tended to regard it as being a sort of illegitimate child of the other.

This unsatisfactory situation meant that it could be – and was – disowned by either or both when expediency appeared to demand that it be disowned. While those geographers who opposed it did so largely on the grounds that it was more political than geographical, political scientists were disinclined to treat geographical factors as being of central importance in politics. While generally nodding in the direction of Napoleon's famous assertion that the policies of states were determined by their geography, they were far from conceding the implications of this for political decision-making in the international arena. Both disciplines incorporated aspects of the other into their discourses, but they were reluctant to recognise any justification for a separate subdiscipline to be shared between them.[3] Although the term 'geopolitics' had been originally coined by a political scientist, from the outset it had been appropriated more by geographers, who, despite its controversial status, considered it as being a part of political geography, even if only for the purposes of demolishing its credibility. Behind their stated concern at its disquieting characteristics lay an uneasy sense of its potential importance and of the dangers which it might pose for the traditional practice of geography (see Chapter 2).

The distrust shown by political geographers centred on the question of the subject's fundamental nature and purpose. During the first half of the twentieth century geopolitics as understood by most Western geographers consisted of the mobilisation of geographical knowledge for the purposes of the state.[4] It followed that this made it subject to manipulation by states in order to justify those particular policies which they wished to pursue. It was this perceived closeness to policy-making which led Harold Sprout to dismiss it as in reality 'geo-policy' and therefore lacking the objectivity to be expected of an academic discipline (Sprout, 1968: 120). To Derwent Whittlesey, writing on the eve of World War II, political geography was the study of the relationships between the earth and the state, and of necessity this included geographical aspects of the relationships among states themselves. Whittlesey used 'geopolitical' as the adjective governing political geography. 'In brief', he wrote, 'its subject is geopolitical patterns and structures.' He considered 'geopolitical' to be 'a portmanteau adjective' which was much better than 'the cumbersome "politico-geographical"' (Whittlesey, 1939: 1). However, he considered that what he called 'the dogma known as geopolitics' was an attempt 'to make political geography serve the purposes of this or that particular state' (ibid.: 4). Richard Hartshorne, in his seminal work *The Nature of Geography*, published in the same fateful year, defined political geography quite simply as being 'the geography of states', which he contrasted with what he called 'the special field of *Geopolitik* ... in which geography ... is utilised for particular purposes that lie beyond the pursuit of knowledge' (Hartshorne, 1939: 404). Political geography was thus considered by Hartshorne as being the proper discipline for everything to do with the political side of human activity viewed spatially. This was because it was regarded as being the 'pure' academic discipline, in contrast to that 'impure' one which prostituted itself to the needs of politics and politicians. Hartshorne's general conclusion was that there was no place for geopolitics in what in his estimation was 'one of the major aspects of geography'. He clearly considered this to be the view generally held among geographers at the time. 'That *Geopolitik* can provide a suitable substitute for political geography', he asserted, 'will hardly be accepted by geographers or political scientists outside Germany, or indeed by few political geographers inside Germany.'

Since that time all has changed. During the 1970s and 1980s a new generation of academics in both geography and political science has rediscovered geopolitics and brought it back into the centre of the international discourse. This rediscovery has involved returning to its pre-Nazi origins, and this has made it possible to make a thorough re-evaluation of the discipline's role. While the effect of this has been to add a new dimension to the study of international relations, it has also made possible the further exploration of the link between politics and the earth, which is one of the keynote themes in the study of contemporary world issues. Political science and the earth sciences meet in geopolitics, and the new light which it sheds has been one of the factors which has added to its legitimacy. As a result it has become distinguished from 'traditional' political geography not because of questions as to its objectivity but because of very real differences in its subject matter, methodology and purpose. While geopolitics certainly merits the prefix 'new', the two component parts of this compound word mean basically what they always did. The central purpose of the exercise was thus 'to reclaim the tradition of geopolitics', and to do so by its disassociation from the state and its policies (O'Loughlin and Heske, 1991: 37).

The basic definition of geopolitics used in this book is quite simply the study of international relations from a spatial or geographical perspective. It is thus based on that 'new' geopolitics which emerged in the 1970s and which has since been developed particularly in the United States, France and Great Britain. It therefore includes much of what between the 1940s and the 1970s was subsumed into the general field of political geography. The principal tool of geopolitics is the political map, and its methodological approach consists in the examination of its characteristics with a view to understanding the phenomena which it reveals and the processes which have produced its morphology. The component parts of the world political scene are considered as spatial objects and their interactions as producing spatial phenomena. The purpose of the study is to seek explanations of the behaviour and interactions of the spatial objects as component parts of the whole, its ultimate goal being to reach an understanding of the totality of geopolitical space and of the processes which are at work within it at any given time. The study has to be a holistic one, since in seeking to examine and explain the behaviour patterns of particular objects in geographical space it is necessary to take into consideration many different aspects of the functioning of these objects.

This is a far broader and more all-embracing project than the traditional geographical line of enquiry, which has centred on the examination of the 'influences' of geographical factors such as climate, physical resources and relief features on human activity. Geographical space is treated as being a totality, and the existence of phenomena which may be considered as being 'factors' in the more traditional geographical sense constitutes a component part of this totality. The technique thus consists of the examination of the geopolitical objects within the totality. Treated in this way, geopolitical analysis is inclusive, and phenomena which may appear to be essentially local and particular are incorporated into the interpretation of the whole of which they form a part.

The understanding of interactions and relationships thus entails the examination of those entities which are in course of interaction. The premise which underlies this is that their spatial characteristics will themselves supply clues as to the causes of their behaviour. Their collective behaviour patterns together then produce the sum total of geopolitical space.

Geopolitical analysis has to be undertaken in three stages. First comes the examination of the characteristics of the primary spatial objects themselves. Second comes the examination of the interactions of the spatial objects and the spatial patterns which are produced by these interactions. This includes the observation of differences in the interactive patterns in different areas of geographical space. Finally there is the examination of geopolitical space as a whole with a view to assessing its overall characteristics. This is the world political map, and the extraction of meaning from the map constitutes the final stage and the ultimate purpose of geopolitics as an academic discipline. 'Meaning' in the geopolitical sense consists of the detection of repeating patterns of activity to which the overall name 'order' can be given. The essential thing is that this search for order is conducted objectively, without, as so often happened in the past, the constant refrain of the special interests of particular states. This is the essence of the 'reclaiming' of geopolitics in the interests of the earth as a whole rather than in the interests of particular segments of it.

The use to which geopolitics may be put is thus considered as being an entirely different matter from the methodology employed in its study. Because this distinction has not in the past been made clear, much of geopolitics has stood condemned in Sprout's estimation as being 'geo-policy'. However, the fact that geopolitics has been viewed and studied in an *engagé* manner has not really been its biggest problem. In the intellectual sense the real problem has been the lack of a clear distinction between study and application. The nature of the subdiscipline has been dictated by the purposes of those who have engaged in it and who have then found what they wanted to find, or more precisely, what their political masters required them to find. Academic objectivity has been muddled up with political ambitions, and intellectual rigour has been sacrificed to reasons of state.

The fact is that there is nothing wrong with an *engagé* geopolitics as such, any more than there is anything wrong with an *engagé* approach to any knowledge. It would be a strange view of anatomy which advocated the academic study of the human body exclusively for its own sake and with no practical applications. To Hartshorne, geopolitics was 'the application of geography to politics' and, he added, 'the estimate of its value and importance will depend on the value that one assigns to the political purpose it is designed to serve' (Hartshorne, 1939: 404). The essential requirement is that it should be seen quite clearly as being something distinct and different from academic study and be conducted as such. It must be recognised that, as with all science, there are both 'pure' and 'applied' versions.

The new geopolitics which arose in France in the 1970s was in its way quite as *engagé* as had been that in Germany in the 1930s. It was the purposes for which it was intended which were different. Hartshorne's question was not with the application to political purposes *per se* but with the value assigned to those political purposes. 'Since it is designed to serve national politics from the German point of view', he wrote, 'its positive value from that point of view may be considered as offset by its negative value from the point of view of other countries' (Hartshorne, 1939: 404). The essential difference between this and the new generation of geographers in France is that they have been concerned with humanity as a whole rather than exclusively with the interests of one particular country. As with many other disciplines, geopolitics can be used for many different purposes which 'lie beyond the pursuit of knowledge', and the evaluation of these will depend upon the perspective of the observer and the value that he or she assigns to any particular political purpose. These are basically moral issues, and whether they be labelled 'good' or 'bad' in the contemporary geopolitical sense must depend on the evaluation of their impact on humanity as a whole rather than one small section of it. However, important as they are, moral questions must remain outside the remit of a 'pure' academic discipline.

Finally, it is necessary to address the question of how geopolitics as here defined relates to political geography, which, in the days when geopolitics was considered to be 'impure', was the 'pure' version of it and took under its wing the whole geographical dimension of political activity. To Whittlesey, political geography was essentially the study of the relationship between 'the earth and the state'; this also included the geographical aspects of the relationships among states themselves. In the context of the definition of geopolitics as the spatial study of international relations, the question of where this leaves political geography needs to be addressed, and this can lead either towards a narrower or a broader definition. In the narrower definition political geography becomes the study of the state as a political entity with a view to understanding the influence of government and governmental decision-making on the overall human geography of its territory. For example, electoral geography illuminates internal variations in attitudes to the pursuit of particular policies and the reasons for these variations. In the broader definition political geography is viewed as being the parent discipline, which includes geopolitics as part of the totality of political activity viewed spatially. Whichever of these one selects, there is clearly an area of overlap between the two, as both must remain concerned with the nature of the state as an entity existing in geographical space. However, the exact nature of the overlap between political geography and geopolitics is of little real consequence so long as the distinction between them, together with the purposes of their study, are kept firmly in mind. While geopolitics has been defined here as being the study of international relations from a spatial perspective this should be seen not as being the end of the matter but rather as being an objective for a subject which has been transformed since the 1970s.

In order for us to understand more fully the extent and importance of the change which has taken place in the perception of the nature and purposes of geopolitics an examination will be made of its origins and development during the first part of the twentieth century.

NOTES

1. Henry Kissinger was assistant for national security affairs to the American President from 1969 to 1975, and Secretary of State from 1973 to 1977. Kissinger used the term geopolitics in order to emphasise the growing diversity of the political world and what he considered to be the unrealistic approach of considering all American foreign policy in the light of the superpower confrontation.

    The return of geopolitics in France took place in the wake of the great student disturbances of 1968. It centred on the journal *Hérodote*, edited by Yves Lacoste, the first issue of which appeared in January 1976 (see Chapter 4). The journal's first subtitle was *Stratégies, géographies, idéologies*, but in 1983 this was changed to *Revue de géographie et de géopolitique*.

2. *Vidalien* refers to the ideas of that school of French geographers founded by Paul Vidal de la Blache in the early part of the twentieth century. Its most basic idea was that of environmental 'possibilism', a doctrine which maintains that the physical environment contains a number of possibilities from which humankind must choose. This idea stands in marked contrast to the doctrine of environmental determinism, which asserts that the geographical environment determines what humanity can do and that there is little real choice but to accept this and to act within its constraints. The geopolitical implications of possibilism and determinism are discussed in Chapters 3 and 4.

3. Many geographers in the early part of the century denied that political geography constituted a separate subdiscipline at all. This was particularly so in the French school, in which Vidal de la Blache himself had maintained that the whole of human geography was a seamless fabric of which the political aspects were integrally a part. The political could therefore be fully understood only within of the context of the whole. Vidal's pupil Jean Brunhes wrote dismissively of 'so called' political geography, which he considered actually to be a part of historical geography (Brunhes, 1947: 273; Parker, 1994b: 30–1).

4. The most important schools of Western political geography at the time were the American, British and French, and it is to their reactions principally that reference is made here (Parker, 1985).

CHAPTER 2

GRAND LINES ON THE DOCILE PAPER: THE ORIGINS OF GEOPOLITICS

The term 'geopolitics' has Greek roots: *Ge* or *Gaia*, the goddess of the earth, and *polis*, the city-state of classical Greece. *Ge* represented humankind's terrestrial home in all its variety and abundance, while the *polis* was the control and organisation of it by humankind. The etymological derivation of 'geopolitics' is thus the earth and the state and the relationship between the two, but its implications range well beyond this. They imply the concept of the state as one of the phenomena not just *on* the earth but *of* the earth; its nature derives from the fact that it is a component part of geographical space. The idea of *Ge* as representing the whole earth leads on to the relationship of that portion of the earth occupied by one particular state to the earth as a whole, and that of *polis* to the relationship of one single state to the rest of the states. In other words, there is the wider relationship of the local geographical and political circumstances to the physical and human totality of which they form a part.

The origins of geopolitics can be traced back to the Swedish political scientist Rudolf Kjellén and the German natural scientist and geographer Friedrich Ratzel. Both were active during the late nineteenth and early twentieth centuries, and, although there is no evidence that the two ever met, the symbiosis of their ideas produced a new dimension of thought within the social sciences. While Kjellén is acknowledged as having been the inventor of the term itself, his interest was initially stimulated by the ideas of Ratzel, and it was through the latter that it became widely known.

Rudolf Kjellén (1864–1922) held the chair of political science at the University of Uppsala. He was for some six years a Conservative member of the Swedish Parliament, where he put forward his right-wing and nationalist views on the functions of government and voiced his concerns for the future of his own small country in a world dominated by great powers (Holdar, 1994: 138–42). In his early career his main academic concerns had been with historical and constitutional aspects of the state, but the turning-point in his life came as a result of the influence of Ratzel's teaching. The German geographer's ideas on the influence of geographical factors on the nature and behaviour of the state were a revelation to Kjellén, and introduced him to an entirely new way of thinking about international relations and the state.

Friedrich Ratzel (1844–1904) was born in Karlsruhe, and after an early career in the natural sciences he gravitated towards geography. He saw this subject as being a synthesis of natural and human phenomena which contributed to the explanation of the nature and distribution patterns of human activity. He became Professor of Geography first at the University of Munich and then at Leipzig (Heske, 1994a: 205), and it was there that he developed his ideas on *Anthropogeographie* (human geography). Ratzel took a particular interest in the political aspects of human behaviour, and in 1897 his book *Politische Geographie* was published (Ratzel, 1897). This is generally considered to be the seminal work in modern political geography, and it proved to have considerable influence on the development of the subject both in Germany and elsewhere. Most importantly, its influence on the work of Kjellén was to have far-reaching consequences in the application of geography and geographical methods to politics.

In the late nineteenth century the application of the geographical method to the understanding and explanation of political and international questions was quite new. There had long been maps which revealed the physical and human features of the earth with reasonable accuracy, but their official use had been largely restricted to military purposes and war. The existence of such governmental organisations as the British Ordnance Survey and the French *Cartes de l'armée* demonstrates the military purposes which had underlain official mapmaking. What had been lacking was the interpretation of the data which the maps revealed for purposes other than the planning of the next campaign, in other words the extraction of deeper meaning from the data which they revealed. The influence of geographical factors on the fortunes of states had long been accepted as a general principle. For example, geographical considerations had played a significant role in French strategic thinking since the seventeenth century, and by the time of the Revolution they became important in systematising the French view of France's role in Europe (Pounds, 1951). That such ideas were also very much in evidence in Napoleon's thinking is seen not only in general comments about the importance of geography but more specifically in his conviction that the most formidable of all his military adversaries had been 'le Général Février'.[1] However, statements of this sort appeared to arise from an idea of geography as a kind of stage, the scenery of which sometimes influenced the human drama taking place on it.[2] There had been no serious attempt at assembling the diverse elements making up the spatial dimension with a view to examining them collectively. Nor could such a thing have been anticipated much earlier, as the great increases in the knowledge of the geography of the world since the sixteenth century had not been accompanied by an equal advance in the capacity of humankind to make sense of the infinite variety of terrestrial phenomena. Darwinism had represented a great advance in explanatory science, but its application to the human world remained controversial. Social Darwinism had made this leap, but it was strongly opposed by those who saw humanity as lying outside and above the natural world.

While Ratzel, the natural scientist, was clearly motivated by the prospect of applying the methods of science to humanity, the motivation behind Kjellén's interest in this innovative thinking appears to have been a rather different one. He was deeply troubled by what he perceived to be the marked deterioration in the international situation in the 1890s. It appeared to Kjellén, and to many others at the time, that the established order which had existed throughout the greater part of the nineteenth century, and which had underpinned the great advances of the time, was breaking down. That 'Concert of Europe' which had emerged out of the 'Congress System' at the end of the Napoleonic Wars had worked reasonably well at keeping the peace.[3] The fact that for over eighty years there had been no general war and that the wars which had taken place had been effectively localised made the nineteenth century unique in modern European history. International congresses were periodically convened for the purpose of maintaining the European order in place and dealing with those disputes which might have disrupted it. However, as the nineteenth century approached its end there were disturbing signs that new and potentially destructive forces were being unleashed. The great powers in concert proved to be less well adapted to finding solutions to these than they had been to containing unrest in the Balkans or apportioning colonial spheres. The growing political and economic unrest led to more intense international competition and to the strident assertions of imperial power.

In many ways this looming breakdown arose from a more general sense of unease which had long been building up. The *fin de siècle* atmosphere of impending doom was captured by such philosophers as Nordau in Scandinavia and Nietzsche in Germany. Not only were established patterns of behaviour at both national and international levels being radically questioned, but apocalyptic visions were in the air. 'In the civilised world there obviously prevails a twilight mood,' wrote Nordau, and out of this twilight he saw threatening political philosophies emerging (Nordau, 1993: 43). Racism, anti-Semitism, anarchism and communism all challenged the relative tolerance of the established order, and all had influential advocates. To Barbara Tuchman the image most evocative of the whole epoch which preceded World War I was the 'Proud Tower' from which, in Edgar Allan Poe's poem, 'Death looks gigantically down'. While, like the tower, the epoch appeared to be splendid on the outside, its foundations were being steadily eroded (Tuchman, 1966: 102–3).

While the sense of foreboding which pervaded much of Europe produced a tendency to look back to the past for security and reassurance, this retrospection took on different forms in different countries. A particular feature of the situation in Scandinavia, which was Kjellén's principal concern, was the tendency to return to older, pagan ways of thought. In the atmosphere of the *Sekelskiftet* (*fin de siècle*) the Nordic idea of the *Ragnarök* (Twilight of the Gods) came to be transformed into the Twilight of the Nations and the impending chaos which would be its inevitable accompaniment (Nordau, 1993: 1–7).

Kjellén himself shared the pervasive feelings of gloom which nurtured such ideas, and his political views were to a large extent a product of them. He reached the conclusion that the great powers of Europe were drifting towards war with a kind of grim inevitability, and he was concerned for the fate of Sweden in the chaos which would follow. He was all too well aware of the vulnerability of his own small country and its powerlessness either to prevent the catastrophe or to fend off its effects (Kjellén, 1897). To Kjellén, the state was of the highest importance, and its existence was the only real source of order and protection from chaos. He believed it to be the fundamental unit of territorial organisation and for him its safety was the highest priority. His geopolitical thinking led him to the conclusion that the state was 'a person ranking higher than the individual' and that it was the clash of state ideas which was 'at the root of the world war that is coming' (Kjellén-Björkquist, 1970: 38). His espousal of the spatial dimension derived most specifically from what he regarded as being the inadequacy of conventional political science to understand, or even to address, the true nature of the contemporary world and of the menace which was looming. On the other hand, the geopolitical perspective was one which pointed towards more realistic courses of action in pursuit of the national interest. It was something positive which allowed for optimism that Europe, and Sweden in particular, could extricate itself from that grim scenario arising from *Sekelskiftet* thinking.

While the immediate causes of this atmosphere of gloom and apprehension were the seeming intractability of the political, social and economic problems of the time, underlying it was that 'closure' which can be seen, with hindsight, as having been at the root of the first global geopolitical crisis. This was caused by the end of that long period of discovery and expansion which had commenced nearly five centuries earlier. It was seen to be of such significance that, in Lord Bryce's words, 'it closes a page for ever'. By the end of the nineteenth century the world was at last revealed in something like its entirety, and the implications of this revelation appeared to produce more dismay than hope. In the final years of the nineteenth century the great world powers faced the realisation, like the dying Alexander at Babylon, that there were no more worlds left to conquer. 'The exploration of this earth is now all but finished,' observed Bryce in his Romanes Lecture of 1902. 'Civilised man knows his home in a sense in which he never knew it before' (Bryce, 1902: 5). This signified the completion of what Bryce called 'the World-process', something which he saw as being 'an especially great and fateful event' (*ibid.*: 8). The American geographer Ellen Semple, disciple and interpreter of Ratzel, put this 'fateful event' into the longer historical perspective when she referred to it as being the culmination of a long process in human history. 'The geographical horizon of the known world has widened from grey antiquity to the present,' she observed, and, alongside this widening of the horizons, 'the geographical outlook' of humankind had also widened. She termed this process 'the expanding field of advancing history' and saw it as being 'a driving force in the progress of the world' (Semple, 1911: 69). True as this may have been in what Fernand Braudel was later to call *la longue durée* (the long term), its effect in the heightened tension of the *fin de siècle* atmosphere was to produce a sense of urgency. It was an entirely new situation for Europeans accustomed for centuries to think of boundless horizons beyond which lay endless new lands, and this intensified the rivalry for the limited global real estate, and the great wealth and resources which it was believed to contain. It was this impending closure of the world which, more than anything else, was the geopolitical basis for the psychological environment in which late-nineteenth-century European imperialism flourished. Hard on the heels of those discoverers who had been engaged until that time in pushing out the bounds of the known world came the assertion of imperial control over the newly discovered lands and their encasement in a mesh of political boundaries. 'At present, as it seems, the occupation of the world is ... being peacefully completed,' wrote Ernest Lavisse. 'They trace grand lines on the docile paper' (Lavisse, 1891: 159–60). The new polychromatic political atlases, highlighting the possessions of the great powers in their favoured imperial colours, appeared to depict political acquisitions as solid and enduring as those natural features upon which they were superimposed. Indeed, little distinction appeared to be made between the 'grand lines' which depicted the new geopolitical landscape and those other 'grand lines' which depicted coasts, rivers and mountains. The adjective 'natural' could have been used with little distinction to denote the human and the non-human elements, and the crisp new horizons were from the outset viewed through imperial tints. The filling in of the remaining blank spaces of the world came to be inextricably bound up with the assertion of political control over them, and what had until then been dark areas on the map, places of myth and mystery, were transformed into precisely delimited territories within finite global space.[4]

It was this new cartographic precision, producing a sense of geographical finality, which lay behind the heightened international tension, increased rivalry and great-power imperialism. 'What will happen when all the attainable territory is occupied it is not difficult to conjecture,' commented Lavisse prophetically. His earlier caveat as to the 'seeming' peacefulness of the European occupation of the globe was followed by the more menacing but prescient conclusion that 'Here, as everywhere, there are indications of war' (Lavisse, 1891: 160). To Bryce too, the completion of the 'World-process' was particularly fateful, and he added, 'it may be deemed to mark a crisis in the history of the world which will profoundly affect the destiny of all mankind' (Bryce, 1902: 8). Nevertheless, Bryce, unlike Lavisse, was ultimately optimistic. While he used the words 'fateful' and 'crisis', his parallel observations struck a different chord. The completion of the process, he said, 'opens up a new stage in World-history', and this has 'given the world a new kind of unity'. As a result, the features of the home of mankind had 'passed from the chaos of conjecture into the cosmos of science'. He concluded that 'the clouds seem to hang heavy on the horizon of the future; yet light streams in' (*ibid*.: 46).

Bryce's idea of the passage from 'chaos' to 'cosmos' was founded on a firm belief in the power of science to bring about change for the benefit of mankind. This was the basis of his optimism and of the optimism of many others who struggled to find some hope in the enveloping *fin de siècle* foreboding. One aspect of this was that desire to anchor humanity into that natural world which appeared at the time to be largely free of the problems of the human world. This naturalistic view of humanity and human activity derived from a long tradition going back to the Renaissance which recognised no fundamental opposition between the human and the natural. On the contrary, nature, in the widest sense, was taken to include humanity. The proposition underlying this was that since the human and the non-human were manifestly both part of the same all-embracing physical universe, to be successful human activity had to be based on an awareness of nature and of natural laws. It was therefore assumed that humanity was subject to the laws of nature in much the same way as everything else. Francis Bacon's observation that 'in order to conquer Nature it is necessary to obey her' encapsulates the naturalistic idea which was also present in the seventeenth and eighteenth centuries and was to act as a warning against the arrogance of the Age of Reason (Bacon, 1924). The assumption that humankind was a part of nature was also present in much of the scientific thinking of the late nineteenth century. 'I cannot conceive of a physiography from which man has been excluded,' wrote the anarchist geographer Peter Kropotkin, and he expressed the opinion that the study of nature without studying humanity was a pointless and 'scholastic' exercise (Livingstone, 1992: 255).

However, what made late-nineteenth-century naturalistic thinking essentially different from that which had preceded it was the presence of two new elements in the scientific firmament. The first of these was the dominant position held by evolution theory in the explanation of natural phenomena and the second was the increasing tendency to specialisation of scientific disciplines. Knowledge, the essential unity of which had been inherent in the ideas of the Renaissance, was disintegrating into separate compartments. The underlying proposition of late-nineteenth-century geography was that this compartmentalisation should be resisted at all costs and the principles of the unity of terrestrial phenomena should be reasserted (Mackinder, 1887: 13–29). This had been the basic contention of the great German geographer Carl Ritter, who was an important pioneer of human geography during the first half of the nineteenth century. He viewed the world as *Ganzheit*, a functioning whole, and Ritter's disciples believed that the new specialist studies should take this into account (Hartshorne, 1939: 96). David Livingstone termed this assertion of unity 'the geographical experiment', and it entailed 'keeping nature and culture under one explanatory umbrella'. For the success of this, as Livingstone observed, evolutionary theory held out the best prospect. The favoured term for this theory was 'social Darwinism', but its fundamental ideas were actually more neo-Lamarckian than Darwinian (Livingstone, 1992: 177). The Lamarckian principle that the characteristics of an organism modified during its lifetime could then be passed on appeared to accord more closely with the application of evolutionary principles to the development of social organisms. This also made more sense if they were considered in the geographical context as being spatial organisms which were capable of modification and change. The map proved to be an especially useful way of presenting human and non-human data in one great matrix. As such, it was the ideal method of demonstrating the application of scientific principles to human activity. It was the 'collective perception' of the map, said Stephen Hall, which made possible 'the construction of a conceptual link between scientific knowledge and social worldview' (Hall, 1993: 20).

Thus the *Zeitgeist* at the turn of the century was made up of an uneasy and unstable mix of pessimism and optimism, both of which had important geographical facets. Both of these were present in Bryce's 1902 paper. The closure of geographical space produced an atmosphere of claustrophobia and apprehension while the move from 'chaos' to 'cosmos' and the application of the scientific method to the understanding of the world as a whole gave cause for hope. This mixture is reflected in the work of Rudolf Kjellén himself. He perceived that the way out of the Nordic foreboding lay in the application of scientific principles to politics, and he found the approach for which he was looking in the work of Friedrich Ratzel (Haggman, 1988: 3).

Ratzel's methodology was based on the application of his experience of the natural sciences to the understanding and explanation of human activity (Ratzel, 1882). In his seminal work on political geography he then developed his ideas on the geographical dimensions of the state and state behaviour (Ratzel, 1897). His basic thesis was that the state was an organism, like those of the natural world, and its behaviour could best be understood as being that of an organic whole. It itself was greater than the sum of its component parts, and these included both its physical and human components (*ibid.*: 1–16). He termed this *die biogeographische Auffassung* (the biogeographical concept) of the state. What made this different from other biological entities was that it was *ein Stück Boden*, a spatial entity, as well as being *ein Stück Menschheit* (a human entity). It was *bodenständiger Organismus*, an organism which not only existed in geographical space but was part of it. The most important characteristics associated with this spatial quality were those of *Raum* and *Lage*, territory and location, and the success of a state depended largely on the interactions of these two (*ibid.*: 180–383).

Ratzel then put forward a theory of the state as an organic phenomenon which was subject to laws in its territorial growth and development (Bassin, 1987: 128). These were laws which related to the behaviour of the state as an entity existing in geographical space, and in this context he examined the nature of the state and its requirements for survival and success. In so doing he applied the theory of evolution to states and compared their patterns of behaviour to that of the organic phenomena of the natural (non-human) world. The success of states, maintained Ratzel, was firmly based on their territory, and their continued success was dependent on the maximisation of their territorial advantages. In order to be successful the state needed to secure adequate and suitable *Lebensraum* (living space). This was the basic ingredient of state power, and the more of it which the state possessed, the more it was likely to secure a position of *Herrschaft* (domination). The principal objective of the state was seen as being the pursuit of *Macht* (power). Success in this led to the state becoming a *Grossmacht* (great power) and eventually attaining *Weltmacht* (world power). For the dynamic state territorial expansion was a necessity, and this was what distinguished successful from unsuccessful states. In presenting these organic theories, Ratzel was not arguing by analogy but was asserting that political phenomena were themselves, in a very real sense, both natural and organic, undergoing the same processes and subject to the same laws as the other phenomena of the natural world. His basic proposition was that the main purpose of scholarship lay in the search for universal laws and that these should then be applied objectively to the understanding of geopolitical phenomena.

Kjellén rapidly realised that Ratzelian thinking was an entirely new way of viewing the state, and it was this which led him to that new method of thinking and theorising about the state and its behaviour which he called *Geopolitik*. This appears to have first taken form in 1899, and his first definition of the subject was 'the science of the state as a realm in space' (Haggman, 1988: 8), and he later elaborated this to 'the theory of the state as a geographical organism or phenomenon in space' (Kjellén, 1916). His earlier work on political science had led him to the conclusion that this particular perspective, which had hitherto been given insufficient attention, was likely to make a significant contribution to the fuller understanding of the behaviour of the state. For Kjellén, *Geopolitik* was actually one category in a wider system of analysis which he devised, the other major ones being *Demopolitik* (demopolitics), *Economopolitik* (economo-politics), *Sociopolitik* (sociopolitics) and *Cratopolitik* (power politics) (Holdar, 1994: 94). While each was concerned with particular aspects of the state and its functioning, Kjellén came to the conclusion that *Geopolitik* was the most important of them all since it underlay all the others (*ibid.*: 94–5). He accepted the Ratzelian premise that the state was a spatial organism and that its most fundamental characteristics and behaviour patterns derived from this fact. However, he added a third characteristic to Ratzel's two. Kjellén's three were *Topopolitik*, *Physiopolitik* and *Morphopolitik*. The first two corresponded closely to Ratzel's *Lage* and *Raum*, and *Morphopolitik* was concerned with the form or shape of the state as a distinct characteristic and the implications which this had for its success or failure (Kjellén, 1920).

Kjellén thus conceived of geopolitics as being a science which gave clarity to phenomena which had in the past been subject to conjecture and speculation. In this he echoed Ratzel's call for complete objectivity in the study. Up to then the state had been treated as being primarily a legal and constitutional entity. Its legitimacy and authority were considered as deriving from a combination of the successful conclusion of treaties, dynastic marriages and alliances together with the blessing of the Church on the pursuit of its objectives. It was a game of chess in which the right moves, both in peace and war, determined the outcomes. Without necessarily rejecting these traditionally accepted indicators of legitimacy, Kjellén's geopolitics was founded on the proposition that there was another, and higher, form of legitimation of the state and that this lay in its geographical space. It was the effectiveness of the state as a geographical entity which was seen as being both the most important factor in its success and the most powerful justification for its existence. Following Ratzel, Kjellén also considered that it was its nature as an entity in geographical space which converted it into essentially something more than the sum of the individuals who made it up. He stressed the fundamental importance of such spatial factors as location, physical resources, morphology, territory and population in reaching a full understanding of the state and its behaviour. He also took into account what he called 'the historical side' in understanding the evolution of the state into its contemporary form. Thus he conceived of the state as being very much a person having a life cycle from youth through maturity to old age. It possessed a kind of 'mind' and a 'consciousness', and out of this arose the perception of its needs and the means by which these could best be fulfilled (Kjellén-Björkquist, 1970: 38). He made a distinction between what he termed 'proper' and 'special' geopolitics, the former being concerned with the spatial attributes of the state and the latter concerned with the state as part of the larger system. 'Special' geopolitics thus placed the state in the wider context, and the relationships among states constituted an essential part of the understanding both of the state itself and of the workings of the system as a whole. This included the factors involved in territorial expansion and in particular the international role of the great powers (Haggman, 1988: 9). Kjellén considered the use of the scientific method, and the objectivity which went with it, to be central to the whole project. 'It should be noted', he observed, 'that the system is independent of every preconceived view of the nature of the state. It is a matter of complete indifference whether one views the state as a form of life or as a legal or ethical entity. There is no room for subjective views of any kind. The method addresses all states, great or small, friends and enemies and measures them by the same measuring rod' (Kjellén, 1919: 279). It is clear from this that the question of whether the state was an organic entity was not the most fundamental matter for Kjellén. The most important thing for him was the role of science as the only method for ensuring objectivity, and this he considered to be the essential feature of the geopolitical approach.

Kjellén continued to develop and refine his ideas, and they were published in 1916 at the height of World War I in a book entitled *Staten som Lifsform*. This was immediately translated into German and published in the following year as *Der Staat als Lebenform*. (Kjellén, 1917). Just as Kjellén had himself been strongly influenced by German, and particularly Ratzelian, thinking, so in turn his work was to have a considerable impact on subsequent developments in Germany itself.

Central to the work of both Kjellén and Ratzel was the illumination of what appeared to be otherwise dark and forbidding corners. Both of them were endeavouring to move away from Nordau's twilight and dusk towards the light which Bryce saw streaming in at the window, and they both came to the conclusion that the geopolitical approach offered the best prospect for doing so. However, they both retained a partially hidden political agenda which sat ill with those principles of objectivity which they deemed to be essential. This was the paramountcy of the interests of their own particular country, but while Ratzel sought to use the new insights in order to rationalise and promote Germany's place in the world, Kjellén sought to use them to help overcome the looming dangers facing Scandinavia in a turbulent world. While Ratzel died before the Proud Tower was finally swept away and events took a decisive turn for the worse, Kjellén lived on into the aftermath of World War I. While he was fully aware that what he advocated was not going to be accomplished overnight, he nevertheless remained optimistic to the end and observed that 'It is a delight to hear the crowing of the cock even if one will never see the sun' (Kjellén-Björkquist, 1970: 95).

In assessing the importance of Kjellén's ideas, Ruth Kjellén-Björkquist saw him as having been very much 'en männska i tiden kring sekelskiftet' (a man of his times at the turn of the century) and in his thinking he reflected this (Kjellén-Björkquist, 1970: 95). However, although like Ratzel he sought to use his work to address the problems of his times, like Ratzel he also transcended them by advocating an approach which had a wider applicability in time and space.

'Germany is a land of geographers,' said Michel Korinman. Since the eighteenth century the study of geography, 'the eye of history', had been given serious attention (Korinman, 1990: 9). The country's location at the heart of Europe was also to make it a land of geopoliticians. It was in Germany that the new geopolitical ideas fell on the most receptive ground, but, despite an early recognition of Kjellén's pioneering role, it was the work of Ratzel which had the greatest impact on the development of the subject there. The implications of Ratzel's ideas were soon realised, and they were disseminated widely throughout the German-speaking world. While to Ratzel the search for general laws was fundamental, it was those particular problems arising out of Germany's geographical location which proved to be of greatest interest in Germany (ibid.: 51–85). This reflected the division within Ratzel's work between pure scholarship and its application to the national needs (ibid.: 9–30). It struck a chord in a country which was disposed to regard itself as being a kind of victim of its geography. The conditio Germaniae, the curse of the central location, which had been inherited from Prussia, had been viewed fatalistically as a burden which had to be born stoically (Parker, 1985: 53). Ratzelian thinking had the attraction of presenting the country's geography in a more positive way. The disadvantages of the central location could become advantages if circumstances in Europe changed. When the country had been weak, Germany was always the cockpit of Europe, the battlefield of the great powers. However, the situation could be completely transformed by a powerful Germany within a strong *Mitteleuropa* (Central Europe). The idea of geography being transformed from disadvantage to advantage, from problem to solution, was thus at the root of Ratzel's appeal in his homeland.

Less than a decade after the appearance of Ratzel's *Politische Geographie*, a book on just this theme was published. Joseph Partsch saw unity as being the most important way in which Central Europe could achieve strength and power (Partsch, 1903). The author, Professor of Geography at the University of Breslau, sought to identify and delimit a large transnational region at the heart of the continent which he saw as having the potential to become a major centre of power. He examined *Mitteleuropa* as a geopolitical region and analysed its strengths and weaknesses in relation to the rest of Europe, and in particular to the great powers surrounding it. His theme was 'the essential unity of this great civilised region' which in the past had so often been torn apart by war. Now, maintained Partsch, there was peace and cooperation within it, and the frictions of the past had been replaced by the 'blessings of peaceful industry'. The key to this felicitous situation lay in the alliance between the empires of Germany and Austria-Hungary. Significantly, Partsch's book appeared in English before being published in German, and it provided the first opportunity for English-speaking readers to become acquainted with the new German thinking in the general area of political geography.

Partsch's *Central Europe* appeared in a series entitled the Regions of the World edited by the British geographer Halford Mackinder.[5] Mackinder had been a pioneer of the new geography in Britain during the late nineteenth century and, like Ratzel, had realised the importance of political geography in a world dominated by the great powers (Mackinder, 1887: 28–9). His book *Britain and the British Seas* had been the first of the series and was an attempt to put British world power into its geographical and geopolitical context (Mackinder, 1902). Two years later, and shortly after the appearance of Partsch's book, Mackinder delivered a paper to the Royal Geographical Society entitled 'The geographical pivot of history' (Mackinder, 1904). In this Mackinder did what Kjellén and Ratzel had not done, and that was to propose a geopolitical scenario on a world scale. In the tradition of Ritter, this was based on the proposition that the world viewed geographically was a functioning whole which could be explained rationally. Like Ratzel, Mackinder applied this to political geography, but while Ratzel had been content to deal with states as autonomous organisms competing for existence within a finite geographical space, Mackinder proposed the existence of a repeating pattern of relationships among states. At virtually the same time as Bryce was predicting the end of the 'World-process' and the looming crisis which arose from this, Mackinder was addressing the same problems from a different perspective. What had been to Bryce the 'World-process' was termed by Mackinder the 'Columbian Age', which was that great period of European expansion and world domination

which began in the fifteenth century. He too saw this age as approaching its
end and predicted that this would be followed by the rise of other parts of the
world which had until then been in the shadow of the European maritime
powers. Central to his thesis was that the period of dominance of maritime
power was coming to an end and that land power was poised to make a
comeback.

Mackinder's basic geopolitical proposition was that world history could be
explained geopolitically as being the confrontation of land power and sea
power, and he traced this confrontation back through history. There had been
constant oscillation in the fortunes of the two protagonists, but there had been
an underlying balance of power between them so that neither one of them had
been able to secure a permanent position of dominance over the other. Each of
them possessed a certain set of advantages to which they had recourse in order
to redress the balance. This was responsible for the persistence of the bipolarity
underlying what was on the surface a highly complex pattern of inter-state
relationships. In 1904 Mackinder applied his thesis to the situation in the early
years of the new century, and he identified the two principal players in the
global confrontation as being the British and Russian Empires. He saw this
situation as being a kind of culmination in the closed world of something which
had been steadily expanding in the open world of the past. He was
apprehensive as to the final outcome as he saw the greater advantage as lying
with the land power (Mackinder, 1904).

Just as Ratzel focused his concerns on the situation of Germany, so
Mackinder focused his concerns on that of Britain, and in particular on the fate
of the British Empire in the rapidly changing world of the early twentieth
century. However, Mackinder was able to discern global realities above the
contemporary world situation, and he was the first to present a comprehensive
geopolitical world-view. Dubbed the 'Heartland' thesis because of its concern
with the rise of land power, this was to be one of the most important formative
influences on the development of both political geography and geopolitics in
the English-speaking world (Chapter 5). Together with the work of Ratzel, it
was also to have a considerable impact on the subsequent development of
German Geopolitik.

Despite all this, Ratzelian thinking was not seriously introduced into the
English-speaking countries until over a decade after the publication of Politische
Geographie, and by this time Ratzel himself was dead and the international scene
had already considerably changed. Ratzel's ideas became known largely
through the work of the American geographer Ellen Semple, who had been one
of his students in Germany. To English-speaking readers Ratzel's work, said
Semple, was 'a closed book, a treasure house bolted and barred'. In Influences of
Geographic Environment she explained and developed Ratzel's ideas of the state
and the territorial dimension of state behaviour, particularly emphasising 'the
importance of the land factor in history' (Semple, 1911). She emphasised the
Ratzelian objective of 'searching for the permanent and common in the

outwardly mutable'; in other words, of establishing geographical laws. 'At the bottom of changing events', she wrote, 'is the same solid earth' (*ibid.*: 68). This led her to emphasise the scientific character of the subject. Ratzel had placed it 'on a secure scientific basis'. He was the first to have investigated the subject 'from a modern scientific point of view ... and based his conclusions on world-wide inductions, for which his predecessors did not command the data' (*ibid.*: v). While accepting much of Ratzelian thought, Semple dismissed the organic theory of society and state. The reason why this permeated Ratzel's ideas, she maintained, was 'because Ratzel formulated his principles at a time when Herbert Spencer exercised a wide influence on European thought'. This theory, which she considered in 1911 to have already been 'generally abandoned' was eliminated by Semple from her 'restatement of Ratzel's system' (*ibid.*: vii). It might be assumed that such an exercise would have left a huge hole in the system, but in her opinion this was not so, and she went on to contend that it had never been really central to Ratzel's work. 'It stood there ... as a kind of scaffolding around the final edifice; and the stability of the structure after this scaffolding is removed shows how extraneous to the whole it was' (*ibid.*).

Much more important for Semple was the positive foundation of Ratzel's thinking. Her work was fundamentally optimistic in tone, and this optimism was founded both on Ratzelian ideas and on the reassuring 'solid earth' itself in which they were rooted. The significance of 'the land, in which all activities finally root' was linked in her mind with the idea of progress in history. 'For a theory of progress', she maintained, 'it [the land] offers a solid basis' (Semple, 1911: 69).

Ratzel's ideas made more of an impact in France than anywhere else outside the Germanic bloc itself. There knowledge of the German language, particularly in those eastern border regions adjacent to Germany, was much greater than in either the United States or Britain. Paul Vidal de la Blache had immediately recognised the seminal importance of the work of the German geographer. However, in his lengthy review of *Politische Geographie* he immediately took issue with what he considered to be Ratzel's determinism, his organic concepts, and his premature attempts to 'formulate laws' (Vidal de la Blache, 1898). The most that Vidal was prepared to concede in this respect was the existence of what he called *principes de méthode* (a methodology). He made it quite clear that, in his view, political geography was 'a part of a whole', which was 'the geography of life'.

Despite these early reservations by Vidal himself, Ratzelian thinking went on to play an important role in the establishment of modern French political geography. Camille Vallaux's *Le Sol et l'État*, which appeared in the same year as Semple's *Influences of Geographic Environment*, was even more permeated with Ratzelian thinking than was Semple's work (Vallaux, 1911). While, like Vidal, Vallaux was clearly an admirer of Ratzel, he did not accept the latter's political geography uncritically. In particular the idea of the state as organism and what was perceived as being environmental determinism were both vigorously questioned (Parker, 1994g: 229–30). Vallaux also took issue with Ratzel's German nationalism, which he considered to be a major detraction from the objectivity of his work. Vallaux maintained that his own book differed profoundly, 'both in method and inspiration', from *Politische Geographie*. *Le Sol et l'État* appeared as one of the volumes in the *Encyclopédie Scientifique*, which included organic and inorganic sciences, and Vallaux's stated aim was to make the subject into 'une science véritable' (a genuine science), the objective of which was to understand and explain the spatial dimension of political phenomena (Vallaux, 1911: 2). Although the idea of general 'laws' was not acceptable there had to be general 'principles' of analysis of phenomena, as 'there can be no science of the particular' (*ibid.*: 18).

Despite this early recognition of the importance of Ratzel there was a widespread disquiet over the role assigned to Germany in his work, and this was nowhere more in evidence than in France. The Darwinist ideas of struggle and survival appeared from the other side of the Rhine to be tailored towards the notion of the hegemony of Germany in Europe. Ratzel's analysis certainly reinforced the idea of Germany as a dynamic state, the destiny of which was to expand territorially and to attain a position of dominance. This scenario was too close to what were widely perceived as being the ambitions of Germany's political and military leadership to be accepted in a completely 'academic' way. On the other hand, Ratzel's supporters within Germany maintained that the Leipzig geographer was a serious academic concerned above all with reaching a deeper understanding of the laws of state behaviour from a scientific perspective. The French geographer Brunhes shared this view when he maintained that Ratzel's spirit was too elevated ('un ésprit trop élevé') to allow him to dismiss the contributions of other nations. He was able to transcend the immediate political preoccupations of the time and retained the capacity to discern humanity through Germany (Brunhes, 1947: 273–81). However, many of Ratzel's self-proclaimed disciples were subsequently to prove to be less scrupulous in this regard.

In the development of his geographical and geopolitical ideas Ratzel chose to use the term *Politische Geographie* to describe his work, but his subject matter was virtually indistinguishable from what Kjellén called *Geopolitik*. Ratzel was coming from the natural sciences, of which he considered geography to be an essential part, and the 'political' – like the earlier 'anthropo' – was an indication of the particular aspect of the subject which was being examined. Kjellén, on the other hand, was coming from the social sciences, and he put the 'geo' in the position of being an indicative prefix. Later his thinking processes appear to have become highly geographical, but geopolitics retained its position as part of the wider analytical system which he had devised. While this difference of terminology reflected the different emphases of two individuals, it was to have momentous consequences for the subsequent development of geopolitical study.

That it was political geography rather than geopolitics which was to enter the mainstream as the 'legitimate' discipline for the study of 'the earth and the state' may be attributed in part to the fact that the impact of Ratzel, writing in German, was greater than that of Kjellén, writing in Swedish. At the time German was also the only foreign language into which Kjellén's work was translated, and it was in the land of *Politische Geographie* that the term *Geopolitik* came first to be used. The origins of the gulf which opened up between the two lie in the divisions within the German geographical establishment in the years which followed World War I. The future role of the subject was much debated, and out of this debate the term *Geopolitik* came into use to describe a particular school of thought which advocated the active participation of geographers in affairs of state. This distinguished them from the academic mainstream which sought to distance political geography from politics. This divide became a chasm, and for over half a century it was to render virtually impossible the development of the study of the earth and the state along those lines which both Kjellén and Ratzel had wished it to go.

NOTES

1. *Le Général Février* (General February) was a metaphor for the ferocious weather conditions which *La Grande Armée* encountered during the Russian campaign of 1812. Napoleon believed that it was the Russian winter, rather than the Russian army, which had been his greatest enemy and the main cause of his defeat and downfall.
2. The first modern world map, that of Ortelius in 1570, was entitled *Theatrum Orbis Terrarum*. 'Theatre' could have become the accepted name to denote the world as a whole had not Mercator and his successors decided that 'Atlas' was a more appropriate term to use.
3. The Congress System, an early attempt at internationalism, arose from the Congress of Vienna, which took place at the end of the Napoleonic Wars and which brought about a general peace on the European continent which was to last for a century. The Congresses were meetings of representatives of the five great powers of the early nineteenth century, these being Great Britain, Russia, Austria, Prussia and France. Congresses were subsequently held at Aix-la-Chapelle (1818), Troppau (1820), Laibach (1821) and Verona (1822). A final Congress, held at St Petersburg in 1825, was attended only by Russia, Prussia and Austria. The Congresses were increasingly seen as being ineffective in addressing the problems of the continent. They were replaced by *ad hoc* congresses and international gatherings which were convened to address matters of particular importance. The most famous of these was the Congress of Berlin (1878), called to address the 'Eastern Question', that is to say the problems of the Balkans, and great-power involvement in this turbulent region.
4. The whole frantic process culminated in the late nineteenth century with the 'Grab for Africa', the 'Dark Continent', the interior of which had been virtually unknown to Europeans until then. This was the high-water mark of European imperialism,

and the frenzy for possessions was certainly underlain by the sense of the closing of the world. It was the great time of the 'tracing of lines' in the chancelleries of Europe, and there was a considerable increase in the size of the territories under the control of the British, French, Germans and Belgians, most of which was accounted for by the new African possessions.

5. The series was published by William Heinemann. According to Partsch's preface, Mackinder invited him to write *Central Europe* in 1897, which was the year in which *Politische Geographie* first appeared. Its content and proportions were to accord with those of Mackinder's own *Britain and the British Seas*, which appeared in 1902. A longer version of Partsch's *Central Europe* subsequently appeared in German. While both these books were published as regional geographies, there was a strong political element in them both, and the basic objective appeared to be the evaluation of the strengths and weaknesses of the great world regions viewed from a geopolitical standpoint. Interestingly, two other contributions to the series were Elisée Reclus's *Western Europe and the Mediterranean* and Peter Kropotkin's *The Russian Empire*. These were two famous anarchist geographers who both had very different ideas on the role of geography from those of either Mackinder or Partsch. However, they, and most of the other geographers who contributed to this series, shared a strong sense of the political vocation of geography and of the importance of the regional dimension.

CHAPTER 3

WAR AND THE FALL OF *GEOPOLITIK*

By 1914 the German Empire, founded less than half a century earlier, had become economically and militarily Europe's most powerful state. In addition to its position in the front rank among the great continental powers, it was also on course to becoming a maritime power with a global reach. Underlying Germany's dramatic rise through the ranks of the great powers during the late nineteenth century had been its rapid economic growth, and this was most in evidence in the heavy industrial sector. The production of coal, iron and steel was at the time the most important measure of a state's real power, since its capacity to produce modern armaments was dependent upon them. Yet there was widespread dissatisfaction in Germany that the country's new industrial might was not fully reflected in its international status and a corresponding desire that this situation should be rectified without delay.

This general feeling of dissatisfaction was spearheaded by the Emperor Wilhelm II (the Kaiser). This ambitious and energetic monarch was at the root of the restlessness and agitation which came to characterise German foreign policy at this period. It was quite apparent that the achievement of the desired objectives entailed mounting a major challenge to that world order which had been in place throughout most of the nineteenth century. In this order Great Britain held the hegemonic position, possessing by far the largest global empire and having a preponderant share of the world's wealth and international trade. The growth of Germany's industrial strength, which in the all-important sector of iron and steel overtook Britain in the final decade of the century, led to ever more strident demands for a larger share of the world power and influence which went with it (Table 3.1). This particularly took the form of a general desire for a greater German participation in world affairs, encapsulated in that favourite phrase of the Kaiser, 'a place in the sun' (Gauss, 1915: 180–3).[1]

Michel Korinman referred to this as the period when Germany *pensait le monde* (thought in global terms), and since Germany was 'a land of geographers' the aspiration to *Weltmacht* had been firmly grounded in a tradition of geographical and geopolitical thinking (Korinman 1990: 9).[2] The vital importance for Germany of the alliance with Austria-Hungary was stressed by geographers such as Partsch (Partsch, 1903) and political scientists such as Naumann (Naumann, 1916), and the consolidation of *Mitteleuropa* around the two Germanic powers was seen as being essential to the strength and security

Table 3.1: The industrial strength of Great Britain, France and Germany in 1900 and 1914

	Great Britain		France		Germany	
	1900	1914	1900	1914	1900	1914
Population (millions)	37.0	40.8	38.5	39.1	56.4	64.9
Coal	228.8	270	33.4	27.5	109.3	161.4
Iron ore	14.2	15.1	5.4	11.3	12.8	20.9
Pig iron	9.1	9.1	2.7	2.7	7.5	12.4
Steel	5.0	8.0	1.6	2.8	6.5	13.8

Source: B.R. Mitchell, *European Historical Statistics*, Basingstoke: Macmillan, 1975.
Note: All production figures in millions of tonnes

of the German Empire. There was also a parallel conviction that truly global power could be attained only through the development of sea power, and the Kaiser reiterated his belief that Germany's future lay 'on the water' (Gauss, 1915: 126–7). In *Politische Geographie* Ratzel had shown himself to be well aware of the importance of sea power (Ratzel, 1897: 486–542). Anticipating Mackinder, he had pointed out the historic opposition between the *Landmächter* (land powers) and the *Seemächter* (sea powers), reaching the conclusion that *Seemacht* provided the quickest and easiest route to the attainment of world power. However, Ratzel considered that a truly great power had need of both (Ratzel, 1900: foreword). This was a view which had already been expressed by the American naval strategist Alfred Mahan, and his book *The Influence of Sea Power upon History* was well known in Germany. Mahan developed his thesis on the primacy of sea power by particular reference to Great Britain and the British Empire, and this was to have a profound impact on German thinking during the years leading up to World War I (Mahan, 1890).

The result of this was that informed German opinion divided into two schools of thought. These consisted respectively of those who favoured the primacy of land power and those who felt that greater emphasis should be placed on sea power. Given the budgetary constraints, it was inevitable that the two views came into conflict with one another. The former stressed the importance of an army strong enough to deter aggression and the consolidation of a powerful Central European bloc at the core of which lay the Dual Alliance of Germany and Austria-Hungary.[3] Above all, the land policy entailed looking towards the east as a source of strength, and it came to focus particularly on the idea of the *Drang nach Osten* (drive to the East). This entailed both the development of closer relations with the countries of Eastern Europe and the undertaking of grand projects, most notable among which was the Berlin–Baghdad Railway. The object of this was to create a direct land link between Germany and the Middle East via the Balkans and Turkey. Sea power was promoted by the *Deutscher Kolonialverein*, which advocated the acquisition of colonies and the buildup of that naval strength which was seen as being an essential prerequisite for national greatness. The ideas of Mahan were central to this school of thought (Tuchman, 1966: 133). They had a particular appeal for the Kaiser, who, while very much disposed to view Great Britain as being Germany's arch-rival, saw that country also as being the principal model in the implementation of the policy of *Weltmacht*.[4] This was the rationale for the construction of a powerful fleet, something which was to cause particular alarm in Britain and to lead to that naval arms race which brought relations between the two countries to breaking-point in the years leading up to World War I (Massie, 1992).[5] In practice Germany embarked upon a dual approach, entailing an attempt both to consolidate her position in Europe and to acquire possessions overseas. Thus land and sea power together played a significant part in the German perception of Germany's future international role, entailing the dangerous strategy of challenging the status quo both in Europe and in the world as a whole.[6]

Geopolitical perspectives of this sort have been seen by some historians as underlying German middle-class opinion in the years before World War I. Calleo, for instance, maintains that the Germans were not only aggressive against the status quo but also had ultimate hegemonic ambitions (Calleo, 1978: 152). However, it is difficult to substantiate the existence of some Machiavellian plan for world domination by reference to the geopolitical literature alone (Parker, 1985: 56). Partsch saw peace as being the great prize of the *Mitteleuropa* policy, and this was to be secured by constructing a strong political edifice (Partsch, 1903). Likewise, many of the advocates of the colonial policy envisaged proceeding stealthily by means of agreement with Great Britain on a more equitable distribution of the world's land and resources (Taylor, 1938). Yet the idea of *Weltmacht*, widely disseminated in German political and academic circles, provided a focus for German ambitions, and by so doing certainly contributed to the build up of the heady atmosphere of the times (Amery, 1939: 45–64). When it came, the war was seen by a number of political and geopolitical writers as providing the historic opportunity for the challenge to be mounted and for the grand ideas to be put into practice. During the first two years of World War I there were substantial additions to the literature on this subject. Most influential among these was Friedrich Naumann's *Mitteleuropa*, published in Germany in 1915 and translated into English in the following year (Naumann, 1915, 1916). The whole tenor of this book is far more strident than had been that of Partsch a decade earlier. Naumann stressed the importance of war in bringing about change. 'It is only in wartime that our mood enables us to entertain broadly transforming thoughts of reconstruction,' he wrote. The foundations of what he called 'this new structure' (*Mitteleuropa*) had to be laid during the war 'in the midst of bloodshed and the upheaval of nations' (*ibid.*: 1). Naumann saw the creation of a united *Mitteleuropa* as being central to the German war aims. '*Mitteleuropa* is the fruit of war,' he maintained. 'We have sat together in the war's economic prison, we have fought together, we are determined to live together' (*ibid.*: 287). In his introduction to the English edition, W.J. Ashley expressed the opinion that this was 'far away the most important book that has appeared in Germany since the world-conflict began'. Naumann, said Ashley, had been the most widely read political writer in Germany, and the war 'gave him an opportunity he was quick to seize'. Ashley considered the book to be 'largely the formulation of current German thought' and as such was not an original contribution. The consolidation of *Mitteleuropa* as 'one of the world powers of the future', he said, had become 'the dominating thought in German politics,' and Naumann had translated 'aspirations' into a 'systematic scheme' (*ibid.*: vii–xiv).

During World War I German translations of some of Kjellén's most important works also appeared. These included *Die Grossmächte der Gegenwart* (1914) and *Der Staat als Lebenform* (1917). These books made a considerable impact on thinking about Germany's future role and the importance of the war in the promotion of this. 'War', said Kjellén, 'is like wine, it always tells the truth' (Kjellén, 1916: 3). Like Naumann, Kjellén believed that the war gave the opportunity for the creation of a new geopolitics, and his proposed *Mitteleuropa* bloc included Scandinavia and the Baltic region as well as the Balkans. It thus envisaged the creation of a geopolitical region of formidable proportions in the centre of Europe, and the inevitable consequence of this was seen by Kjellén as being the marginalisation of the influence of both France and Russia. Desires such as these were then translated into the 'war aims', which came to be more clearly enunciated as the war progressed. While what Ashley termed the 'systematic scheme' was most in evidence in the East, necessary adjustments in the West came to focus on the acquisition of Belgium so as to secure firmer control over the Rhinelands and give Germany better access to the sea.

The German geographical community as a whole applauded ideas of this sort and proved ready to swing into line behind the use of geography in order to promote Germany's national interests. Korinman observed that it was the war which focused the 'theoretical reflections' of the German geographers on matters which had previously been of only marginal concern to them (Korinman, 1990: 135). 'War is the motor of geography,' said Richard Hennig, and it had to be used in order to bring about desirable changes to the national situation (Hennig, 1917).

The development of such grand and transformational schemes for the future made the defeat of November 1918 all the more traumatic. Such was the magnitude of the reversal of the country's fortunes that there was massive resistance to accepting the permanence of the condition to which it had been reduced. 'We are sitting in a waiting room called Europe,' observed Kastner. 'We are living provisionally' (Stirk, 1945: 89). Underlying the collapse of Germany as a great power lay the total failure to bring about that transformation of the world order designed to give Germany the 'place in the sun' so coveted by both Kaiser and people. Instead of a *Mitteleuropa* stretching from the Rhine to the Danube and beyond was a minuscule Austria, shorn of its enormous empire, and a truncated Germany from which the Treaty of Versailles had detached a large slice of the old Prussia in the east and Alsace-Lorraine in the west. It is unsurprising that in this atmosphere of exceptional bleakness the nation turned towards political ideas which appeared to give hope, and these ranged from the far left to the far right of the political spectrum. Both National Socialism and *Geopolitik* were among such ideas, and they shared a common place of origin: Munich. In the turbulence of post-war Germany, no place was more turbulent than the Bavarian capital. Located as it was in the middle Danubian region at the heart of the Germanic world, Munich was where some of the most extreme solutions to Germany's problems were proposed and attempts were made to translate them into reality. It was inevitable that the paths of National Socialism and *Geopolitik* should have crossed. German National Socialism represented an adaptation of Italian Fascism to the conditions of a weak and ruined Germany, while *Geopolitik* represented an adaptation of *Politische Geographie* to the needs of national recovery. In the melting-pot of Munich in the 1920s the two were to forge an uneasy alliance which lasted for a generation.

The *Geopolitik* which arose in Germany after World War I had its roots in the ideas of both Ratzel and Kjellén. Its practitioners subscribed to the Ratzelian principal that a thorough knowledge of a country's geography is an essential requirement for the formulation and implementation of policies in its best interests. In the context of its times, the main purpose of the *Geopolitiker* was to produce an effective strategy for the recovery of Germany so as to enable it to resume its position as a great power. Furthermore, they were convinced that the rise of Germany in the late nineteenth century had been very much a hit-or-miss affair and that the defeat had been in part brought about by an imperfect understanding of the country's geographical situation and the limitations which it imposed. It was intended that *Geopolitik* should rectify this and thus from the outset it entailed the application of geography to the needs of the state. '*Geopolitik* is concerned with the spatial requirements of the state while political geography examines only its spatial conditions,' said Maull, 'and by its conclusions [it] seeks to guide practical politics' (Maull, 1936: 31).

Throughout the 1920s and 1930s the leading exponent of *Geopolitik* was Professor General Karl Haushofer (1869–1946). A geographer and a former general in the Bavarian army, Haushofer increasingly came to see geographical knowledge as being something which could play a major role in Germany's recovery from defeat and humiliation. He identified the 'ignorance of geographical realities' displayed by Germany's leaders as having been one of the main causes for the country's defeat, and set out vigorously to remedy this situation (Stoakes, 1986: 141). The challenge of geopolitics, said Haushofer, came from an 'elementary craving for better scientific protection of the political unit' (Haushofer, 1929: 711). His geographical background made him well acquainted with the work of Ratzel, and he and his associates embarked on the adaptation of *Politische Geographie* to the problems of post-war Germany. The key date in the development of Haushofer's geopolitical thinking was 1908, when he was sent on a mission to Japan and the Far East (Heske, 1994d: 111– 14). It was as a result of what he saw there that he began his project on the geographical foundations of world power. He was well aware of Kjellén's works, and these and his correspondence with Kjellén himself influenced the formulation of his ideas (Stoakes, 1986: 141 note 6).

Following the defeat of 1918 the feeling was widespread among German geographers that the Treaty of Versailles had been a harsh and unjust settlement and that it should be overturned. However, there was considerable disagreement within German geographical circles as to the extent to which geographers should be directly involved in political action. The geographical community divided on this issue, and Haushofer was among those who became convinced that geographers had a positive duty to play an active role. A bitter debate then followed between those who upheld the claims of 'classical' political geography and those who were attracted by the 'new' *Geopolitik* (Korinman, 1990: 152). According to Haushofer, political geography was the study of the distribution of states on the surface of the earth and the conditions in which they operated while geopolitics was the study of 'political activity in natural space' (Haushofer, 1925: 138). This rather general distinction was taken further by Lautensach, who maintained that while in political geography the state is seen as being a static object, 'geopolitics concerns political processes in the past and the present. The concept is essentially a dynamic one' (Korinman, 1990: 155). 'The assumption that scientific investigation could provide some insight into the mysterious workings of political destiny', observed Stoakes, 'effectively marked the point of departure from political geography to geopolitics' (Stoakes, 1986: 148).

In 1924 Haushofer became the editor of the journal *Zeitschrift für Geopolitik*, published in Munich. While the avowed purpose of this journal was the study of the new 'science' of geopolitics, its underlying purpose was the examination of the geopolitical elements of the German situation with a view to altering them to Germany's advantage. The territoriality of Germany was analysed in order to understand the realities which lay behind it and the implications which these had for effective policy-making. Such matters as British world power and the problems faced by Italy and Japan were given space in *Zeitschrift*, and attention was also paid to wider issues, especially those which had an impact on Germany. A fundamental difference from Ratzel was that while the latter had, in Brunhes's phrase, been able 'to discern humanity through Germany', the discernment of Haushofer and *Zeitschrift* usually stopped at Germany. Underlying Haushofer's concerns was a Spenglerian perception of the more general decline of Europe as a whole and his conviction that Germany was the country which was destined to lead the continent back to its old position at the heart of a Eurocentric world.

Just as the immediate concern of *Geopolitik* was with Germany, viewed in the context of *Mitteleuropa*, so its wider concern was with Europe viewed in the context of the world as a whole. In this part of the project Haushofer was strongly influenced by the ideas of Halford Mackinder. He considered Mackinder's 1904 article to be 'the greatest of all geographical world views', referring to it as a 'geopolitical masterwork' (Parker, 1985: 58). Its adaptation to Germany became the basis for his own world-view (*ibid.*: 73–5). The development of the *Geopolitik der Panideen* (the pan-regions) demarcated a future German sphere of influence which was placed into the global context (Haushofer, 1931). Subsequently the whole project was extended to the geopolitics of Italy and Japan, the two countries which were to be Germany's principal allies during World War II. Mussolini's ambitions for Italian domination in the Mediterranean, *Mare Nostro*, were examined and justified on geopolitical grounds, and they were deemed to be quite consistent with Germany's own aspirations to domination in *Mitteleuropa*. Despite Italy's long-held ambitions to great-power status, its inferior industrial base consigned the country to being a far weaker power than Germany, and therefore Haushofer considered that Italy posed no threat to the dominant position of Germany in Europe as a whole.[7]

From the outset, Haushofer had always taken a particular interest in Japan, a country which he saw as being a kind of prototype for geopolitical analysis (Haushofer, 1913). When Japan became an ally with the signing of the Anti-Comintern Pact in 1936, its importance in German geopolitical thinking was considerably enhanced. Japan's projected role as the dominant power of the Far East was then justified in *Zeitschrift* in much the same terms as was German dominance in Europe. Japan was presented as being one of the great world powers of the future, the centre of one of the pan-regions, and instrumental, together with Germany, in replacing the old Anglocentric world order with a new one jointly controlled by Germany and Japan (Haushofer, 1924).

Other important geopoliticians working in Munich and elsewhere in Germany included Ewald Banse, Wulf Siewert, Colin Ross, Johannes Kühn, Richard Hennig, Kurt Vowinckel and Karl Haushofer's own son, Albrecht. They and many others played a significant role in setting the geopolitical agenda. As editor of *Zeitschrift*, Karl Haushofer remained the dominating presence, but by the 1930s the whole project had become a collective one.

From the outset it was claimed that *Geopolitik* was *Wissenschaft und Kunst* (a science and an art), and the basic theory which underlay it was that of evolutionary biology. As developed in Munich, *Geopolitik* became a sort of synthesis of history, economics, politics and the physical sciences fused together by the application of the spatial or territorial perspective. The state was looked upon as being an organism, 'a supra-individual living being' which conformed to biological laws (Stoakes, 1986: 148). This state organism was territorial and the requirements for its success were spatial. The terminology used to express this condition was basically a Ratzelian one. Thus the state existed in *Raum* and its growth and development necessitated *Lebensraum*. *Lebensraumkunde* (the science of living space) was the study of the significance of geography in the success of states (Korinman, 1990: 252–4). The possession of *Grossraum* (large space) was the key to the freedom and security of the powerful state. *Grossraum denken*, thinking in terms of vast spaces, was the hallmark of a great power (Parker, 1985: 60). It was part of that *Selbstbestimmungstreben*, the strife for self-determination, which distinguished such powers from the others. Dynamic states expand and inevitably absorb the smaller and less successful ones. Those states with a truly global reach are the *raumüberwindende* (space-hopping) states, and they are to be contrasted with those lesser states which are *raumgebundende* (space-bound).

Although *Geopolitik* was regarded as being a science, it was an applied science. Geographical knowledge was to be 'the "scientific" basis by which to forecast developments and to prescribe future policy' (Stoakes, 1986: 147). In Haushofer's words, it is 'applied theory, capable of directing practical policies up to the necessary point of departure from firm ground' (Haushofer *et al.*, 1928: 27). However, Haushofer admitted that the distinction between the pure and applied was never made very clear. 'The borderline between pure science and practical science is easily crossed,' he said, and in the end he admitted that he had 'overstepped those borders occasionally' (Stoakes, 1986: 148).

There was thus bound to be a close relationship between *Geopolitik* of this sort and state policy objectives. In this relationship, 'policy would be gleaned from the study of ways in which political processes were bound by earth-realities' (Livingstone, 1992: 247), and its objective was quite simply 'to discover the geopolitical determinants of political action' (Stoakes, 1986: 148). While it was claimed that *Geopolitik* was nomothetic, the preoccupation with one particular state meant that the reality was a rather different one. As Vallaux had put it, there can be no science of the particular.

The whole question of the dichotomy of land and sea power was seen by Haushofer as having been 'one of the most pervasive phenomena of geopolitics' (Haushofer, 1927: 23). Both were important, but there were geopolitical constraints on their use. Thus while sea power was acknowledged to be the most effective for *Raumüberwindende*, he conceded that it was also possible for land power to assert control over great spaces in a different way. Land power was seen as being essential to Germany's best interests, and this entailed the pursuit of both the policies of *Mitteleuropa* and *Drang nach Osten*. Haushofer saw Germany's future as being above all an eastern one linked to the Middle East, Russia and Central Asia. Out of this he developed the thesis of the *Panideen*, which envisaged the rise of *Grosslebensformen*, large geopolitical entities on a continental scale. The most important of these were *PanEuropa*, *PanAsien* and *PanAmerika*, and their formation and growth centred on the *Schicksalsraumen*, the spaces of destiny. Needless to say, Europe's *Schicksalsraum* lay in Germany and that of Asia lay in Japan.

One of the most central features of *Geopolitik* was its environmental determinism. The basic proposition underlying such concepts as *Boden* (soil) and *Schicksalsraum* was that the destiny of a people was written in its physical environment. It was essentially places rather than people which determined the course of history and the rise and fall of powers. Inevitably such environmentalism came into conflict with the racialist agenda of the Nazis. In its pure form geopolitics was at variance with that racialism, derived from Darwinism, which had made so powerful an impact on European thought during the later nineteenth century and which was used to justify notions of European supremacy. It was also used to justify imperialism as the onward march of progress and civilisation, and this became particularly important in German ideas. While the concept of the *Volk* was part of the geopolitics of the nation and the state, the cultural characteristics of this were rooted in the *Boden*, and the *Volk* itself was always subject to the constraints of the environment. The *Volksboden*, manifestations of which were the *Kulturboden*, the *Sprachsboden* and, ultimately, the *Reichsboden*, underlay all else (Parker, 1985: 64).

It is clear from the above that, far from being identical, the basic propositions upon which the ideas of the Nazis and the geopoliticians were based were very different. *Geopolitik* was emphatically not the geography of Nazism in the way in which it was assumed to be by many Western political geographers during World War II. There was certainly a close relationship between the two which went back to the early days in Munich. The key to this was the close friendship between Karl Haushofer and Deputy Führer Rudolf Hess, who had been introduced to *Geopolitik* when a student of Haushofer at the University of Munich after World War I (Hess, 1986: 33–4). Clearly a convert, Hess believed that 'the ruler trained in political geography has a comprehensive conception of the world' (*ibid.*: 32), and he became the conduit for acquainting the higher echelons of the Nazi party with geopolitical ideas. As part of this, Haushofer was invited to give talks to selected Nazi gatherings. After the Munich *putsch* of 1923 both Hitler and Hess were imprisoned in the fortress of Landsberg, and Haushofer paid frequent visits there to see his friend and disciple.[8]

It was during this time that Hitler wrote *Mein Kampf*, and in it he employed such geopolitical concepts as *Mitteleuropa, Lebensraum* and *Drang nach Osten* (Hitler, 1939). It is virtually certain that, on his visits to Hess, Haushofer also met Hitler, and the use of geopolitical terminology suggests the influence of Haushofer's ideas – possibly via Hess – on the Führer's thinking. The most one can say with certainty is that the whole climate of the times was congenial to the dissemination of geopolitical ideas and that these certainly entered the potent mix which passed for Nazi doctrine. These were then used to justify the policies pursued by the Third Reich, particularly in the field of territorial expansion.

While Haushofer was a strong advocate of Germany's eastern destiny, this did not lead him to the view that war with Russia was either a necessary or an inevitable consequence of this. On the contrary, he saw cooperation with the Soviet Union as being the best strategy for Germany to adopt. He held to his early conviction that in the drive towards *Weltmacht* it was Great Britain rather than Russia which was the major global adversary. His vision thus made him much closer to the policy which underlay the Treaty of Rapallo in 1925 than that behind the Treaty of Brest-Litovsk in 1918 and, subsequently, to the policy underlying the Nazi–Soviet Pact of 1939 rather than Operation Barbarossa in 1941.[9] He certainly envisaged a greater *Mitteleuropa* led by a powerful Germany and extending deep into Eastern Europe, but he did not consider that this would necessarily involve a massive programme of military conquest.

In May 1941, six weeks before Operation Barbarossa, which unleashed the *Wehrmacht* on the Soviet Union, Germany was shaken by the news that Rudolf Hess had flown to Great Britain on his own. While the official explanation of the whole bizarre event was that it was nothing more than an unwise personal attempt by the Deputy Führer to terminate the war with Great Britain so as to give Germany a free hand in the east, recent research has suggested that the connivance of elements within the top leadership of the Third Reich, and even of Hitler himself, cannot be discounted (Sereny, 1995: 240–4). Hitler had made it clear that he did not welcome the continuation of the war with Britain and appears to have been quite prepared, in any peace settlement between the two countries, for Britain to have kept its empire. Whatever the truth behind the Hess mission, it appears that both Karl and Albrecht Haushofer had been in the know about it (Korinman, 1990: 323). Karl himself had been deeply involved in the idea of a peace mission and was associated with a number of activities having a bearing on it (Sereny, 1995: 242). Both the Haushofers were immediately arrested and, although they were soon released, from then on Karl's influence waned, and *Geopolitik* itself was more carefully scrutinised and brought more closely into line with Nazi ideas and policies (Korinman, 1990: 318–21). Unfettered territorial aggression and racialism reigned supreme during the remaining years of the Third Reich, and the two in combination produced the Holocaust. The gulf which lay between the Nazis, with their belief in the German *Herrenvolk* (master race), the parallel belief that the Slavs were *Untermenschen* (subhuman) and their strident and obsessive anti-Semitism, and *Geopolitik*, with its environmentalist philosophy and its emphasis on the importance of *Raum* in the destiny of nations, now became ever wider.

Since the establishment of the Third Reich, the geopoliticians had had to live with the knowledge of what their political masters were really like, and over the years most of them appeared to have found little difficulty in reaching a *modus vivendi* with them. In any case there had always been a grey area between the two. Some geopoliticians were themselves racist, while some – but not many – Nazis were prepared to concede the importance of the environment. As a result of this, 'certain mergings' took place between 'the rationalistic, causal, law-bound, scientific, environmental determinism' which characterised *Geopolitik* and 'the romantic, subjectivist, Herder-like fascination with the *Volk*' (Livingstone, 1992: 247). The extent of this is to be seen in the way in which *Rassenlehr* (race theory) was developed as a category within *Geopolitik*. The concepts of *Volk* and *Raum* came to be specifically integrated and there was a shift from an emphasis on the physical environment of the *Boden* to the overall *Kulturlandschaft* (cultural landscape) created by, and imbued with, the imprint of its human occupants (*ibid.*: 247–8). This was encapsulated in the ideological theory of *Blut und Boden* (blood and soil), which asserted that *Geopolitik* was the theory of the connections between *Rasse und Raum im Volkerschicksal* (race and space in the destiny of nations). This was then used in the justification of the occupation and settlement of Eastern Europe by and for the *Herrenvolk* during the early 1940s (Heske, 1994b: 20–1).

Thus, as the struggle intensified after 1941, *Geopolitik*, the ideas of which had been derived from Kjellén, Ratzel and Mackinder and reformulated by Haushofer, was overwhelmed and altered by its powerful and terrifying political partner. 'Unreformed' *Geopolitik* came to be viewed by the Nazis as placing undue emphasis on space and environment at the expense of race and was therefore quite unacceptable to them (Livingstone, 1992: 247).

From the outset Haushofer appears to have wanted to put some distance between *Geopolitik* and the Nazis. After World War I there had been many right-wing parties in Germany which had objectives similar to those of the geopoliticians. However, as the Nazis grew rapidly in power and influence the very real possibility of putting their theories into practice proved irresistible for the practitioners of a discipline which by its own admission was *engagé*. By 1944 many of the geopoliticians had become increasingly concerned about the way both the war and the Nazi regime were going. They had come to question radically not just the role played by *Geopolitik* itself in formulating German strategy but the wisdom of its close association with the Nazis. None was more critical than Karl's son Albrecht Haushofer. Albrecht, who had followed his father into the study of *Geopolitik*, was by profession a diplomat with considerable knowledge of German foreign policy. Despite also being a close friend of Hess, he had always been less warm than Karl towards the Nazis, and from 1941 on he became increasingly troubled by them and the effects which they were having on Germany. By the time of Hess's flight he was in close contact with opposition groups and was a member of the Kreisau Circle, which was engaged in planning a post-Nazi future for Germany.[10] He certainly had knowledge of the failed attempt on Hitler's life (the 'Bomb Plot') which took place at the Fuhrer's East Prussian headquarters on 20 July 1944, and he, together with Karl, was arrested and interrogated by no less a person than Reinhard Heydrich, head of the Reich Security Office (Korinman, 1990: 324). While Karl was again quickly released, Albrecht was held throughout the winter of 1944–45 while the *Volksgericht* (People's Court), presided over by the infamous Roland Freisler, daily passed sentences of death on opponents of the regime. On 23 April 1945, with the Russians already in occupation of the eastern half of the city, Albrecht was executed in Berlin. *Zeitschrift für Geopolitik*, which had become more and more impregnated with Nazi racialism, had already ceased publication in October 1944. Following the arrival of the

Americans in southern Germany, Karl was arrested, but after interrogation the decision was taken to release him. On 13 March 1946 the bodies of Karl and Martha Haushofer were found at their home in Bavaria. Both had committed suicide.[11]

During the autumn of 1945 Haushofer had met Colonel Edmund Walsh, the self-styled American 'geopolitician' who was impressed with Haushofer and his ideas. Walsh accepted the legitimacy of *Geopolitik* as a discipline and saw its main crime as having been its association with the Nazis rather than its ideas *per se*. 'I am categorically opposed to [Haushofer] in the political consequences which he has drawn from his theory and writings,' he later wrote, but conceded '50% scientific truth' in his work (Walsh, 1946: 8). Walsh then accompanied Haushofer to Nuremberg, where in October 1945 Haushofer was interrogated as a witness and met Rudolf Hess for the last time. As a result of this experience Haushofer then wrote his *Apologie der deutschen Geopolitik*, in which he attempted to justify his work (Korinman, 1990: 324–6). Maintaining to the end the scientific character of *Geopolitik*, he claimed that he had never held to the principle of 'right or wrong my country' (*sic*). However, he admitted to not having made an adequate distinction between pure and applied science and having transgressed the boundaries between the two. While he continued to maintain that *Geopolitik* was scientific, he maintained also that the geopolitician could not be expected to be just 'a machine to produce science', as he was also 'a man of flesh and blood' (*ibid.*: 325). It was only to be expected, he wrote, that after 1918 geopoliticians would be concerned with the sorry state of their truncated country and particularly with the inadequacy of its *Lebensraum*. Despite this, Haushofer claimed that there was nevertheless a 'pure' geopolitical thinking which was neutral and independent of particular interests and players. The conclusion of his *Apologie* was interesting and significant. He asserted that although his interest in *Geopolitik* had in the first instance been stimulated by Ratzel and Kjellén, his thinking was essentially founded on the work of the Anglo-Saxon geographers. Among these he singled out particularly Alfred Mahan, Brookes-Adams, Thomas Holdich, Halford Mackinder and Isaiah Bowman. This statement was clearly intended to link geopolitics with political geography as it was understood in the Western countries, and in making it he was asserting that German *Geopolitik* was to be seen not as something uniquely aberrant but as being part of a great tradition with a common scientific methodology. It was also an assertion that, even though they might not choose to use the term 'geopolitics', Western geographers were in fact engaged on the same project (*ibid.*: 325–6). It was Haushofer's Parthian shot into a geopolitical world which was already collapsing in the ruins of war.

Political geographers in the Western countries had from the outset expressed considerable disapproval of the whole project of German *Geopolitik*. Halford Mackinder was swift to dissociate himself from the work of the geopoliticians and invariably used the term 'political geography' to describe his own work (Parker, 1982: 147–85). The search for laws, and the determinism associated with it, was particularly unattractive to Mackinder. The relegation of free will and the restriction of human choice was quite as unacceptable to him as it was to the geographers of the *vidalien* possibilist school in France. It was its association with the Third Reich and its policies which particularly drew the attention of American political geographers to *Geopolitik*, and Isaiah Bowman was among the first to warn of its implications. 'Geopolitics has simplicity and certitude,' said Bowman, 'but what is shown in its writings and in German policy is illusion, masquerade, apology and bavardage' (Bowman, 1942: 658). During World War II, German-speaking political scientists working in the United States, many of whom had themselves fled from the Nazis, were quick to alert Americans to the dangers of the sort of geopolitics which was being practised in Germany and the support which it was giving to the policies of the Nazis (Parker, 1985: 103). Important among them were Andreas Dorpalen, Karl Wittfogel, Andrew Gyorgy, Robert Strausz-Hupé and Hans Weigert. Commenting on Haushofer's debt to Mackinder, Strausz-Hupé asserted that 'Mackinder's vision accorded only too well with the martial philosophy of world power or downfall which explains so much about German national pathology'. Referring to what he called the 'Wagnerian mentality' he went on to observe that 'The impending struggle promised to be titanic; the goal – the domination of the Eurasian Heartland – was as challengingly remote as the far-off places towards which Wagner's heroes interminably travel' (Strausz-Hupé, 1942: 70). The nature and objectives of the new German 'science' were given considerable coverage everywhere from the newspapers to the learned journals (Parker, 1985: 102). Hans Weigert was convinced that geopolitics lay behind the Nazi strategy for world conquest. Writing of 'Dr Karl Haushofer and his Geopolitical Institute in Munich, who owes much to Sir Halford Mackinder's teaching', Weigert asserted that 'It is here that this cold, hard, dynamic science of war-geography, backed by propaganda and maps of terrifying suggestion, is hammered out' (Weigert, 1941: 3). Weigert quoted Frederic Sondern's, dramatic assertion that there were '1000 scientists behind Hitler' led by 'Major-General Dr. Karl Haushofer'. 'Their ideas,' asserted Sondern, 'their charts, maps, statistics, information and plans have dictated Hitler's moves from the very beginning' (*ibid.*: 5). 'Dr. Haushofer and his men', he asserted, 'dominate Hitler's thinking', and, in Sondern's opinion, Haushofer had virtually dictated *Mein Kampf* (*ibid.*: 6). While Weigert dismissed the more extreme assertions of Sondern and others, he certainly took the view that the geopoliticians lay behind the policies of the Third Reich. 'It is apparent', he wrote, 'that the Haushofer school has, to a certain degree, abandoned strict geographical determinism and has expanded into the realm of metaphysics' (*ibid.*: 11–12). Weigert concluded that 'The *Weltanschauung* of geographic materialism is but a dynamic nihilism which can flourish only in a nation which has buried its gods and which instead is worshipping Mars' (*ibid*: 31).

Thus geopolitics, now firmly in the guise of German *Geopolitik*, was utterly condemned by those Anglo-Saxon geographers from whose ranks Haushofer claimed to have drawn his inspiration. Weigert saw this kind of geopolitics as being in its 'twilight' and having no future (Weigert, 1942). However, the difference between what such geographers termed political geography and *Geopolitik* of the 'unreformed' variety lay less in the subject matter than in the use to which it was being put. What thinkers like Walsh opposed was the conclusions drawn by the German geopoliticians and the political consequences arising from these. Considerations of national self-interest also underlay much of the political geography practised in the Western countries, and many of its leading exponents had themselves been actively involved in the political world. Halford Mackinder had been for a time a Member of Parliament and Lord Curzon, an enthusiastic political geographer, had held the offices of Viceroy of India and Foreign Secretary. Both had seen Russia as being the greatest threat to the British Empire and, in the wake of the 1917 Revolution, Curzon dispatched Mackinder to Russia as his emissary (Parker, 1982: 47–9). Mackinder's secret brief was to encourage nationalism in the Ukraine and among other non-Russian nationalities, and in this way to weaken the new communist state. Underlying the famous world-view which Mackinder had first presented as the Pivot theory in 1904 (see Chapter 7) lay his concern for the future security of the British Empire. Securing the national interests was also the underlying theme in the work of the French political geographers. *La France de l'Est*, Vidal de la Blache's last work, written during World War I, was in many ways a geopolitical polemic justifying the reunion of Alsace-Lorraine with France (Vidal de la Blache, 1917). In 1919 a number of French geographers acted as specialist advisers on the new international frontiers at the Congress of Versailles, and their conclusions accorded well with French policy in regard to Central and Eastern Europe (Parker, 1987c: 14). The appeal to French geographers by Lucien Gallois in *Annales de Géographie* to pay more attention to the new political geography of Europe sounds almost like a clarion call to fulfil their duty to the nation. He clearly had French interests foremost in mind when he wrote of the importance of 'the study of states and political organisations which these [new] arrangements will bring into being' (Gallois, 1919: 248). André Chéradame's *Le Plan Pangermaniste Démasqué* was in many ways a riposte to Naumann's *Mitteleuropa*. Dismissing the German writer's 'peace state' in the heart of Europe, Chéradame saw the Pan-Germanist agenda as being nothing less than the domination of the continent. Pan-Germany was to extend from the Baltic Sea to the Persian Gulf and its axial belt was the Berlin–Baghdad railway (Chéradame, 1916). After the Congress of Versailles, German geographers were bitter in their condemnation of the 'politicising' of geography by their French colleagues. 'They are now accusing us of having founded political geography,' wrote Johann Solch. 'What, then, do they think French geography is?' (Korinman, 1990: 147). De Martonne's *l'Europe Centrale* came in for harsh criticism from across the Rhine. 'The author is making propaganda under the cover of scientific objectivity,' wrote Solch in his review of the book in *Geographische Zeitschrift*, and he accused the French geographer of 'the mixing of science and politics'. 'What has become of French geography?' bemoaned Solch. 'Does it not frequently cease to be a science when it is considering political problems?' (Solch, 1933: 236). Korinman comments that after World War I German geographers reproached their French colleagues for engaging in what was soon was to be known as *Geopolitik* (Korinman, 1990).

A similar concern for American interests is clearly discernible in the works of Alfred Mahan and Isaiah Bowman. There had been a growing realisation after the Spanish–American War of 1898 of the emergence of the United States as a world power of the first rank, and even of the possibility of its becoming the successor state to Great Britain. Mahan intended his analysis of the importance of sea power less as an academic exercise than as an argument for an American global role and of the necessity for a powerful fleet in order to bring this about (Mahan, 1890). The fact that his ideas made more of an impact in Germany than they did in his own country was little more than an unwelcome side-effect. Similarly Bowman in *The New World* was not simply engaged in presenting a totally objective geopolitical analysis of the situation in the wake of World War I (Bowman, 1922). That 'New World' of Bowman's agenda entailed bringing to an end the territorial exclusivity of the European empires and extending the 'open door' policy, which had been proving so successful in the Far East where American influence was at its strongest, to the rest of the world.[12] It involved a global reorganisation which, in its way, was as fundamental as that proposed by Haushofer. Like Haushofer, Bowman was engaged in promoting what he saw as being the best interests of his own country, and in this capacity he came to be dubbed 'the American geopolitician'. 'Bowman affected to disdain geopolitics as a pseudo-scientific ideology,' commented Livingstone, 'but ... this was an apologetic move designed to out-manoeuvre the danger of witnessing himself cast as the American mirror image of Haushofer' (Livingstone, 1992: 252). Neil Smith is of the opinion that Bowman was 'keen to be the American counterpart of Haushofer' but did not want to be 'cast as the American Haushofer *per se*' (Smith, 1994a: 23–4). This demonstrates Bowman's own ambivalence about geopolitics, which he clearly found attractive yet from which he wanted to keep his distance. He was either afraid of it, or – in Livingstone's view – was afraid of the geopolitician which he saw in himself. Livingstone's conclusion was that 'Bowman's political geography was every bit as conditioned by social circumstances as the German variety'. He observed that 'The territorial border between science and politics was one boundary Bowman just could not map' (Livingstone, 1992: 253).

While the geographical study of the national interest in the United States was thus pursued under the overall designation of political geography, following American entry into World War II there was a surge of interest in geopolitics. This was the age of 'barbershop geopolitics', and there was considerable fascination with the new 'German science' (Parker, 1985: 102). 'Geopolitics has migrated from Germany to America,' said Bowman (Bowman, 1942: 648). A poem in the *New Yorker* by M. Tagoff contained the couplet:

> Ah blessed styptic on the nicks!
> O brave new geopolitics.

This new interest was in complete contrast to the relative indifference to foreign policy which had characterised the isolationist years. 'Global geography was simply not in our blood,' lamented Hans Weigert, and this lack had to be addressed. It meant sweeping away what he called 'yesterday's geography', and so 'letting us see the world in the image of dynamic maps, instead of the static maps of times past' (Weigert, 1942: 131). That ignorance which had encouraged the 'myth and magic' aspect of *Geopolitik* would then give place to a better understanding of what it was really all about. Weigert justified this objective by using one of Haushofer's favourite Latin quotations, *fas est ab hoste doceri* (it is a duty to learn from the enemy). The knowledge so gained could then be used to create what Weigert called a 'humanised geopolitics' which would enable Americans to comprehend more clearly the nature of the world and the role which their own country now was called on to play (*ibid.*).

Despite the great interest which it provoked, geopolitics did not prove to be as readily adaptable to the American academic scene as might have been thought from the first wave of interest in it. The resistance to it within the American geographical community in the 1940s was very similar to that of many German geographers two decades earlier. Basically this was because it had been altogether too evidently involved in the political process to be acceptable as an academic discipline. Also, it was seen as being an import from the enemy, and as such it was an uncomfortable guest in the Allied camp. The most that Edmund Walsh would concede was guilt by association, but others were harsher in their judgements. Those American geographers of German or Central European descent were the most disapproving, and most of them knew more about it than did their Anglo-Saxon colleagues.

In the end there were few who followed Weigert's call for a 'humanised' geopolitics. Perhaps the most important among them was Walsh. Defining geopolitics as 'a combined study of human geography and applied political science', he saw it as having an 'ancient and mixed ancestry' dating back to Aristotle, Montesquieu and Kant. He was inclined to believe in the scientific credentials of Haushofer, and he cited instances in American history, such as the acquisition of Louisiana in 1803, which had been essentially 'geopolitical'. 'All these precursors of the Munich specialists lacked only classification; they were geopoliticians without portfolio' (Walsh, 1943: 13). He maintained that geopolitics could be viewed in several ways, and the main trouble with the German variety was that it was too materialistic and lacked a spiritual dimension (*ibid.*: 32). He expressed the opinion that 'the best prophylaxis in the field of external strategy will be an American geopolitics based on international justice'. Unless spiritual values were taken into account, 'they [the present statesmen] will simply create another plague of spurious geopolitics'. He expressed the opinion that 'the pattern of a future geopolitics ... is even now beginning to grow discernible in broad outlines', and this would be based on justice and respect rather than on power and force. 'Geopolitics can ennoble as well as corrupt,' he concluded. 'It can choose between two alternatives – the value of power and the power of values'. Finally he invoked Mackinder's 'airy cherub', who had enjoyed such notable lack of success at Versailles, 'if still in office' to warn the statesmen not to imagine that the Anglo-American programme for a new world order had descended direct from Sinai (ibid.: 35).[13]

While Hans Weigert advocated a 'humanised' geopolitics and Edmund Walsh was advocating a 'spiritual' one, there were some at the time who were inclined to accept the geopolitics of Haushofer in a less modified way. George Renner's proposed European 'pan-regions', which included a kind of Mitteleuropa centring on Germany, resulted in his being accused by Walter Lippmann of concocting a bigger Pan-Germany than even the Nazis had claimed (Renner, 1942: 14–21). Renner then contributed to World Political Geography, the first important book in American political geography after World War II (Pearcy and Fifield, 1948). This became a standard textbook for the post-war generation of political geographers. 'During the recent war against the Axis,' wrote Renner, 'Americans became aware for the first time of the existence of political geography', and most significantly, he went on, 'they learned of it under the name of geopolitics'. As a result of this, 'Many Americans, because they had never previously heard of geopolitics, ... deduced that this whole field of knowledge was of very recent origin. Moreover, because they observed that some of the German political geographers ranted about Nordic "race superiority" and the "Aryan super-man", they concluded that geopolitics was therefore intellectually fictitious ... They, therefore, inferred that political geography was a German National Socialist invention for conquering the world. Actually, none of these inferences was true.' On the contrary, it had a long tradition, and he considered its 'father' to have been the philosopher Immanuel Kant. The American people were generally unaware, he said, 'that geopolitical principles were being used by the United States itself, almost from the outset of World War II, in fashioning the pattern of military victory' (Renner, 1948a: 4). Renner wrote of 'that subdivision of the subject known as political geography (and called by some people geopolitics)' and went on to assert that 'Geopolitics may be regarded as a shortened designation for political geography'. Renner used Griffith Taylor's definition of geopolitics as 'the study of the outstanding features of the situation and resources of a country with a view to determining its status in World Politics' to justify this assertion. 'Thus defined and clarified by Taylor,' he wrote, 'geopolitics might well be inferred to be synonymous with political geography, and consequently one may also infer that the dissimilarity between the two resulted, not from any difference between the subjects, but from differences between German geographers living under a national psychosis and non-German geographers in a democratic regime.' He concluded that 'to label geopolitics as an immoral science was to box with a straw man. Science is neither moral nor immoral, it is amoral. It is only the ends to which science is used that may be moral or immoral.' Now, in peacetime, asserted Renner, geopolitics has even greater utility. 'It affords a way for a nation to appraise its own national strength and to estimate the strength of its enemies. It provides a system for projecting graphically one's probable military moves and the probable military moves of one's enemy in the event of war ... As such it provides the basis for winning and maintaining peace.'

Thus in the 1940s geopolitics was commended to the Americans on the grounds of humanism, spirituality and practical politics. But the commendation did not work. In the second edition of *World Political Geography* Pearcy comments that 'German geopolitics was used to blueprint world conquest, and the Nazi creed incorporated those portions of political geography that served to justify German expansion'. It was this which had caused 'some scholars to divorce the discipline of political geography from geopolitics' (Pearcy *et al.,* 1957: 4–5). Geopolitics had been banished and was to remain banished for a generation.

There were two principal reasons for this. The first was that the revulsion with the Nazi regime became greater, not less, after the end of the war as the full extent of its crimes became clear. *Geopolitik* was too tarnished for redemption. Secondly, the onset of the Cold War meant that the world situation froze and geopolitics froze with it. Geopolitical analysis became geostrategic analysis for fighting the Cold War, and political geography deteriorated into a rather bland description of countries and resources. In this respect the differences between the first and second editions of *World Political Geography* was striking. It needed signs of a real thaw in the Cold War before recovery began to take place, and this did not come until the end of the 1960s.

NOTES

1. This famous phrase, attributed to Blaise Pascal, was frequently used by Kaiser Wilhelm II. 'Ein Platz in der Sonne' came to signify Germany's entitlement to a full recognition of its status as a world power.
2. 'Quand l'Allemagne pensait le monde' (when Germany thought in global terms) was regarded by Korinman as being a geopolitical project.
3. The Dual Alliance of 1879 between Germany and Austria-Hungary was the keystone of Bismarck's European policy. It represented the reconciliation of the two Germanic powers after the Austro-Prussian War of 1866.
4. *The Influence of Sea Power upon History* (Mahan, 1890) made a great impact on the Kaiser. By his order copies of the book were placed in every ship in the German navy. Significantly the book was also translated into Japanese and became required reading in all Japanese military and naval colleges.
5. The maritime school of thought was led by Grand Admiral Tirpitz, and it gave rise to the construction of a new generation of powerful battleships and a naval arms race with Great Britain. British policy was to ensure that the British navy was

more powerful than any combination of two foreign navies, but the costs imposed by the arms race with Germany stretched both British and German finances to the limit.

6.   The ideas of 'a place in the sun' and 'our future lies on the water' were coupled together by the Kaiser in a speech made at Hamburg on 18 June 1901. The subject of this was the happy outcome of the events in China and the crushing of the Boxer Rebellion by the Great Powers. It gave the Kaiser particular satisfaction that Germany had made a substantial contribution to this and was thus incontrovertibly in the ranks of the world powers. The relevant quotation is as follows:

In spite of the fact that we have no such fleet as we should have, we have conquered for ourselves a place in the sun. It will now be my task to see to it that this place in the sun shall remain our undisputed possession, in order that the sun's rays may fall fruitfully upon our activity and trade in foreign parts, that our industry and agriculture may develop within the state and our sailing sports upon the water, for our future lies upon the water.

7.   Bismarck largely discounted Italy in his European policy. He summed up Italy as having such a large appetite but such poor teeth.

8.   The Munich *putsch* of 1923 was an attempt by the Nazi Party (NSDAP) to take over the government of Bavaria. It was led by Hitler and General Ludendorff, a leading German military figure of World War I.

9.   The Treaty of Brest-Litovsk, signed between Germany and Russia in March 1918, gave Germany overwhelming preponderance in the East. It was completely overturned by the provisions of the Treaty of Versailles. In 1925 Germany and the Soviet Union signed the Treaty of Rapallo. Both were by then 'pariah' states in the international community, Germany because of the 'war guilt' and the Soviet Union because it was a communist state. They agreed to cooperate on such matters as trade, armaments production and military training. For Germany this provided a way around the restrictive provisions of the Treaty of Versailles.

10. The Kreisau Circle (*Kreisauer Kreis*) was established by Helmut von Moltke in 1940 for the purpose of building up resistance to the Nazi regime and discussing practical post-Nazi alternatives. These included a 'rehumanised' Germany which would be less inclined to seek military and authoritarian solutions to its problems. Underpinned by strongly held religious convictions, the Circle included professional and military people, as well as a number of academics of whom Albrecht Haushofer was one. He introduced a non-Nazi geopolitical dimension into its deliberations. Although the Circle was not directly involved in the Bomb Plot on Hitler's life in June 1944, some of them, including von Moltke and Haushofer, were eventually executed.

11. Martha Haushofer had collaborated with her husband throughout and was the translator of Fairgrieve's *Geography and World Power* (1915) into German (*Geographie und Weltmacht*, 1925).

12. After the Spanish–American War of 1898 the United States acquired its only substantial colonial territory, the Philippines. Kipling's famous poem, 'The White Man's Burden', was an invitation to the Americans to take up the 'burdens' of empire. However, although in 1900 the United States was one of the powers

involved in putting down the Boxer Rebellion in China, its policy was subsequently different from that of the other powers. The United States did not seek to acquire a sphere of influence in the manner of the other powers but rather proposed that China should be opened to trade by all. This was the origin of the 'open door' policy which the United States pursued in the Far East until after World War II.

13. Mackinder's 'airy cherub' (p. 105) was responsible for warning the Allied statesmen assembled at Versailles to take into account the realities of world power. This warning was delivered in the form of a triptych which summed up Mackinder's whole thesis of the dichotomy of land power and sea power. (Mackinder, 1919).

CHAPTER 4

PEACE AND THE RISE OF
GÉOPOLITIQUE

In January 1976, just three decades after the suicide of Karl and Martha Haushofer, the first issue of a new geographical journal appeared in Paris. Entitled *Hérodote*, it was edited by Yves Lacoste, a professor of geography at the University of Vincennes, and its objective was to examine the issues of the day from a radical geographical perspective. The term which Lacoste decided fitted his purposes best was none other than geopolitics, and *Hérodote* was subsequently subtitled '*Revue de géographie et de géopolitique*'. Geopolitics had returned, not to the country where it was initially developed but to the country which had been its most uncompromising opponent. *Geopolitik* had become *géopolitique*.

Since World War II, French geographers had had little to do with geopolitical matters. Even the far more respectable *géographie politique* had been considered to be tarnished by association with it and had been deliberately avoided by most geographers. For the French during the 1930s *géopolitique* was a straight translation of the German *Geopolitik*, and as such was subject to the severest criticism. At the time French geographers did not oppose *Geopolitik* with their own version of it but used *géographie politique*, which, like their Anglo-Saxon counterparts, they considered to be the real academic discipline. Thus in considering the nature and development of geopolitics in France one must be conscious of the fact that, during the first half of the century, the thinking on this subject constituted in reality a kind of 'anti-geopolitics' which cannot be fully understood without reference to what was happening in Germany. The chapter in *Western Geopolitical Thought in the Twentieth Century* entitled '*L'Esprit vidalienne* versus *Geopolitik*' focuses on the basic differences between the geopolitical thinking in France and Germany during the inter-war period (Parker, 1985: 87–101). The key word is 'versus', since the French geographers of the *vidalien* tradition rapidly reached the conclusion that what was taking place in Germany was a terrible perversion of the subject.

As has been observed, the emergence of political geography in France had owed a great deal to the work of German geographers and especially to Ratzel himself. In his review of Ratzel's *Politische Geographie* in *Annales de Géographie*, Vidal de la Blache had recognised the importance of the work of the German geographer (Vidal de la Blache, 1898). While taking exception to Ratzel's concept of the state as a 'living organism', he was indulgent in assuming that Ratzel was using the term only by analogy (*ibid.*: 111). However, from the outset Vidal took the view that political geography was not something which could be studied in isolation from the rest of geography. It was deeply rooted, he maintained, within the totality of human geography and it could be studied only as 'partie d'un ensemble' (part of a whole).

Those of Vidal's successors who embarked upon its study did not subscribe to the master's stated desire to plunge the infant political geography back into the totality of human geography as a whole. This may be put down to two factors: the profound changes to the European geopolitical scene brought about by World War I, and the rise of *Geopolitik* in Germany. It was acknowledged that geographers had to examine the changes which had taken place from their own perspective, and this made it all the more essential to define the purpose and methods of political geography and to scrutinise its academic credentials (Gallois, 1919). The success of this approach is to be seen in the work of a number of geographers during the inter-war years. *Le Déclin de l'Europe*, the first book written by Albert Demangeon, the most influential French human geographer of this period, dealt directly with the issues at the interface between geography and international politics (Demangeon, 1920). The process of defining and applying the subdiscipline in France was soon to be overtaken by the rise of German *Geopolitik*, which cast a long shadow over French political geography. Weigert observed that French geographers, 'closer than we are to the arising dangers from without', were ahead of their Anglo-Saxon colleagues in appreciating the true nature of *Geopolitik* and responding to it (Weigert, 1941). Referring to the French political geographers as 'geopoliticians', Weigert maintained that they had criticised 'German geopolitical thinking by the accusation that, to it, space and earth meant everything; the human being almost nothing. They tried to fight against the fatalistic conception which makes man more or less an object of geographic factors' (*ibid.*: 31). The attack on it had been led by Demangeon, who found *Geopolitik* 'disquieting' and in a series of articles and reviews went on to demolish its credibility (Demangeon, 1922, 1932, 1939). At the root of his criticism lay what he considered to be its total lack of scientific spirit and the placing of geography so blatantly at the service of the state. He regarded it as being a part of 'the German war machine' and concluded that 'the old *Drang nach Osten* is again the order of the day' (Demangeon, 1932: 537). In contrast, he conceived of *la géographie politique* as deriving from that creative interplay of *civilisation* and *milieu* which produced those *genres de vie* (ways of life) of which the states were themselves important manifestations.

The lead of Demangeon was followed by other French political geographers. Yves-Marie Goblet accused the German geopoliticians of producing 'a kind of metaphysics', and he equated their base in physical reality with that of the medieval alchemists. The resulting *Geopolitik spagyrique* was dismissed as being 'a false science at the service of politics' and 'a state anthropomorphism pursued

... with dark fanaticism' (Goblet, 1936: 16–17). Likewise, Jacques Ancel dubbed *Geopolitik* 'pseudo-geography', regarding it as little more than propaganda which had renounced all claim to scientific authenticity. Its role was to provide the justification for 'an infinite expansion' (Ancel, 1938: 186).

These French geographers, who were so strident in their condemnation of *Geopolitik*, viewed political geography in a very different light. Possibilist rather than determinist and emphasising the pre-eminent importance of environment over race, they took the view that states were the result of the dynamic interaction between human and physical phenomena. To Vidal, states were *des faits en mouvement*, dynamic entities which were products of evolution in space and time. As a consequence, the idea of their being 'natural' phenomena went completely against the grain. Demangeon emphasised that *la circulation* (movement) was the essential factor in ending the isolation of states, and 'the great axes of movement' were the highways of change and integration. To Ancel the frontier was not a *barrière rigoureuse* (an absolute barrier) but a *périphérie toujours provisoire* (an always temporary periphery), and there was thus nothing 'natural' about it. 'The boundaries of a state oscillate, the result of perpetual flux ... the frontier is a political isobar' (Ancel, 1938: 195). It followed from this that the geopolitical surface at any given time was something essentially transitory, and a refusal to recognise this fact divorced it from the true realities of the human world. These realities were the *civilisations* arising from the *genres de vie* of a people existing in a particular environment. An example was *la civilisation rhénane* (Rhineland civilisation), which was an enduring reality continuing to exist beneath what was essentially an imposed an artificial political surface. This surface Ancel considered to have been produced by what he called Prussia's '*Anschluss* rhénane' and the *Musspreussen* (forced Prussianisation) which was its accompaniment. To Ancel, the existing states, and the great powers in particular, were all artificial geopolitical creations which, although they had an air of power and permanence, were in reality fragile and doomed to eventual extinction. He concluded that 'The walls of these Jerichos will fall at the sound of the trumpets which will awaken the bound and sleeping nations' (*ibid.*: 188). The way forward lay not in further acquisitions of power but in the creation of *ententes* and *groupements* (flexible groupings) sensitive to the underlying human realities.

The idea of there being alternative geopolitical realities to those represented by Lavisse's 'pale lines on the docile paper' pervaded French geopolitical thinking during the inter-war years. Thus in *Le Déclin de l'Europe* Demangeon identified the European continent as being the great whole of which the states constituted the parts. He emphasised that the states themselves were not autonomous geopolitical entities but parts of a wider geopolitical whole, and thus had to be recognised if there was to be any chance of halting their decline, and that of the continent as a whole. Demangeon was convinced that it was essential that the geographical unity of Europe be rediscovered, and saw the 'the great axes of movement' as constituting the underlying geopolitical framework around which the continent could be refashioned. In this context, the Rhineland was viewed as being a geopolitical reality which underlay its political component parts (Demangeon and Febvre, 1935). Far from being a natural frontier, the Rhine was a human unit which was the natural link, not the divide, between France and Germany. Demangeon and Febvre looked beyond present realities to 'the rich and luminous routeway' which they opposed to 'the bloody and sterile frontier' that existed at present (*ibid*.: 291). Demangeon thus saw 'the force for unity which comes from the Rhine' as constituting a transcendent geopolitical reality embedded within the still greater European reality. In this context the Rhineland was postulated as being an example of a category rather than as something unique and, in proposing this categorisation, Demangeon used the concepts of *ententes régionales* and *groupements*. At a time when the Rhinelands was the main bone of contention between Germany and France, and its role as frontier was seen as being paramount, Demangeon's view was a revolutionary one. His partner Febvre considered that *la civilisation rhénane* transcended the national characteristics and encapsulated those human realities which lay beneath – and were obscured by – the political surface (Parker, 1994c: 80). To Febvre the state was 'never a given; it is always man-made', and the only geopolitical entities which he considered to be 'givens' in this sense were what he termed 'the natural regions of the great states'. Febvre called these *mondes* (worlds), and it was in them that the major world civilisations had arisen. Since its civilisation transcended the artificial frontiers of those states of which it was made up, Europe was regarded as being a *monde* in this sense (Febvre, 1932: 314–15).

Demangeon's world-view, of which his European view was a part, was predicated on the impending end of European hegemony and the emergence of new geopolitical entities. In *Le Déclin* he identified the two most important of these as being North America and the Far East, dominated respectively by the United States and Japan. He considered that Europe could be a third, but only if the Europeans were prepared to submerge their differences and unite. Pointing to the leading role of Japan in developing the Orient, he even went on to suggest a Japanese sphere of influence and a Japanese Monroe Doctrine for the Far East (Demangeon, 1920: 179). Demangeon appeared to accept Japanese imperialism in the Far East in a way in which neither he nor any other French political geographer would have accepted a similar position for a single power in Europe.

While Demangeon and other geographers concerned themselves with internationalist approaches, in his final years the doyen Vidal de la Blache had actually moved back towards a more state-centred view. *La France de l'Est* was basically a plea for the reunification of the eastern *départements* with France, to which he considered them 'naturally' to belong (Vidal de la Blache, 1917). He wrote of 'the natural vocation of France' as being both to maintain *le Tout géographique* (her geographical wholeness) and to act as the link between Central and Western Europe (*ibid*.: 206). *Mitteleuropa* had demonstrated a worrying propensity to become closed within itself, and he went so far as to assert dramatically that this was 'against the laws of life'. It was in the interests of all for this huge and powerful region to be opened up to wider influences so that it could then return to a harmonious relationship with *le Tout terrestre* (the world as a whole). This sounds very much like an early call for a globalist approach, and Vidal indeed asserted that the world vocation of France conforms to the very nature of *La France de l'Est*.

It is possible to detect two distinct strands running through French geopolitical thought during the first half of the twentieth century. One of them centred on the idea of *le groupement* (grouping) and the other on *le pouvoir* (power). While the former was idealist, seeing the way forward as being a cooperative one, the latter was realist about the continued existence of national power and the need to come to terms with it. Both of these strands can be detected in the work of Vidal de la Blache himself. In *La France de l'Est* he appeared to move from idealism towards realism and placed greater emphasis on power. It is possible to observe a similar change taking place in the work of his successors during the years leading up to World War II. There was a marked difference in Ancel's emphasis between that of *La Géographie des frontières*, written during the mid-1930s (Ancel, 1938) and *Slaves et Germains*, his last work, completed during the first year of World War II (Ancel, 1947).[1] During less than half a decade his advocacy of *entente* was replaced by that of 'the defence of the Western democracies against Hitler's pan-Germanism'. The change clearly relates to the perceived failure of the principle of *entente* and the re-emergence of *Anschluss* and *Musspreussen* in the affairs of Europe during 1938 and 1939. Ancel displayed a full awareness of the implications of the German policy of *Lebensraum* for Germany's neighbours and the need for it to be resisted (*ibid.*: 209–12). As early as 1934, just after the Nazis had come to power in Germany, Goblet wrote of the darkening of the international scene as *le crépuscule* (twilight) (Goblet, 1936). Nevertheless, Goblet concluded optimistically with the belief that the night which would follow would not be a long one and that the opportunity to convert failure into success would once again present itself. He emphasised the necessity for 'experiments' in new forms of geopolitical (or politico-geographical) organisation, and saw the situation in the early 1930s as still providing the opportunity for these to be made (*ibid.*: 256–9). Goblet envisaged that the setting up and analysis of such experiments would be the major role of the political geography of the future.

In 1945, and for many years afterwards, anything 'political' was regarded by most French geographers as being something to be avoided at all costs. There was a propensity among geographers to seek solace by a return to the purer air of the regional monograph, while the strongest practical thrust lay in the fields of post-war planning and regional development. Although this attitude persisted well into the 1960s, developments on the European scene were very much in line with many of the ideas of the French political geographers of the 1930s. With the establishment of the first of the organisations of European cooperation in the 1950s the geopolitical idea of *groupement* was being translated into a reality. It is now clear that the French political geographers of the earlier part of the century played a considerable role in the formulation of the European idea. In *La France de l'Est* Vidal de la Blache had used the term *la communauté européenne*, and the language used by French foreign minister Aristide Briand, particularly in his speeches to the League of Nations, was almost exactly that of Demangeon in *Annales de Géographie* (Parker, 1987a). The French political and geographical worlds, which had encountered one another at Versailles after World War I to draw up the new political boundaries, were to go on meeting in Geneva in the 1930s and again in London in the 1940s. Important geographical influences were brought to bear on political decision-making in both these places (Claval, 1994: 60–3). The overall influence of geographers on internationalist thinking was significant, and Goblet's 1934 idea of 'experiments' in new forms of politico-geographical organisation was inherent in the European Community (Parker, 1983).

In the event, the Community represented both a dramatic change in French foreign policy and the beginning of a new paradigm for international relations in Europe. It represented a break with traditional solutions based on the nation and a sublimation of the national self-interest within an international framework. (Parker, 1983: 7). While the relative political and economic strength of France over its continental neighbours made this a more attractive option to Paris, looked at geopolitically the implementation of the community idea was the triumph of *groupement* over *puissance* and of Europe over the nation-state (*ibid*: 1–16).

The arrival on the scene of *Hérodote* in January 1976 represented a major turning-point in geopolitics and geopolitical thinking in France. It was the child of that revaluation of geography which took place in the context of the *événements* which shook the country in 1968 and which contributed to the fall of General de Gaulle's government. Although during this period at the universities the social sciences in general had played a central role in giving ideological direction to the student movement and pointing to future directions of policy, at first geography, emasculated by decades of avoidance of involvement in political issues, appeared to have little to contribute. Yves Lacoste embarked on a project to demonstrate that this was not the case.[2] He posed the question: 'What is geography for?', and the answer which came back to him was that 'La géographie, ça sert, d'abord, à faire la guerre' (the title of his book, meaning 'the purpose of geography is, above all, the making of war'). In the past, he contended, it had been used by the state for its own purposes, and these involved mainly enhancement of the war-making capacity (Lacoste, 1976b).

The accusation of war-making was Lacoste's initial broadside against the traditional role of geography and the geographical establishment which had sustained it. Nevertheless, he maintained, it could be otherwise; geography could also be used for other purposes, but in order for that to happen radical changes had to be made in the approach to the subject. The *Hérodote* project was initially about how this could be achieved, and it involved the return of geopolitics (Lacoste, 1994). It was from then on that geopolitics, 'proscribed until then, began to reappear', said Lacoste (*ibid.*: 127). As mentioned in note 1 to Chapter 1, the journal's first subtitle had been '*Stratégies, géographies, idéologies*', but from 1983 this was changed to '*Revue de géographie et de géopolitique*'. From the outset, the stated purpose of *Hérodote* was to use the spatial methodology to understand the issues better and to facilitate more effective action (Lacoste, 1994: 19). While distancing itself from *Geopolitik*, *Hérodote* distanced itself equally from the traditional French political geography. Despite strong criticism of much of *vidalien* geography, the immense contribution to geographical thinking which had been made by Vidal himself was fully acknowledged (Lacoste, 1979). Criticism was directed at the pretensions of the practitioners of *la géographie politique* to have been more truly academic than those of *Geopolitik*. In *La géographie ça sert, d'abord à faire la guerre* Lacoste asserted that geography had always been used by the state for its own purposes. He accused geographers of having too readily acquiesced in being put at the service of domination, war and political control. He maintained that the whole ethos of *la géographie dominante* exalts the national territory, obscures political contradictions and camouflages the *état* (state) with the *pays* (land). The view was taken that the role of the new geopolitics lay in overcoming chauvinism and moving towards greater objectivity, and this has remained its avowed intention. In moving away from the traditional statist approach, *Hérodote* and the new geopolitics came to be linked with ecology and wider environmental issues as well as with such matters as world poverty and the using up of finite resources (*Hérodote*, 26. 1982). In this context, the work of the early-twentieth-century anarchist geographers Peter Kropotkin and Elisée Reclus, who were both deeply concerned with environmental issues, was examined and re-evaluated (*Hérodote*, 22. 1981).

Hérodote represented a radical reappraisal of the nature and role of geopolitics, and central to this was its disassociation from the state and its policies. Typical *Hérodote* subjects of the 1970s included anarchist geography, ecogeography, anticolonialism, Latin American revolutions and the transformation of geography from a *discipline asservie* (a servile discipline) into an objective – but *engagé* – science. In its relationship to the traditions of French geopolitical thought, it came down firmly on the side of *groupement*. Born into what Lacoste termed a *manichéan* world situation dominated by the 'the two great geopolitical groupings', one of its self-appointed tasks was the investigation of alternative geopolitical scenarios. A recurrent theme has been the identification of the emergence of *des nouvels ensembles* (new groupings) in the world, the emergence of which lessened the Manichaean duality. Lacoste's designation of such formations as *les grandes plaques* (the great plates) is a geological analogy which is particularly significant in view of the implications of too close an association with such naturalistic concepts in the past. Such terminology constitutes an implicit recognition of the continued importance of *le pouvoir* as *les plaques* have the makings of future centres of world power. The distribution of power and the implications of this distribution was being discussed around the fringes of the *Hérodote* circle during the 1980s. In *Pour une géographie du pouvoir*, Claude Raffestin observed that *Macht* in the Ratzelian sense of the term had always led to totalitarianism, and instead he proposed a geography of autonomy as an antidote to it. Raffestin discussed the possibilities of the dissemination of power outwards to those regions and social groups which had never experienced it and placed this in the context of wider political change (Raffestin, 1980).

While the distinction made between *la géopolitique* and *la géographie politique* had been an attempt to emphasise a fundamental difference of approach by the use of a different terminology, one of the most significant contributions made by *Hérodote* was to remove this distinction and to demonstrate that, far from being opposed, they are complementary to one another. To Lacoste, geopolitics is based on firm academic foundations, but is in the *engagé* tradition of addressing problems and issues. While both, in their different ways, are concerned with states and with the structures of state power, a more basic distinction can be made between the ideas of *le groupement* and *le pouvoir* which have been present in French geopolitical thought throughout the century. However, while *le pouvoir* is much the same as the German *Macht*, *le groupement* represents a radically different alternative to *Anschluss*. The relationship between all such ideas has been a subtle one, each representing different interpretations of closely associated phenomena. While from Vidal to *Hérodote* the concept of *groupement* has been most associated with an innovative approach to regional structures, the concept of *pouvoir* has been more associated with the global scale of analysis.

The reinvention of geopolitics in France in the 1970s recalls the basic argument of the American political geographers of the 1940s that the baby should not be thrown out with the bathwater. In the opinion of Weigert and others, geopolitics should be humanised rather than abolished, but the circumstances of the post-war era proved to be uncongenial for this humanisation process to take place. The return of geopolitics in the United States also began during the 1970s, but initially it made less of an impact on the academic world than was the case in France. As mentioned near the start of the chapter, Weigert had commented that the French were far more aware of geopolitics than their Anglo-Saxon colleagues, and he attributed this awareness to their having been being closer to its source (Weigert, 1941: 31). Much of the credit for the reintroduction of geopolitics into the United States during the 1970s, and its subsequent popularisation, has been attributed to Henry Kissinger, who favoured its use when considering global issues. However, Kissinger used the term rather randomly, with little apparent precise or specific sense of its meaning (O'Loughlin and Nijman, 1994: 137–8). It was soon taken up by politicians and commentators, who found, like Lacoste, that it was the word they needed for formulating and presenting ideas in a way which emphasised the territorial dimension. The 'barbershop' geopolitics of the 1940s returned as 'media' geopolitics in the 1970s before American geographers came to terms with the full implications of its new use. As with Kjellén in the early 1900s, it became the term for the times and it fitted well with the new interest in humanistic and radical geography.

The objective of humanistic geography was to bring back humanity to the centre of the stage and, in Max Sorre's phrase, to 'humanise' human geography (Ley and Samuels, 1978). Radical geography focused on contemporary issues including those concerning inequality, race, environment and underdevelopment (Peet, 1977). Peet's *Radical Geography*, subtitled *Alternative Viewpoints on Contemporary Social Issues*, included a re-evaluation of the relevance of geopolitics as an *engagé* subdiscipline which had a contribution to make to the fuller understanding of the profound changes taking place in the world. Asserting as 'fact' that geopolitics had held 'a dominant position in the field of political geography before the 1930s', Anouar Abdel-Malek blamed its subsequent neglect on what he called 'elitist intellectual circles, mainly those of the cosmopolitan, anti-national leftist type' (Abdel-Malek, 1977: 301). Maintaining the necessity to assert 'the role of geopolitics ... in the social dialectics of our times', he went on to discuss 'the possible uses of geopolitics in the shaping of the world to come'. With the Cold War balance of power now in its final stages and 'subordinate contradictions' coming to the fore, he saw the emergence of 'a pattern of intensified and complex struggles'. In these circumstances the role of geopolitics was 'fundamental' in addressing the issues of the future and the new world scenario which was coming into being (*ibid.*: 305–6).

Ten years later the Cold War was drawing to its close, and what Abdel-Malek had termed 'the shape of the new world balance of power' was beginning to become apparent. Claval saw the emergence – or re-emergence – of geopolitics as being the result of 'the crumbling of blocs, the falling of walls'. In the resulting 'hostile and uncertain environment it [geopolitics] is about concentrating and employing one's forces in the most effective manner' (Claval, 1994: 4). Seen in this way, geopolitics is about using a knowledge of the real world to understand and manage change. When the political ice age of the Cold War had been at its height, the intensity of the confrontation had effectively obscured the real world from view. The ideological ice cap which covered the greater part of the Northern Hemisphere for nearly half a century had the effect of burying the previous geopolitical landscape beneath it. The melting of the ice cap revealed the continued existence of a living geography and, in the peri- and post-ideological world, a variety of global issues began to replace the single-issue world of the Cold War.

Geopolitics thus emerged as one of the manifestations of a new earth-consciousness and the one which treated political phenomena as being essentially environmental in their implications and part of a multi-dimensional and holistic human world.[3] Here lies the most fundamental philosophical difference between the old geopolitics, as expressed in the *Geopolitik* of the 1930s, and the new *géopolitique*/geopolitics of the 1970s. The perspective of the old geopolitics focused on one particular segment of territory, the state, and on the single-minded pursuit of what were regarded as being its best interests even if these led, as all too often they did, to confrontation and war. Its recurring themes were space and power and the relationship between the two. The perspective of the new geopolitics, on the other hand, is global, and its fundamental proposition is that the world as a whole is the proper unit for the addressing of those issues which have global repercussions. There is no such thing as the solutions of a 'local' issue seen in isolation and out of its wider context.

In France and the United States the initial return of geopolitics in the 1970s was driven by the intellectuals and the politicians. It was thus respectively *engagé* and 'neo-barbershop' in its origins but it rapidly gained considerable media attention. In Great Britain, despite the return of political geography, there was little enthusiasm for the reintroduction of geopolitics. It continued to he held at arm's length and to be regarded as being something different from, and inherently less desirable than, political geography. While dictionaries of geopolitics appeared in both France and the United States, nothing similar appeared in Britain. During the 1990s the new 'critical geopolitics' in both Britain and the United States is an attempt to develop a new geopolitical discourse designed to examine international issues in an objective manner. This has gone some way towards bridging the gap between political geography and geopolitics (Ó Tuathail, 1996).

The severing of the close links between geopolitics and the state has been the most significant feature of the period since the 1970s. It has been accompanied by a radical questioning of the role of the state itself and of whether states as at present constituted are the best forms of organisation for the contemporary world. Quite apart from their obvious inability individually to tackle such urgent questions as environmental decay and global warming, it is they who have been responsible, through their aggressive and selfish behaviour, for the situation which confronts humanity. They can be thus regarded as being part of the problem rather than the solution.

With the end of the Cold War, at first sight the newly revealed geopolitical landscape appeared to be gentle and attractive in its variety and subtlety, a human and humanised landscape compared to the harshness and monotony of its ideological predecessor. A landscape, the existence of which owed much to the ideas of one German thinker, Karl Marx, appeared to have given place to that owing much to the ideas of another, Friedrich Schumacher.[4] Yet it soon became apparent that the newly revealed geopolitical landscape was not quite what it seemed in that it contained a propensity to violence. It is basically the same geopolitical landscape as that which existed at the time of the onset of the Cold War in the 1940s. It is made up of territorial states, and with the unfreezing of global geopolitics the former conflictual behaviour of states whose behaviour patterns had been frozen for nearly half a century have been in many places resumed. While the immediate causes of these post-Cold War conflicts have included disputes over frontiers and physical resources, underlying them has been a deeper cause. This is the nature of the territorial state and the problems inherent in its functioning in a world of similar states.

Kjellén's definition of geopolitics as 'the science of the state as a realm in space' is a closer and more binding one than Semple's definition of political geography as 'the state in relation to the land'. It implies not so much the study of the 'relationship' between two independent phenomena as the integrated study of a single phenomenon: the state as a spatial entity. The implication of this is clear. It is that the state is not just a juridical or political entity which is influenced in some degree by geographical factors. Rather it itself constitutes a spatial phenomenon which can and should be studied as such. This was something far more basic to Kjellén than the question of whether the state was organic or not. It may or may not be considered as being an organic entity, said Kjellén, but it was certainly first and foremost a spatial entity. It is this which marks the real divide which runs through the whole combined field of geopolitics and political geography. It is between those who have remained in the 'relationship' mode, viewing the central task as being to establish the existence of 'influences' emanating largely from the physical environment which affect the nature and behaviour of the state, and those, following Kjellén himself, to whom the state was a holistic spatial entity which could be fully understood and explained only by being treated as such.

For both Ratzel and Kjellén it was the nation-state, as it was conceived of at the time, which constituted the most significant geopolitical level. To them it represented stability, order and purpose, and its existence was the guarantee of the continuation of these things. In this their thinking derived from Hegel, who had asserted that the state, by which he meant the nation-state, was the highest form of political existence, embodying as it did the common purposes and aspirations (*Hérodote*, 2., 1976). Looked at geopolitically, the nation-state had also brought clarity and precision to the complexities of the political map and replaced the diverse and ramshackle empires of the past with a logical system based on the idea of the nation. Ratzel and Kjellén considered it to be the indispensable level of organisation, and without it there appeared to them to be the very real possibility of a slide into chaos. This was the philosophical basis of that attachment to the interests of the nation-state which characterised geopolitics from its inception.

A century later the nation-state no longer holds the sacrosanct position which it formerly did and this is reflected in the fact that geopolitics is no longer tied to it as in the past. On the contrary, its role is being vigorously questioned and there is a new interest in the possibilities of the other levels of organisation which lie above and below it. In particular, what O'Loughlin and Heske refer to as 'global-scale (structural) mechanisms' are now central to the whole project, and are considered as being the essential prerequisites for the conversion of geopolitics from 'a discipline of war to a discipline of peace' (O'Loughlin and Heske, 1991). Before embarking on an examination of the global level, it is first necessary to consider the nature of the component parts of the world's geopolitical space and their relationships to one another.

NOTES

1. Jacques Ancel wrote *Slaves et Germains* at the time of the *drôle de guerre* (the Phoney War), which lasted from the outbreak of war in September 1939 to the German invasion of the Low Countries and France in May 1940. After the defeat and occupation of France Ancel was arrested and imprisoned in the concentration camp of Compiègne. He died shortly after his release in 1943 and his last book was not published until after the end of the war.
2. A student slogan at the University of Vincennes in 1968 read 'la géographie est complètement crétine et complètement réactionnaire'. Yves Lacoste agreed with the students that geography was reactionary but certainly not that it was cretinous. Thereupon he and a number of his colleagues embarked upon a project to rehabilitate the subject. It was out of this project that *Hérodote* was conceived.
3. This world consciousness was holistic and based upon the ideas of the organic unity of the planet as a functioning whole. What David Livingstone termed 'the geographical project' of putting all the social sciences under one conceptual umbrella fitted in well with thinking of this sort (Livingstone, 1992).
4. Schumacher contended that the grandiose ideas of communism had obscured humanity from view. In his book *Small Is Beautiful: Economics as if People Mattered* (1973) he maintained that the truly human scale was the small scale. This should be returned to if humanity's real needs were to be fulfilled.

CHAPTER 5

TOWARDS A SPATIAL TYPOLOGY OF STATES

The political map of the world consists of a jigsaw of territorial units of various shapes and sizes. These units are the sovereign states and each constitutes the ultimate political authority within that territory for which it is responsible. Below and above the level of the state there are likely to be other types of units. Its territory is segmented into smaller political units (local states) and it itself may be a member of groupings of states set up for particular purposes. However, it is the states which are the principal actors on the world stage and it is at state level that the major decisions are taken. Such authority as exists above and below the level of the state is largely what the state has granted to it, and the continuance of such authority is dependent upon its acquiescence. Thus the political map of power, varied and unclear at the intra- and inter-state levels, crystallises and comes into focus at the level of the state. The state surface is therefore the most important one and is the key to reaching an understanding of the processes involved in the geopolitics of power.

While the sovereign states can thus be regarded as being the essential pieces of the global jigsaw, they are far from possessing the relative uniformity of size of a jigsaw's pieces. They range in size from those of continental or subcontinental dimensions, such as Russia and China, to tiny islands and peninsulas such as Singapore and Qatar. In view of its colourful cartographic conventions, the world political map thus gives an initial impression of being a riot of shapes, sizes and colours, more kaleidoscope than jigsaw. However, unlike the kaleidoscope, the political map does not resolve itself into easily identifiable patterns or spatial arrangements. Unlike on those physical maps showing world climates or soils, there are few immediately recognisable patterns which give clues to the existence of general principles or laws underlying the incidence and disposition of the phenomena depicted. On the surface, at least, there appears to be more chaos than cosmos in the distribution of the phenomena depicted.

The states which constitute this all-important geopolitical surface are, in the contemporary idiom, generally known as 'nation-states'. This distinguishes them from other types of 'states', such as the constituent states of the United States of America, which, as the American Civil War clearly demonstrated, do not possess the attributes of sovereignty. It also introduces another dimension to their nature, a dimension which is emphasised by the fact that 'nation-state' is more usually abbreviated to 'nation' than to 'state'. Thus we have a world which is apparently made up of 'nations' as the all-important units of organisation and authority. We have the 'nations' which constitute the European Union, those of the Organisation of African States, those of the Olympic Movement and, of course, the United Nations itself. While the word 'state' refers to political organisation, 'nation' refers to the characteristics which give identity to a particular people, and as such it has formed the basis for independent statehood in a world of nations (Cobban, 1969: 13–23).

While such a world has proved satisfying to the protagonists of the idea of nationality, since each such nation is an independent sovereign entity there have been considerable problems in achieving some form of overall organisation among them. The United Nations and its associated bodies represent attempts to rectify this situation. The UN itself is an umbrella organisation established for the purpose of dealing at the highest level with the relations among states and attempting to ensure that these relations do not break down again as they have done in the past with such catastrophic results. The intention of those who founded the organisation was to ensure that in future disputes were solved peacefully. The whole concept of 'union' implies an end to the chaos and disorder of total sovereignty and the creation of order based on authority. Since the beginning of the twentieth century, when the closure of the world had put a virtual end to that seemingly limitless expansion by the Europeans which had characterised most of the previous four hundred years, the urgent necessity of bringing order to the closed and finite world became apparent. The United Nations itself was the post-World War II successor to the League of Nations, which had been established in the wake of World War I. This League had also assumed that the basis of the units of organisation was the nation, but 'league' implied a rather looser form of grouping than was implied in the term 'union'.[1]

In the late nineteenth century the favoured term associated with sovereign political authority had not been 'nation' but 'power', and among these powers were seven or eight 'great powers' which together dominated the world. The term 'empire' had also returned to general use to denote the territorial extent and geographical variety of the global possessions of the powers.[2] One of the justifications put forward by the Allies for World War I was that it was 'the war of the nations', and President Wilson's 'Fourteen Points' included the principle of national independence. When extended to their dependent territories outside Europe, this was to cause considerable embarrassment to the imperial powers. After World War I, when nationality became an accepted principle of sovereignty, conferring on it the sort of legitimacy which in the past had been founded on dynastic and legal considerations, 'nation' increasingly took over from 'power'. Until that time nations – and the 'nationalism' which went with them – had still been widely considered to be subversive and dangerous, and too closely associated with those 'progressive' movements which made the powers, and particularly their rulers, so fearful for the future. However, following the collapse of the more fragile of the empires, the term 'nation' came to be adopted, even by those who had previously condemned it, as being more desirable than either 'power' or 'empire'. It was endorsed by such bodies as the new British Broadcasting Corporation, which boldly proclaimed in its motto that 'Nation shall speak peace unto nation'. By this time a dozen new nation-states had risen in Europe out of the ruins of the former empires, and the League of Nations itself had 25 members. Twenty years later in 1944, when it was established in San Francisco, the infant United Nations had 40 members and by 1996 the membership of the world body had risen to 130. It is now an assumption that the world political map is made up of 'nations' and only a relatively small part of it is taken up by discontinuous dependent territories.[3]

As has been observed, although used together to designate a single unit, in reality 'nation' and 'state' refer to quite different attributes, and these need not necessarily be territorially coextensive. A state, from the Latin *status*, meaning appointed or fixed, is defined as being a sovereign and organised political structure the government of which constitutes the legitimate authority over a particular territory. 'Nation', on the other hand, from the Latin *natio*, meaning birth, is usually taken to signify a population group having common origins and characteristics. Generically it is a term which has been used in modern times to indicate the cultural attributes of a particular people rather than their political status. Such cultural attributes are normally taken to include such things as language, history, religion and artistic heritage (Minogue, 1967). 'Nation-state' can thus be more precisely defined as being a population group sharing common cultural attributes, occupying a particular territory and having a common government. In fact this represents a kind of idealised model rather than a usual or normal situation. From the nationalist perspective it has an idyllic quality about it which is pervaded by a sense of rightness and wholeness. This is an ideal which is expressed cartographically in the favoured colour on the polychromatic political map, which serves to reinforce the idea of homogeneity within any particular territory. The geopolitical colour coding serves to reinforce the idea of there being a 'natural' territory, having the same kind of permanence as the natural features which run through it. This implies a link between a people and a territory which transforms a physical landscape into a psychological one. Thus hills and mountains, rivers and forests, may be deemed to constitute an inalienable part of the national heritage, giving physical expression to the psychological attributes of the nation. This essentially deterministic set of ideas is frequently reinforced by national myths and legends and by a national iconography designed to reinforce the bonds between a people and a territory, and in so doing to weld them into a single entity (Vidal de la Blache, 1926: 163f.).

Such a neat fit between a people and a territory, between 'nation' and 'state', is in practice extremely rare. There is likely to be considerable internal diversity, both physical and human, which belies both the stridency of the colouring of the political map and the assertiveness of the iconography which accompanies it. For example, the term 'nation' is habitually used in reference to France, Spain and Britain, but in not one of them do the attributes of nationality actually correspond with the boundaries of the state as at present constituted. In each case there are, in fact, clearly definable sub-state cultural entities within their boundaries to which the appellation 'nation' can also be applied, and, conversely, many attributes of the dominant nation are to be found outside the state's boundaries (Figure 5.1). As has been frequently seen in the recent past, the strongest sense of nationality has often been associated with the smaller sub-state nations rather than with the dominant nation itself. Thus Scotland, Catalonia and Brittany have evoked stronger popular emotions than have the states of which each has formed a constituent part. Ireland, the Basque Country (Euskadi) and Corsica have demonstrated an alienation from the nation-state which led to persistent and violent attempts to establish their own alternatives.

The collective name for states which is favoured at any particular time in many ways reflects aspiration rather than reality. Thus 'nation' is a more evocative term than 'state', and its use has been promoted by governments in order to humanise what is otherwise a political framework established as a result of physical force, divine sanctions, dynastic claims or a combination of all three. It has come to be adopted for reasons of state in much the same way as the Roman Empire finally adopted Christianity. Thus the evocative and emotional concept of 'nation' is injected into the legal and administrative concept of 'state' in order to engender a popular sense of enthusiasm and loyalty. It is easier for governments to justify control over something which can be shown to be living and vibrant rather than merely a slice of territory produced by the past accidents of power politics. It has been the objective of states, for their own purposes, to develop that homogeneity within their territories which is associated with the national principle. In this context, Y.-M. Goblet asserted that the state preceded the nation and that the nation is actually a creation of the state rather than the other way round (Goblet, 1956: 105–6).

Just as, for reasons of state, diversity has been played down by governments and homogeneity has been played up, the corollary of this is that diversity among states has been emphasised and encouraged. Thus the attributes of State A are seen as being totally different from those of its neighbour, State B. One state may even gain its sense of individuality by contemplation of the very different characteristics of its neighbours (Parker, 1985: 94). The 'naturalness' of one state as territorial unit is bound to imply the 'naturalness' of others and therefore, by definition, of the whole world of states. In this way the polychromatic map becomes a representation of a tangible reality in much the same way as do maps of climate or soil types. As such it becomes a political tool, and its component parts consist of space so sacred that blood may be spilled to defend its inviolable frontiers (Goblet, 1956: 55–9). While it has often been a difficult task to conceal the fact of diversity and to sustain claims to homogeneity within the boundaries of a particular state, it has been a relatively easy matter to do so by demonstrating the existence of diversity among states.

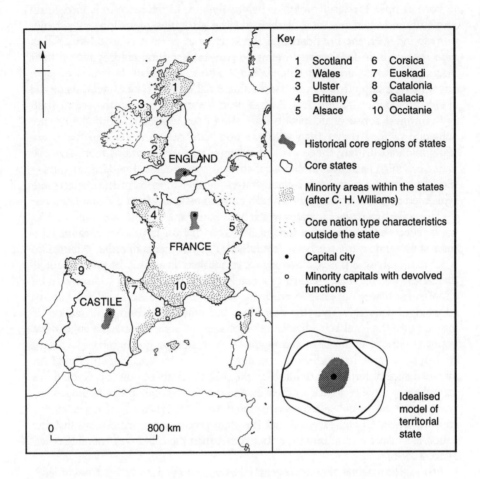

Figure 5.1 Nations, states and nation-states: France, Spain and the United Kingdom

As has been observed, the general categorisation of 'nation-state' includes units of immense diversity in size, shape, population, physical resources, wealth and power. Such diversity calls into question whether they can be grouped into a single category at all. Since they are essentially geographical entities, the existence of such diversity among them has been produced by the particular factors at work during their development. Such factors have a geographical and historical incidence, and the result of this is that in a particular geographical region at a specified historical period there is likely to have been a dominant state type. There have in practice been a great diversity of types of state, but one particular type has tended to become the norm. While they may display considerable differences in many of their attributes, they will have basically the same type of geopolitical structure and relate in much the same way to the rest of the states in the region. Likewise, those states which emerge at another place or time are also likely to possess considerable similarities to one another but to be different from those which preceded them. The key to understanding the great diversity of the states which at any particular time constitute the polychromatic political surface is thus to view the political surface from a diachronic perspective.

Diachronic geopolitical variation and its causes can be clearly demonstrated by reference to the Italian peninsula. In the middle of the first millennium BC the most common form of geopolitical organisation in Italy was the city-state. These cities, Greek and Phoenician in the south and Etruscan in the north, were part of the city-state system which dominated the whole of the Mediterranean world, and they entered into alliances and groupings for the purposes of defence and trade. By the beginning of the Christian era one of these cities, Rome, had moved into a dominant position. This city was in many ways an atypical one among the Mediterranean city-states, possessing a more developed sense of territoriality than was normal among them. It first achieved a dominant position in Italia,[4] and in doing so it subjugated all the other city-states to its will. Rome's dominance of Italia was followed, after the victorious Punic Wars against Carthage, by control over the western Mediterranean basin, and finally over the whole of the Mediterranean Sea. This then became Rome's *Mare Nostrum*, which was thought of as being the 'natural' region over which Rome exercised its authority. This authority was further secured by extending the *Limes* (frontiers) of the Empire northwards to the Rhine and eastwards into Mesopotamia.

At first this immense political entity had taken the form of the *Respublica Romana*, a grouping of largely autonomous cities under the hegemony of Rome, whose function was seen as being that of keeping the *Pax Romana* throughout the immense territories which it controlled. By the first century of the Christian era this *Respublica* had been transformed into the *Imperium Romanum*, in which Rome was transformed from being *Primus inter Pares*, the first among the equal cities of the Mediterranean, to *Caput Mundi*, the dominant city controlling the destiny of the ancient world.

With its fall in the fifth century AD a successor state, the Holy Roman

Empire, held together by the cement of Christianity, arose in northern Europe. The centre of this new empire was located in the middle Rhinelands, which had been on the northern frontier of the Roman Empire. Power moved over the Alps and Italy was relegated to the status of being a subordinate part of an empire which still looked to the Mediterranean for its civilisation and took its name from Rome. Rome retained its position as the religious centre of the new empire and as such was at the southern point of that axis which linked the imperial and the papal power. This in turn soon weakened as a result of the appearance of strong centrifugal tendencies which the Rhineland core region did not possess the economic or political strength to overcome.

As the centre of power weakened, city-states began to re-emerge in Italy. The first of the new type of city-state was Venice, which became central to the revival of the Mediterranean trading system and the prototype for what was to become the dominant political form throughout the Italian peninsula. By the fifteenth century Italy had been transformed into a peninsula of city-states and the centre of the Mediterranean's economic and commercial system.

Around the northern fringes of the Italian peninsula lay a number of states which were culturally peripheral to the Italian world. One such was the Duchy of Savoy, nestling in the Alps and sharing a long common border with France. This state became a sort of southern outpost of northern influences: among these influences being the idea of the nation-state, one of the most influential legacies of the French Revolution. From its Alpine core region Savoy expanded southwards into the Po basin, and in so doing was transformed into the Principality of Piedmont. It was through Piedmont that the northern European idea of the nation then took hold in Italy, and this principality, and later kingdom, also became the conduit for the transplantation of northern ideas to Italian soil. Using Piedmont as its base, and in the name of Italy, the new Italian nationalism absorbed the city-states, removed foreign influences and created that Italian nation-state which came into being in 1860 (Figure 5.2a). The process of 'piedmontisation' transformed the peninsula along the lines which were to become general throughout the whole of Europe by the next century. However, this was still the time when powers and not nations were the favoured geopolitical entities, and the new Italy soon aspired to great-power status. It embarked on overseas empire-building, which was considered to be the most important indicator of a great power. The Italian economic base proved to be woefully inadequate to sustain a successful imperial drive, and the new power, a relative latecomer to the imperial game, was unable to create more than a token empire. After World War I the Italian state was reconstructed on authoritarian lines by the Fascists, led by Benito Mussolini. The Fascist party took its name from the *Fasces*, the bundle of sticks with an axe which had been the symbol of the authority of Rome, and an attempt was made to resurrect the power of the Roman Empire. Nationalism and imperialism coalesced into the ambition to build up the power of Italy through the creation of an imperial state dominating the whole of the Mediterranean. As with

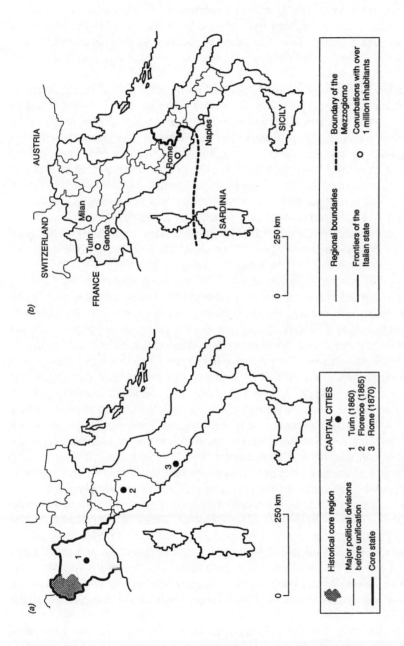

Figure 5.2 (a) The unification of Italy (b) Elements in the geopolitical structure of Italy

Germany and *Mitteleuropa*, attempts were made to justify in geopolitical terms this aspiration to a dominant position in *Mare nostro* (Antonsich, 1995). However, once more the economic weakness of Italy's home base made it impossible for this second imperial drive to be sustained. With the collapse of the Fascist state in 1943 Italy was forced to abandon its imperial aspirations and to return to reliance on the nation which had been created nearly a century earlier.

The aspiration to nationhood appeared easily attainable since the linguistic and cultural identity of Italy was not seriously challenged. However, it was to founder on the social, political and economic chasm which existed between the north and south of the peninsula. The aspiration to the establishment of a strong and centralised nation-state on the French model foundered on the failure to bring the Mezzogiorno, that part of the Italian peninsula south of Rome, fully into the state and to give it the manifest benefits which the more advanced north had gained from unity. The attempts to devolve power, and to loosen that centralised Italian state which was a legacy of French influence, centred on the regions (Figure 5.2b). The post-Fascist constitution of 1947 gave increased powers to these *regioni*, although, in practice, those powers proved slow in being granted and implemented (Parker, 1983: 24–7).

While the internal cohesion of the state was being challenged in this way, externally the failed *Mare nostro* imperialism of the Fascist period gave place to a new spirit of post-war internationalism. Association with its European neighbours, rather than xenophobic nationalism, was seen as being the answer to the country's problems. Mediterranean and colonial solutions had failed, said Prime Minister Alcide de Gasperi, and 'Italy must climb the Alps'.[5] Once more Italy sought solutions in northern Europe to the problems of its identity and position in the world (Willis, 1971). The new idea was supranationalism, which came from France in much the same way as nationalism had done a century earlier. In 1951 Italy became one of the original 'Inner Six' countries which signed the Treaty of Rome and embarked on the new supranationalist approach based on Jean Monnet's idea of 'community'. Italy had climbed the Alps and became part of the new Western Europe, working towards collective solutions to the problems which were the legacy of nationalism and imperialism.

Meanwhile the continued economic and political strains on the Italian state have produced powerful regional movements, some of which, such as the Lombard League, desire that the Italian state should be superseded and replaced by new states based on the regions. As a result of this a question mark again hangs in the 1990s over that Italian state created in the 1860s. The dynamic new regionalism threatens to erode its authority from below, while from above the European Union moves into ever larger areas of the competence of the state.

It can be seen that the political units of the Italian peninsula have been subject to considerable diachronic change. As the centre of a great empire, at its apogee Rome, in addition to making Italy the major centre of power in the

Western ecumene, was able to bring about relative social harmony, economic prosperity and internal peace in Italy and throughout the Mediterranean world. However, the attempt to re-create the Roman Empire by the Fascists in the early twentieth century proved to be an unmitigated disaster. The establishment of the Italian nation-state in the nineteenth century was fraught with problems which de Gasperi and the post-World War II generation of Italian politicians have attempted to solve in a European context.

The evidence from this survey is that the favoured political form at any particular period has owed more to a widespread aspiration towards a desired goal than to a dispassionate assessment of the desirability of the form in the context of the circumstances prevailing. It is thus more an ideal than a practical phenomenon, and its effect on those particular areas which are subjected to it varies greatly in time and place. From this it is possible to identify those geopolitical forms which have been most characteristic of particular periods, and these can be grouped into categories. Viewed from this diachronic perspective, the nation-state constitutes a category of this sort. While nation-state type characteristics can be identified in forms which have existed since the earliest times, it was only during the present century that it became the 'norm' towards which there was a general and widespread aspiration.

Thus while viewed synchronically the world political map gives the initial impression of being a riot of unconnected forms and colours, when viewed diachronically, set in motion as it were, the existence of patterns becomes apparent, and evidences can be detected of processes taking place. Geopolitical forms having particular characteristics give place to others having different characteristics, the later being superimposed on those which preceded them and often interacting with them to produce hybrids. While the chosen new forms become the models towards which others aspire, evidences of the earlier ones are likely to persist. In this way, at those times and places where the city-state is the normal form of geopolitical organisation, evidences of earlier forms have usually persisted. At times when empires have been in the ascendant, vestiges of city-states remain in evidence. At the present day, when the so-called nation-state is the dominant geopolitical form throughout the world, other types of states have continued to exist alongside nation-states. The world political map at any given time is thus a palimpsest, the layers of which date from different periods; it has meaning only when it is viewed as such.

The reality of the existence of non-typical geopolitical forms at any particular time is frequently obscured by the deliberate use of the terminology associated with the dominant forms. The non-typical, and therefore less acceptable, forms are thus clothed in the politically correct terminology of the period. In classical antiquity, *polis*, in addition to meaning the city-state, was often used to describe what were in reality proto-imperial entities. After Rome had changed from being a republic to being an empire, the term 'Respublica' remained for long in use. When the centre of the Empire had moved away from Rome to Constantinople — the 'Second Rome' on the Bosphorus — and the

Italian peninsula was partitioned among barbarian tribes, the term 'Imperium Romanum' continued to be used for another thousand years. The reality was that, long before the Empire's formal end in 1453, what remained had shrunk into little more than a group of city-states and finally into the single Greek city-state of Byzantium. Yet its people still called themselves Romani and it was still ruled by the Basileus (Emperor) and claimed to be the true centre of (Orthodox) Christianity. In the west the Roman idea of *Imperium* continued, and Europe was inherited by the German tribes, who established the Holy Roman Empire, which nominally exercised authority over an increasingly centrifugal Western Europe. This anachronistic empire was central to that *ancien régime* which was a major objective of the French Revolution to overturn, an event which then set Europe on course towards making the nation-state its normative model. During the first half of the nineteenth century 'nation' was widely associated with progress and humanity, while 'empire' was associated with backwardness and oppression. As the great maritime powers of Europe consolidated their world possessions the term 'empire' was at first avoided by them. 'Greater Britain', associated with progress and dynamism, was long used in preference to British Empire (Dilke, 1890). France, a republic which was engaged in building what was in effect a world empire, soon followed suit with *La Plus Grande France* (Betts, 1978: 52–3). In fact Britain was reluctant to acknowledge that it had in effect become the centre of a global empire and, in India, the heir to the Moghuls. The designation of Victoria as 'Queen-Empress' in 1876 thus represented a considerable psychological shift. However, by this time empire was back in fashion and the 'new imperialism' was in full swing. Empire was an aspiration which demonstrated that a state was truly in the first rank of the powers. When Germany was united in 1871, the new state was designated the *Reich* (Empire), and its emperor was quick to recall the medieval splendours of the *Romanisch Reich*. Likewise the Belgians, Dutch and Italians designated their possessions as 'empires' and converted their monarchs into emperors and empresses (Betts, 1976).

The nation-state became the favoured geopolitical form which followed the fall of the empires both in Europe and elsewhere. It represents the aspiration to progress which has usually underlain and impelled all major changes of geopolitical form. However, it has been seen that the nation-state's basic weakness is the problem of the relationship between its two component parts, territory and people. The two extremes in this relationship are the existence of an absolute fit and of no fit at all. However, the usual reality is one of gradations of fit between the two, and its closeness will depend to a large extent on the relationship of the formation of the state to that of the nation, in other words which of them came first. If it was the nation, then the resulting state represents an expression of its sense of identity and its desire for freedom from foreign domination. If it was the state, then the nation becomes subsumed into a territorial process which has more to do with statism than with nationalism. Nation and nationalism are then created and used by the state in the way suggested by Goblet for its own purposes and, when this is the case, the result may more appropriately be called a state-nation than a nation-state.

In reality this whole process is a form of imperialism, and its end-product will be a kind of modified empire masquerading as a nation-state (Williams, 1985: 127–9). It is another version of the recurring phenomenon of the 'imperial nation' which expands and secures a dominant position among adjacent population groups and then seeks to impose its own national identity upon them. Examples of both nation-states and state-nations are to be found in nineteenth-century Europe.

An example of the nation-state phenomenon is modern Greece, which came into being in the early nineteenth century as a result of the general revolt of a population which was highly conscious of its own cultural identity and opposed to that alien cultural identity which the Ottoman Empire had sought for centuries to impose upon it (Darby, 1965: 88–90). Established at the Treaty of London in 1829, the original Kingdom of Greece consisted only of the Peloponnesus, the Cyclades and a strip of land lying immediately to the north of the Gulf of Corinth. A century later at the Treaty of Sèvres (1920), in which, as with Versailles a year earlier, nationality was one of the guiding principles, the Ottoman Empire was consigned at last to history, and the Kingdom of Greece was given almost the whole of the peninsula and the Aegean Sea (Crawley, 1965: 112–18).

An example of the state-nation phenomenon, on the other hand, was the Kingdom of Hungary, which had large non-Hungarian-speaking territories assigned to it in the *Ausgleich* of 1867 in which the Dual Monarchy was established, and the Hungarians became partners with the Austrians in the management of the empire. Although Hungary had been one of the leaders of the nationalism which gripped central and eastern Europe during the second half of the nineteenth century, by the end of the century Hungary was itself behaving in a quasi-imperial manner towards the smaller nationalities within its extended frontiers (Goblet, 1956: 209). Attempts were then made to entrench the dominant position of Hungary and the Hungarian language throughout the whole of the area which it controlled. With the fall of the Austro-Hungarian Empire in 1918 an independent Hungarian state came into existence, but at the Treaty of Trianon in 1920 Hungary lost two-thirds of its territory, and large numbers of Hungarians were left outside the tightly drawn borders of the new state. However, Magyar imperialism and the idea of a 'Greater Hungary' persisted, an idea that was for a time revived under the aegis of Nazi Germany during World War II.

The formation of a true nation-state is thus usually linked to the sense of identity of a particular population group coupled with the threat of foreign domination. The state-nation on the other hand uses a particular cultural group as its base to secure a position of dominance over a wider area. The nation is then modified and developed, and a new nation emerges which is closely associated with the state and its needs. The new national identity is reinforced by the transposition of the identity of the expanding state to the whole of the territory which it occupies.

Spain, France and Great Britain have been considered as being in many ways typical examples of the nation-states of modern Europe, but in each case their creation was actually the result of the process of the formation of a state-nation. All three came into existence as a result of territorial expansion from their respective core regions in the Meseta, and the Paris and London basins into territories having a diversity of languages and cultures and a variety of historical experiences. The policy of the states was to centralise power on the core regions, and then, as part of the process of strengthening the state, to effect a cultural absorption of the conquered territories into the culture of the core regions, and the core states of Castile, France and England which were based upon them. This is the particular characteristic of the state-nation which distinguishes it from either the nation-state or the imperial state. The latter controls a diversity of peoples and territories but remains a remote and usually alien power. There is usually little attempt to effect a full absorption of the subject peoples so long as their expressions of individuality do not interfere with the structures of power and impede the functioning of the empire. The state-nation, on the other hand, attempts a complete absorption of the conquered territory and its people into an enlarged 'nation' based on the dominant culture's possessing a high level of homogeneity.

The dichotomy of continuity and change lies at the heart of the complexity of the world's geopolitical surface. The development of new forms of geopolitical organisation, more responsive to changed circumstances, has been countered by vigorous attempts to resist change and to maintain the status quo. Decaying empires have invariably resisted disintegration, and formerly dominating cities have attempted to hold on to their positions of power. Throughout time successive *anciens régimes* have never been prepared to acquiesce in their own extinction. The attempt to turn the nation-state (or the state-nation) into something permanent and eternal smacks of just such *ancien régime* attitudes. As a consequence, changes to the political map have rarely taken place within a gradual process, but have more often been the result of sudden transformation. This has usually been brought about by general wars caused by the development of structural imbalances between the established geopolitical surface, which those who uphold it regard as firm and fixed, and the pressures caused by changes in the realities of the distribution of power. War produces a new political map which for a time reflects more closely the realities of the distribution of power, and the endurance of the new map will depend on the extent to which it continues to do this.

Observation of the patterns of change over the long term also reveals the recurrence of two opposite spatial processes. These are respectively the centrifugal and centripetal processes, and they have diametrically opposite effects on the political map. The centripetal process is integrative, leading to the formation of larger political entities, while the centrifugal one is disintegrative and results in the creation of smaller entities. The former is the result of the propensity of certain states for territorial expansion, and its success, in other words the extent to which larger states actually come into being and endure, is a consequence of both internal and external geopolitical circumstances at a particular time. Internally these centre on the power of the core region, and its ability to secure and to maintain control. Power in this sense derives from such factors as size and location in relation to the total territory together with the possession of the necessary physical and human resources. If the extended core region, consisting of the area of greatest cultural homogeneity – in other words the core nation – covers a large proportion of the total territory of the state and is economically powerful and demographically strong, then the evidence shows that the state is more likely to be successful in maintaining control. As an example of this, the extended French core region, stretching from the basin of the Seine to that of the Loire and Garonne, is of such size and strength in relation to the later expansion of the French state eastwards to the Rhine and the Alps – territories which had been part of the Holy Roman Empire – as to facilitate the successful establishment and maintenance of a centralised state. The French core is large and powerful in relation to the total area of the state, and this made relatively easy the extension to the conquered regions of a high level of cultural homogeneity emanating from the core. Spain, established by the union of the Crowns of Castile and Aragon in 1479, and Great Britain, established by the union of the Crowns of England and Scotland in 1707, were also state-nations of the same type, but neither of the extended core regions of the new states proved to be strong enough to subsume the strong aspirations to independence which existed among other population groups lying within their boundaries into their own state-based nationality. Despite this, they did possess sufficient real power to assert the dominant positions of the core nations (Castile, England) and to assert that their extended territories were nation-states (Figure 5.1).

In other cases the fiction of nationality has proved to be too great to be sustained and the power of either the core region or the core nation proved insufficient to maintain the unity of the state. A notable example of this was Yugoslavia, the union of the South Slavs. This federal state was established in 1918 following the disintegration of the Austro-Hungarian Empire and it centred on the union of the Serbs and the Croats. It also included Slovenes, Albanians, Macedonians and a number of other population groups. The proto core nation of the new state was Serbia, which had a long and illustrious history as an independent Balkan state and had been fully independent of the Ottoman Empire since 1878 (Kolarz, 1946: 189). Despite its power and influence, its assertion of hegemony in the new Slav state was resisted strongly by the others (*ibid.*: 191). It proved impossible either for the Serbian national identity to be accepted as that of the new state or for some invented national identity to be at all credible. Neither were overall feelings of being 'Slav' sufficiently strong to replace the historically engendered national identities within this artificial state (*ibid.*: 9–11). When the ideological cement of communism crumbled away after 1990, there was virtually no coincidence between 'nation' and 'state'. The state on its own then proved to be insufficiently strong or credible to be able to survive. The position of Serbia in relation to the former Yugoslavia was in many way akin to that of Castile to Spain and England to Great Britain but, unlike them, it did not possess the strength to convert a nation-state into a state-nation (Figure 5.3).

It can be seen from all this that the reason why some states endure and some do not has a great deal to do with their geopolitical structures. This is also true of those states which have become great powers. The most important structural relationship is that between the nation and the state. Thus while, as has been observed, the two actually refer to quite different attributes, and the connection between them is often a tenuous one, a close association exists between them. Each reinforces the other, and the closer the fit between them, the greater the potential for stability and durability. The importance of the core region in relation to the nation and the state lies in the fact that it is the territorial link between the two and is thus the real key to the success of both. The core is the most intensive part of the state and is likely to possess most strongly the attributes of nationality. As one moves away from it, both nation and state attributes become weaker. As a consequence of this, the larger the size of the state, the greater the potential for the success of disintegrative forces becomes. The ultimate consequence of such a situation will be the breakup of the state and, although external factors are likely to play a part in it, the fundamental causes of state disintegration are to be found in its internal structures. Primary among these is the presence of subordinate elements within the state which refuse to accept the dominance of either the core region or the core nation. The larger any particular state is, the more difficult it is likely to become for the core to be successful in asserting and maintaining its control over the periphery, and centrifugal forces will be stronger. If they are strong enough to prevail against the core, then the state will disintegrate. Although the disintegration of any state is likely to have considerable international consequences, since it inevitably alters the situation in some way, the larger and more important the state, the greater, and more widely spread, the effects will be. This both challenges the international system of the time and produces the tools for the creation of a new one. The new system will certainly be founded on those ideas which were instrumental in bringing down the previous system and it is therefore likely, initially at least, to look very different from its predecessor. The centripetal tends to give place to the centrifugal, and the successor to a system based on great powers will be one which contains a large number of smaller states. However, the system also contains within itself the seeds of the re-creation of the preceding one. This is brought about by the attempts of certain of the new states to move into more powerful positions and so to exert more control over the situation. This leads again to the rise of new great powers and to hegemony or collective hegemony within the multi-state framework. The

Figure 5.3 Serbia, Yugoslavia and the Balkans
Source: Kolarz, W. (1946) *Myths and Realities in Eastern Europe*. London: Lindsay Drummond

attempt to assert a hegemonial position by one state inevitably produces a reaction which invokes new centrifugal and centripetal processes.

The categorisation of states can thus be meaningful only when it is approached from a diachronic perspective. Extreme differences in size have behavioural implications at all times and in all places, and the behaviour of large states is likely to have certain characteristics which set them apart from that of small states. Jean Gottmann classified states as being either 'Alexandrine' or 'Platonic' in character (Gottmann, 1980). The former kind of state is typified by a state of gigantic dimensions produced by conquest and cherishing aspirations to universality. The latter is a small state often consisting of little more than a city together with its hinterland. The former is territorial, and the acquisition and control of territory is of prime importance to it. For the latter, on the other hand, the acquisition of territory is of secondary importance and its principal concerns are with integrating itself into wider structures. The former can be seen as being the ultimate product of the centripetal process and its success is measured in terms of the controls which it is able to exercise while, the latter's success is measured in the extent of its integration into the wider system.

While making the same basic distinction, Goblet used the terms 'intensive' and 'extensive' to classify states but he took the distinction between the them further (Goblet, 1956: 185–200). What Goblet called 'extensive' states were not only large but were basically primitive and inefficient in their relationship to the territory which they occupied. They were exploitative of both human and physical resources and profligate in their use. They were not able to manage well what they had, and their urge to expansion arose from this. The 'intensive' states, according to Goblet, 'ranked highest in the scale of evolution' and developed what he referred to as 'qualitatively an optimum anthropo-geographical territory' (ibid.: 188). They thus needed less territory since they were able to manage more wisely the limited land which they occupied. They were more effective and frugal in the use of their resources, and this made them more the agents of progress than were the larger states. Between these two main categories of states Goblet interposed another which he called the 'mixed' state, which possessed both an intensive core and a large territory. The existence of a strong core region gave power, purpose and direction to territorial expansion which otherwise degenerated into random and undirected conquest for its own sake. Goblet's third category also points to another characteristic of the process of expansion. This is that all the most successful and enduring larger states came into being as a result of the expansion of small states and, despite divergent patterns of behaviour, there remains a clear link between the two. Smaller original states were transformed into the core regions and core nations of the subsequent larger states. These often then retained their positions of power within the enlarged states, although with further expansion the economic core regions tended to move into newly acquired areas. Those states successfully moving into positions of dominance can be seen to have characteristic geopolitical structures which set them apart from the others (Parker, 1988).

Although states have varied greatly in their characteristics and have regularly appeared and disappeared from the map, nations have become deeper and more enduring human realities—this despite the fact that their origins are bound up with those of states and, in particular cases, have been the deliberate creations of the states themselves. The same goes for capital cities, core regions and culture areas, all of which are geopolitical phenomena having considerable capacity for endurance, adaptation and rebirth in some new political form. Thus they have been the enduring geopolitical coordinates, as it were, and have acted as links between new systems and their predecessors. As a result the new system becomes embedded into an ongoing geopolitical continuum, the former city-state becoming the capital of a new empire and the core region of a declining empire becoming the revitalised core region of a new nation-state (Goblet, 1956: 206–7).

Geopolitical processes are thus fundamentally transformational, and the political forms of one place and time become the building-blocks for those of another. It is thus essential that the state should be defined in wider conceptual terms than those which are favoured during one particular period. Successive forms of geopolitical organisation can be seen as successive attempts to introduce order into the turbulence and destructiveness of the human world. As one form of territorial organisation breaks down or proves unsatisfactory, new ideas have been investigated and new geopolitical forms have been created. Stephen Jones identified this process of the translation from idea to reality and called it the Unified Field Theory (Jones, 1955). At first, new ideas, and even those realities which are based upon them, are bound by their very nature to have an experimental quality to them (Goblet, 1936: 22). There are always many possibilities, in the *vidalien* sense, as to the most appropriate and effective type of geopolitical organisation, and the one which eventually becomes the norm is the one which most appears to meet the perceived needs of the time. The rise of the cities, and their gradual transformation into city-states in early modern Europe, was a centrifugal response to the breakdown of the authority of the empire and the clear need for effective new structures to replace it. This restructuring along city-state lines was accompanied by a considerable increase in stability and wealth, and the Renaissance was very much a product of the rise of the city culture in Italy and elsewhere. Likewise, the rise of nations and nationalism in the early nineteenth century, and its subsequent use in the process of state formation, was a similar centrifugal response to that oppressive and stagnating system of control by the great powers known as the *ancien régime*.

Thus the predominant form of geopolitical organisation characteristic of any particular period is itself the result of the perceived need for changes to be made. The success of the new form of geopolitical organisation in ousting its predecessor and replacing it as the established order is then dependent on its continuing to embody the aspirations of the time and providing a method for their attainment. Success begets success, and what emerges as a successful form becomes an aspirational and then a normative model. The so-called nation-state is the main contemporary example of this.

However, despite this tendency for a particular form to become predominant, it cannot therefore be assumed that there is only one possible model at any particular time. Different models may appeal at the same time in different places and to different population groups. The victors and the vanquished; the colonisers and the colonised; the dominators and the dominated; the rich and the poor; the great powers and the small powers are each likely to have different ideas as to the most desirable way to progress. Particular groups of states having similar characteristics are more likely to form a set having the same basic aspirational model. Thus as the nineteenth century drew to its close, the acquisition of empire was the favoured objective of the great powers and imperialism was the most important political philosophy. The imperialist model was thus the one chosen by all those aspiring to acknowledged great-power status. The 'Grab for Africa', Africa being the last part of the world still available to European colonialism, was participated in by virtually all the major powers, as mentioned in note 4 to Chapter 2, even though the value of the territory acquired was often highly dubious (Amery, 1939: 52).

At the same time as this was taking place, there was a growing aspiration towards the achievement of freedom by the subject peoples within the empires of Central and Eastern Europe, and by the early years of the twentieth century this was spreading to the overseas empires as well. Having insufficient physical force or technological resources at their disposal to be successful in confronting the imperial power, their principal weapon became the sense of identity of their people and their chosen model became the nation-state. Thus by the early years of the present century, nation-state and empire had come to coexist uneasily as alternative models for the attainment of mutually exclusive objectives. Both of these models were based more on aspiration than on reality, and they often accorded ill with geopolitical realities. Overseas empire often made little sense in terms of satisfying the real needs of particular states, but imperialism was still pursued by leaders who desired the status of great powers. The acquisition of Germany's overseas colonies by Bismarck in the 1880s has been interpreted in this way since they proved to be of little economic benefit to Germany. Empires were in fashion and their emperors needed to have new clothes. In a similar way, the idea of the nation often accorded ill with many of the realities of the situation within the overseas possessions of the imperial powers. Particular colonial territories frequently contained within themselves great human diversities and the human realities often crossed those artificially imposed boundaries drawn by the imperialists themselves. The model of the nation-state, and the nationalism which sought to bring it about, had an air of unreality about it in the context of Africa or Asia.

Thus, as concepts, both nations and empire were used to justify certain courses of political action. They were founded on belief in the inherent virtue of particular forms of organisations. Both were firmly territorial in that the desired end was linked to the possession and management of a particular territory.

After World War II, one of these two models, the imperial one, was rapidly transformed into an anti-model. It came to be associated less with the establishment of order through the world-wide structures which it produced then with global inequality and injustice. Both the colonised peoples themselves and a new generation of Europeans came to see it as being at best irrelevant to the modern world and at worst the instrument of European domination. Powerful forces throughout the world sought to bring about its speedy end. Of the two competing models of the early twentieth century, the nation-state model emerged victorious. The idea of nation had been transposed from Europe to the Third World and the idea of nation-state, long dominant in Europe, had become the aspirational model throughout the dependent territories of Africa and Asia. Thus the two models can be seen in the role of the dominant and challenger model. The great-power normative model in a world dominated by great powers was successfully challenged by a national model which becomes the norm in a world of small states.

However, at the time when the confrontation of nationalism and imperialism was at its height, a third model had presented itself. This was the communist model, which, although developed from ideas which had been prevalent during the second half of the nineteenth century, did not achieve a geopolitical form until the Revolution of 1917 produced the transformation of the Russian Empire into the Soviet Union. While communism purported to present an alternative model to both empire and nation-state, and one which was superior to them both, in reality the particular form it took, represented a kind of synthesis of them both since it was made up of nations cemented together by ideology. Looked at in geopolitical terms it was actually far from being radical since it preserved the territory of the empire almost inviolate as the overall framework, and within this made concessions to its component parts. Only some of these components could with any reality be said to have the attributes of nationhood, but, frequently on the basis of very slender evidence, the major ones were elevated to the status of Union Republics based on the principle of nationality.[6] While the political theory underlying the union was of a devolved system of power, the reality was one of a centralised state operating ever more stringent controls on all aspects of life within its boundaries. Its most radical geopolitical assertion was that the new state was to be egalitarian in territorial terms. Thus the centripetal core–periphery structures characteristic of an empire, and being the basis of its inequalities, were to be replaced by centrifugal structures in which both wealth and power would be widely distributed. These centrifugal structures were based on two types of internal organisation: the political component parts, the most important of which were the Union Republics, and the economic regions, which had the task of development within particular territories. In this way the characteristics of both imperialism, in bringing an overall order, and nationalism, in attending to the particular needs of local communities, were to be retained (Dewdney, 1971: 59).

Following World War II a looser version of this system, in which nation was emphasised over empire, was established under the overall aegis of the Soviet Union in many of the states around the Soviet Union's periphery from Eastern Europe to the Far East. This formidable Eurasian grouping existed for nearly half a century. It was designed to present the Third World with an alternative first to the imperial model and then to the national models. Despite being taken up by Cuba and a number of Afro-Asian states, like the imperialism of the first half of the century this model failed in its second half and disintegrative forces prevailed. Since 1990 the sovereign nation-state has been overwhelmingly the favoured model throughout the world.

In conclusion, while many of the component forms making up the world's geopolitical space show signs of being survivals of past systems, others may be pointers to the next stage in the evolution of the geopolitical surface. This surface is a palimpsest to which new and unfamiliar forms are constantly being added. Some of these forms are destined to become the dominant geopolitical realities of the future. This mixture of past evidences, present realities and future possibilities is the raw material of the world political map. In turn those political ideas which, in the unified field, become translated into reality will determine its future shapes and patterns. The next important question is the extent to which wider patterns of state relationships can be identified and the effects which they have on both the regional and the global scales.

NOTES

1. The idea of a 'League of Nations' had been one of the famous 'Fourteen Points' for a just and lasting peace outlined by President Woodrow Wilson at his Inaugural Address to Congress – for his second term as President – in January 1918. The use of the term 'league' implied a binding together, while 'nation' was a term which fitted in well with the American opposition to the European empires and the desire to promote the freedom of smaller peoples. The Covenant (constitution) of the League was adopted by the Congress of Versailles and was written into the Treaty of Versailles in 1919. Ironically, as a result of opposition in Congress, the United States never became a member of the League of Nations.
2. The word 'empire', from the Latin *imperium*, had been widely used in Europe to denote the idea of the dominance of one people over others and to justify and legitimise it by reference to the Roman Empire. In the late nineteenth century imperialism came to be associated particularly with the creation of the world empires by the great European powers (Parker, 1988: 1–11).
3. The most notable such area is Antarctica, which contains the dependencies of a number of countries which have bases there. Not only has it become one of the world's most important areas for scientific experiment, but it is also an interesting experiment in international cooperation (Chaturvedi, 1996).
4. In ancient times Italia was that part of the Italian peninsula south of the river Rubicon. The first area to be conquered by Rome, it maintained its special position at the heart of the Roman Empire. It came to possess a high measure of that cultural and economic unity associated in later times with the nation-state. It was forbidden for Roman generals to lead their armies into Italia and that was why the 'crossing of the Rubicon' by Julius Caesar was an especially fateful event for Rome, signifying the end of the power of the Senate and the beginning of rule by the Emperors.
5. After having been imprisoned during the Fascist era, Alcide de Gasperi (1881–1954) became the prime minister of Italy from 1945 to 1953. He was an early supporter of European integration and took Italy into NATO, the Council of Europe and the European Coal and Steel Community. It was largely thanks to de Gasperi that Italy's policy in the post-war years was a very pro-European one.
6. Although in the European parts of the Soviet Union the term 'nation' was appropriate, in the Asiatic regions it most certainly was dubious. The peoples of Central Asia, formerly known as Turkestan, were divided into five republics on

national principles even though each one of them contained many different peoples within its frontiers and many different languages were spoken. Finally they all assumed importance at the end as the units into which the Soviet Union disintegrated and the new sovereign states which emerged from it.

CHAPTER 6

MICRO, MESO AND MACRO:
SCALES OF GEOPOLITICAL ANALYSIS

The political map imparts a certain air of permanence to a geopolitical world which is, in reality, in a state of considerable movement. We have seen that, while the units of which it is composed are extremely diverse, they can be grouped into a number of functional categories: the local, territorial (national) and universal (imperial) states. Examples of each of these categories can invariably be found on the world political map but their relative importance alters, and at any given time one of the categories will usually have become the norm. The attainment of such a position owes much to the political *Zeitgeist* which engenders the belief that one particular form or structure is in some way the 'right' one and is more likely than any of the others to promote human wellbeing and progress. Both within and between categories of states, certain states are seen to be increasing while others are decreasing in importance. While an increase in importance is associated with spatial or territorial acquisition, a decrease is associated with contraction and disintegration. When it takes place, disintegration of this sort tends to be into pre-existing component parts, some of which may then themselves become successor states, some be absorbed into other states while others become the nuclei of new states in course of formation. The most spectacular recent example of the disintegrative process at work was the Soviet Union, the collapse of which in 1989 resulted in the appearance of fifteen new states on the political map.[1]

As we have seen, underlying all geopolitical change two distinct processes are at work. One of these is the rise and fall of states of basically the same type. This is caused by the oscillation of centripetal and centrifugal forces within these states together with parallel changes taking place in other states. The other process, which underlies the former, is the replacement of one dominant functional category by another. This will take place over a longer period of time and be associated with fundamental changes in conditions. This represents a paradigm shift which sets an entirely new geopolitical course. These two processes acting together produce two extremes in a geopolitical time and space matrix of great complexity.

While on a global scale this all constitutes a continuum, it is possible to isolate particular times and places so as to view the process from a regional perspective. In other words, one can select parts of the matrix for more detailed chorological and chronological investigation. This regional scale of analysis enables more precise focusing to take place so that situations more characteristic of particular times and places can be identified and explained. However, while there is a global totality which is finite, and therefore a given, it does not follow that it itself is therefore divided into automatically identifiable segments of space. The only areas which stand out clearly on the map as being separate geographical entities are the continents such as Africa or South America, but they do not therefore constitute geopolitical entities. The splitting up of the global totality into convenient and useful sub-units or regions depends less on predetermined circumstances than on the purpose for which such regionalisation is required. Thus it is possible to identify climate, relief or soil regions and even to attempt a synthesis to produce overall 'natural' regions. However, when it come to human activities the particular regions chosen are less likely to be the result of the operation of some absolute criteria than the intention and perspective of those who are engaged in the exercise. Geopolitical regionalisation is thus more likely to be a subjective business strongly influenced by considerations of time and place.

Looked at from a European perspective, those areas which lie on the right-hand side in the Eurocentric map, in which the convention is that North is at the top, have been commonly lumped together as the 'East'. However, since the lands lying immediately adjacent to Europe were in earlier times by far the best known and, from a European perspective, the most important, it was these which invariably loomed largest in ongoing European geopolitical perceptions.

From the sixteenth century this particular 'East' consisted overwhelmingly of the Ottoman Empire, the gigantic and menacing proportions of which bestrode the routes from Europe into Asia and extended deep into the eastern half of Europe.[2] With the beginning of the disintegration of the Ottoman Empire, what had been the eastern menace was transformed into the 'Eastern Question', which preoccupied the statesmen of Europe throughout the second half of the nineteenth century. This was bound up with such issues as the 'Straits',[3] the Holy Land and, after the opening of the Suez Canal in 1868, the security of maritime communications between Europe and the Indian Ocean. Thus, while there existed an overall 'East' in Kipling's sense as an area which was so different from the 'West' that 'never the twain shall meet', there could be little precision in a term which sought to define so vast an area stretching from the Balkans and the Mediterranean to the shores of the Pacific Ocean. It was natural that while the 'near' East loomed large in European perceptions the distant 'far' East was of much less immediate consequence. It was not until the end of the nineteenth century that any real precision began to enter into the distinction between the two. The former was linked to the Mediterranean and centred on the Ottoman Empire while the latter was linked to the Pacific and centred on China. In his survey of the state of the world after World War I, Isaiah Bowman used the regional approach for ease in identifying and examining issues particular to certain areas. Whereas in The New World he identified a 'Far East' which centred on China and Japan, he did not identify a 'near' East at all. Rather this area was examined under the headings 'Constantinople and its thoroughfare'; 'Palestine: a Jewish homeland' and 'Anatolia: the last remnant of the Turkish Empire' (Bowman, 1922: 425). There was little attempt to unify these separate areas or to link together those issues which were common to them all.

Nearly two decades later, on the eve of another war, Derwent Whittlesey in *The Earth and the State* identified the 'Orient' in a very general way. The 'Near East' was considered to be no more than an extension of that 'Mediterranean Realm' the eastern part of which consisted of the 'nexus with the Orient'. While much attention was given to this latter, the Far East was not discussed at all (Whittlesey, 1939: 235). However, in the current affairs atlases of the 1930s and 1940s a 'Near East' and a 'Far East' had been clearly emerging as important geopolitical regions. The presence of oil and pivotal world location emerged as the two principal criteria for defining the former, while the latter consisted largely of that area which was increasingly menaced by the expansion of Japan. In J.F. Horrabin's *Atlas of Current Affairs* there were special sections on 'The Mediterranean and the Near East' and 'Japan and the Far East' (Horrabin, 1934). The Mediterranean, by the 1930s itself menaced by Italian territorial expansionism, was generally seen as being less a 'realm' in Whittlesey's sense than as part of the vital line of communications between Europe and the East. In the perceptions of the European powers, its world role was largely seen as being a strategic one.

After World War II, in the first edition of *World Political Geography* (Pearcy and Fifield, 1948), Bowman's post-Ottoman separation of the Straits (Constantinople and its thoroughfare) and Anatolia was replaced by 'Turkey and the Straits'. In addition another entity, 'The Arab World', made its debut. This huge area stretched from the lands around the southern and eastern Mediterranean deep into Asia, and its appearance served to strengthen the link between the Mediterranean and the lands to the east of it. At the same time, curiously enough, Pearcy and Fifield used the term 'Middle East' very restrictively to denote only Iran and Afghanistan, which were treated as being 'transitional lands between the Near East and the Far East' (Lemert, 1948: 313–25). Seven years later in the second edition the area to which the term 'Middle East' referred had been expanded enormously to include not only Turkey, the Arab countries and Iran but also the newly independent Commonwealth states of India and Pakistan. On the other side of the continent 'Eastern Asia' had also appeared and was linked together with 'Australasia and Oceania' (Pearcy *et al.*, 1957: 643). In 1956 W.B. Fisher had used the term 'South-West Asia' to describe a far more tightly drawn region (Fisher, 1956). Fisher commented that what he called 'the extended use of the term "Middle East" to denote South-west Asia and its immediate borderlands in European Turkey and North-east Africa ... ignores logic', and he went on to pose the question 'Where is, then, the "Near East"?' (*ibid.*: 681). In the following year Hans Weigert used the almost identical term 'Southwest Asia' to delineate what was virtually the same region. Both again emphasised oil resources and strategic location as the principal criteria of definition (Weigert *et al.*, 1957). Despite the reservations of those like Fisher who sought greater precision in regional delineation, in the regional terminology of the Cold War the whole area moved into a position of crucial world significance and 'Middle East' became the favoured term to describe it. In addition to its strategic location between the great power blocs, together with its ever more important oil resources, its new world importance arose from its being the centre of the emerging Arab world. This was increasingly seen as being a distinct cultural entity of great importance, which was courted by both West and East. In *Geography and Politics in a Divided World* Saul Cohen perceived the region as a dangerous 'shatterbelt' lying between the major centres of world power in East and West and threatening to destabilise the balance of power between them (Cohen, 1964: 230–52). To Keegan and Wheatcroft, writing two decades later in the last years of the Cold War, it remained one of the world's major 'zones of conflict', central to which were 'the Levantine entanglement' of Israel and Palestine and the 'permanent flashpoint' of the Gulf (Keegan and Wheatcroft, 1986) .

At the same time as the Middle East was moving into the centre of the world drama, the Far East, on the other hand, sank to being a term used only for geographical convenience and, in geopolitical terms, an increasingly obsolete one. During the Cold War eastern Asia came to be seen less as a distinct geopolitical region than as an integral part of the global confrontation between the Soviet Union and the West. It replicated on the eastern side of the Eurasian landmass the divisions which were so much in evidence in the West. In this view the counterpart of the Iron Curtain stretching across Europe was a 'Bamboo Curtain' dividing communist from non-communist Asia. At the height of the Cold War Carlson distinguished between 'the continental states of East and Southeast Asia', which were part of the communist bloc, and the 'East Asian Offshore Islands', which were curiously categorised as being part of the 'Western' lands of Asia and the Pacific (Carlson, 1962). This same division was put into the global geopolitical context by Cohen, who divided the world into two great geostrategic regions centring respectively on the Soviet Union and the United States (see Chapter 7). The former was 'The Eurasian Continental Power' and the latter was the 'Trade-Dependent Maritime World' (Cohen, 1964: 63). These overall geostrategic regions were divided into a number of separate geopolitical ones. Not only was the eastern part of Asia not considered to be a geopolitical region at all, but the line separating the two geostrategic regions divided it into two parts. These were continental East Asia, dominated by China, which was a geopolitical region within the Eurasian Continental geostrategic region, and 'Offshore Asia and Oceania' – consisting of Japan, South Korea, Taiwan and the Philippines – which lay within the Maritime World geostrategic region (*ibid.*: 56–87). With the end of the Cold War the whole question of geopolitical regionalisation was reopened. In the new world of the 1990s the Middle East has remained inviolate, but its importance has been considerably lessened as a result of the diminished significance both of its strategic location and of its oil. On the other hand, the countries of the old Far East, divided and peripheralised by the Cold War, have emerged to a new global significance. Led by Japan, which had already precociously moved into the front rank of the industrialised countries by the 1970s, its countries have emerged as major players on the world stage, and this has been reflected in new regional terminologies. 'Far East' had been increasingly superseded by 'East Asia' (Cotterell, 1993), which in turn is being replaced by 'Asia Pacific'. This latter term includes a wider area than does East Asia and would normally be taken to be a combination of the old Far East and Southeast Asia. Some, not very logically in view of the 'Pacific' element in the term, have even extended it to include South Asia (Dobbs-Higginson, 1994). The introduction of 'Pacific' emphasises the maritime orientation of the region and its place as an inherent part of the maritime world. This new orientation has been most evocatively captured by the term 'Pacific Rim', the eastern half of which includes those fast-developing countries located in a great arc of islands and peninsulas stretching around the eastern seaboard of the Asian continent from Japan to Indonesia (Jones et al., 1993). This emphasises not just the 'Pacific' orientation of East Asia but the new significance of the great archipelago, which during the Cold War was relegated to being an insular periphery around the all-important Eurasian landmass (Figure 6.1).

While the identification of geopolitical regions of the sort described above changes considerably in relation both to developments in particular areas and to wider global considerations, there is another type of region which has endured over long periods of time and in which it is possible to distinguish the continuation of a particular set of characteristics. The existence of such enduring anthropogeographical regions arises from the longer-term differentiation of the world's human surface. They have been in fact distinct 'worlds', self-sufficient politically, economically and culturally, and they are the products of developments which have taken place in isolation within distinct environments. Alexander the Great bemoaned the fact that there were no more 'worlds' left to conquer and the Portuguese navigators spoke of *mundos* (worlds) in reference to the new lands which they were discovering. Those which lay to the west, the existence of which had been totally unsuspected, became the 'New World' to distinguish it from that 'old' one which had been already – if only vaguely and imperfectly – known. Lucien Febvre revived the term *mondes* to denote those anthropogeographical regions which had developed behind such great physical barriers as the Himalayas and the Central Asian deserts (Febvre, 1932: 314). They are here referred to as 'ecumenes' and they represent a regional differentiation of Whittlesey's world ecumene (Parker, 1988: 9–10). They also possess many of those characteristics attributed by Wallerstein to the 'world-economies', economically autonomous areas able to provide for most of their own requirements (see Chapter 9).

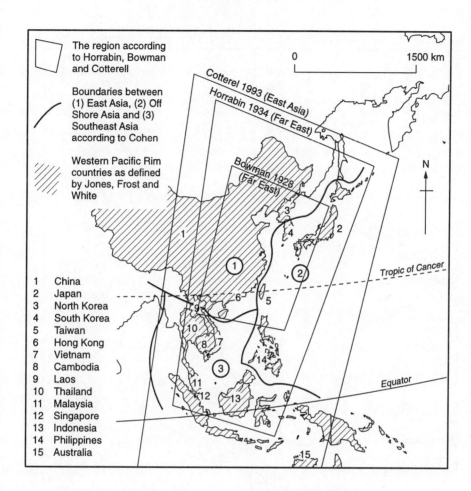

The region according to Horrabin, Bowman and Cotterell

Boundaries between (1) East Asia, (2) Off Shore Asia and (3) Southeast Asia according to Cohen

Western Pacific Rim countries as defined by Jones, Frost and White

Cotterel 1993 (East Asia)
Horrabin 1934 (Far East)
Bowman 1928 (Far East)

0   1500 km

N

Tropic of Cancer

Equator

1   China
2   Japan
3   North Korea
4   South Korea
5   Taiwan
6   Hong Kong
7   Vietnam
8   Cambodia
9   Laos
10 Thailand
11 Malaysia
12 Singapore
13 Indonesia
14 Philippines
15 Australia

Figure 6.1 East Asia as a world region (map projection based on satellite data). The three regions which appeared as regular quadrilaterals in the originals appear as irregular quadrilaterals when transposed to this projection.

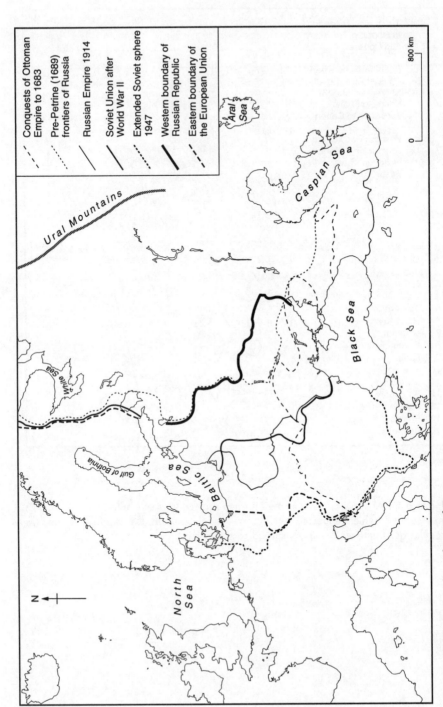

Figure 6.2 The eastern boundaries of Europe

Conquests of Ottoman Empire to 1683

Pre-Petrine (1689) frontiers of Russia

Russian Empire 1914

Soviet Union after World War II

Extended Soviet sphere 1947

Western boundary of Russian Republic

Eastern boundary of the European Union

0 ___ 800 km

Ural Mountains

White Sea

Gulf of Bothnia

Baltic Sea

North Sea

Caspian Sea

Aral Sea

Black Sea

N

It is possible to identify three great historical ecumenes of this type: the Western (Europe–Mediterranean), the Southern (South Asian) and the Eastern (East Asian). Each of them has been a major centre of human development possessing demographic, economic, political and cultural attributes which have evolved particular characteristics in relation to one another in a distinct and limited geographical space. While the centre of the ecumene, the principal area of the development of its distinct characteristics, can be easily identified, a problem arises in precisely delimiting its overall extent. Historically each has expanded and contracted in accordance with changes in its structures of power and influence. The East Asian ecumene can be identified in a general way as covering the eastern lands of Asia as delimited by Cotterell (1993: xi) and the South Asian ecumene the lands south of the great Himalayan barrier as delimited by Spate and Learmonth (1972: 2–14). The delimitation of the Western ecumene has the same problems as those associated with defining the precise extent of Europe. These centre on the eastern extension of the European continent. Traditionally Europe's eastern boundary has been considered as being the Ural Mountains, but more recently it has come to be more tightly drawn along a line extending from the Baltic to the Black Sea. While the former encloses a larger Europe which includes Russia, the latter defines a smaller and more compact continent (Figure 6.2). By drawing the boundary thus, the cultural factors of unity are more clear-cut, and Russia is seen as being a Eurasian state which is linked geopolitically more to the countries of Asia than to Europe. However, the Ural boundary conforms more with the geographical delimitation of the extent of the other two ecumenes, both of which have hinterlands extending into Central Asia.

Since the eighteenth century these three historical ecumenes have been joined by a fourth, the North American ecumene, and signs of proto-ecumenical characteristics can be observed in sub-Saharan Africa, and Latin America.

While the overall characteristics of each ecumene are very different from one another it is nevertheless possible to identify certain common geopolitical features. These include the existence of dominant capital cities, core regions, core cultures, inner and outer peripheries, frontiers and communications systems. They can be examined and compared using this terminology.

The principal historic core region of East Asia lies in the Wei He valley in northwestern China, and political unity was originally brought about from there by the Chin emperor in the third century BC. A high measure of cultural unity then came into being as a result of subsequent consolidation by the Han dynasty, and this 'Han' China became the basic entity known also as 'China proper' or the 'Eighteen Provinces' (Figure 6.3). During periods when the Han Chinese state was powerful, the non-Han inner peripheries which swathe it were incorporated into it. During the periods of greatest territorial aggrandisement by the Chinese state, an outer periphery including Tibet, Xinjiang, Mongolia and Manchuria was also incorporated. While the inner peripheries rapidly became Sinicised and were usually inclined to accept the

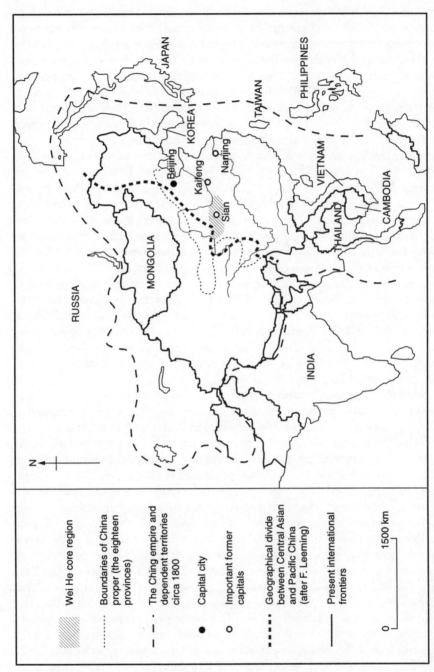

Figure 6.3 China and the Eastern ecumene

Wei He core region

Boundaries of China proper (the eighteen provinces)

The Ching empire and dependent territories circa 1800

● Capital city

○ Important former capitals

Geographical divide between Central Asian and Pacific China (after F. Leeming)

Present international frontiers

0   1500 km

RUSSIA

MONGOLIA

JAPAN

KOREA

Beijing

Kaifeng

Nanjing

Sian

TAIWAN

PHILIPPINES

VIETNAM

THAILAND

CAMBODIA

INDIA

N

dominance of China and Chinese civilisation, the outer peripheries, although strongly influenced by China, always retained their distinctive economic and cultural identities. Han China was bound together by a network of roads, and the Grand Canal was constructed to link the Huanghe core region with the economically important Yangtse region. Grandiose state projects of this kind served to bind the country together both politically and economically, and stimulated the forces of unity. While at its maximum extent this Chinese state covered the greater part of that territory identified regionally as the Far East, the projection of its power into the maritime periphery (the Pacific Rim) was always limited and uncertain. This lack of success can be attributed to the inadequacy of the resources allocated by China to maritime activity and the strongly continental bias of its foreign policy. It was in these circumstances that the Japanese state arose in the maritime periphery and, while using China as a model for its state development, it was able to maintain its independence and to strengthen its grip on the archipelago (Cotterell, 1993: 62). During the first half of the twentieth century, a period when China was weak and divided, Japan then went on to mount a strong but unsuccessful bid to replace China as the dominant power of the Eastern ecumene.

In South Asia the historic core region is at the centre of the gigantic Indo-Gangetic plain, which extends across the north of the subcontinent. The watershed region between them includes the Punjab (meaning 'five rivers') and the upper courses of the Ganga and Jamuna. Together these make up the *Madhya-desa*, the middle land around which the first Indian state (Bharat) was formed (Tinker, 1989: 5–8). The Ganga–Jamuna region has remained the major centre of power since the earliest times. It was here that the principal core regions of the Indian states have been located and where the salient characteristics of Indian (Hindu) culture became evident. The mountains which ring the subcontinent to the north together with the Deccan plateau to the south have also been part of the dominant state during its periods of maximum territorial extent, although the far north and the far south, the latter including the island of Sri Lanka, have only rarely been incorporated into it. The major axis of communication, the 'Grand Trunk Road', extends from northwest to southeast following the line of the river system, and the major centres of political power have almost always been located on or near to it.

Using those characteristics common to these two ecumenes, a normative geopolitical model of a universal state can be tentatively constructed. It has a basic centre–periphery structure with territorial expansion taking place from a peripheral core region to encompass and absorb the major centres of population and economic power of the ecumene. If the core region is strong enough to impose its will and to maintain its authority, this results in the establishment of a universal state covering all or most of the ecumene. Unity is then consolidated through the promotion of cultural attributes such as language and religion, and a system of communications, centring on the capital, serves to bind the state together and to emphasise the pre-eminence of the core region. If the state is strong enough, it will then seek to establish control over the inner and outer peripheries, a move which besides improving its security provides the possibility of additional physical resources (Figure 6.4).

When this model is applied to the Western ecumene it can be seen that, while a number of characteristics are consonant with it, there is also considerable divergence. A measure of political unity was achieved at around the same time as in the other two ecumenes, but since then disunity rather than unity has been the norm. Many subsequent attempts have been made to achieve unity, but, although there has been some success with these, unity has been both a rare and a temporary phenomenon and it has never been properly consolidated. While the continent has retained the overall structure of an ecumene, the superstructure has been subject to constant changes. As Chaunu put it, 'the summit shifts, but the base remains firm. Social plasticity, relative at the best of times, is confined to the summit' (Chaunu, 1970: 26). The attempts to bring about unity have usually involved securing control of particular regions which have core-type characteristics. An important example of such a region is to be found in the Rhinelands, and while this has on occasion acted as a kind of a European proto-core region, it never succeeded in becoming the core region of a fully developed universal state. In addition, despite originally having possessed many of the characteristics of a common culture such as language and religion, the cultural unity of the ecumene has tended to become weaker rather than stronger and a distinct cultural rift has opened up within it between west and east. It is from the latter that the most effective attempts to establish a universal state have taken place but these have proved to be inadequate to bring the west of the continent under its control. In the east, changes in the balance of power in modern times resulted in the core region of the proto-universal state being transferred from the Bosphorus to the *Mezhdurechie*, the historic Russian core region located in the middle Volga basin (Cornish, 1923: 175–91). It was from here that rapid territorial expansion resulted in the establishment of a state of immense size. Russia on its own is comparable in size to the universal states of the Eastern and Southern ecumenes, and by the beginning of the twentieth century 'European' Russia west of the Urals covered half the area of Europe. It had become itself a kind of 'world' and possessed many of the geopolitical characteristics associated with an ecumene (Febvre, 1932: 313–15). Its empire extended westwards to the Baltic–Black Sea isthmus and, by the time of the greatest territorial extent of its sphere of influence – in the guise of the Soviet Union – this extended over the whole of that part of the European continent lying to the east of the Baltic–Adriatic isthmus (see Figure 6.2). However, Russia never succeeded in extending its influence further westwards into peninsular Europe. The establishment of control based within peninsular Europe has been attempted by both France and Germany, and in those attempts they based their power on core regions located respectively to the west and east of the Rhine. Neither of these proved successful in establishing more than a relatively short-lived control over the ecumene (Parker, 1988: 30–63).

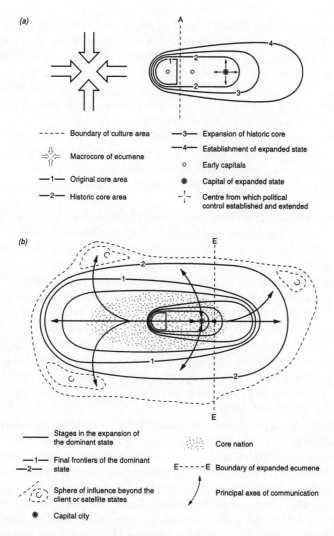

Figure 6.4 Geopolitical model of the universal state: (a) Early stages of territorial expansion (b) Completion of expansion
Adapted from Parker, G. (1988) *The Geopolitics of Domination.* London: Routledge

As a consequence of the successive failures to consolidate a universal state of a type which has been normal in the other ecumenes, smaller territorial units have become the norm in the Western ecumene. As a consequence of this the usual political map of Europe has been more polychrome than monochrome. The major preoccupation of the small states of which Europe is made up has been to maintain their independence from the larger ones and to resist the establishment of large accretions of power. Since the nineteenth century, with the spread of the nation-state model, the average size of these states has tended to become smaller. Only Russia has retained its position as an empire of gigantic proportions and a proto-universal state covering much of the east of the ecumene. However, with the collapse of the Soviet Union Russia also has now shrunk and been replaced, west of the Urals, by nine new states on the nation-state model. The territory of Russia is now smaller than it has been at any time since the late seventeenth century (Figure 6.2).

The discrepancy with the geopolitical model in the case of the Western ecumene is thus attributable to the failure to consolidate the early achievement of unity and to establish a universal state. In explaining the basic reasons for this situation it is possible to detect a number of basic divergences from the model.

The most significant of these divergences is the historic division between the east and west of the ecumene. With the fall of the Roman Empire two proto-universal state core regions came into being, one located around the Bosphorus and the other in the lower Rhinelands. However, while the former consolidated itself and remained the core region of a succession of imperial states, no single state was successfully built around the latter. In the east, although the core regions changed, proto-universal states were able to retain their power. The failure of the western core region to establish itself was linked to the early consolidation of powerful territorial states the core regions of which lay in the European inner periphery. In the Meseta (Castile), the North German Plain (Prussia) and the middle Danube (Austria), powerful states grew up which were able to consolidate and maintain positions of regional dominance over long periods of time (Parker, 1988).

The failure of universal state formation in the west produced the conditions for the development of a different set of geopolitical characteristics. The resistance to domination, and the securing of freedom and independence, became ideals to be aspired to and the geopolitical manifestation of these ideals was encapsulated in the smaller state and the devolution of political power. An example of this was Switzerland, which came into being in the thirteenth century as an assertion by the mountain peoples of the Alps of their freedom from the Holy Roman Empire.[4] It has remained in being through a number of subsequent transformations of the European geopolitical scene as an example of the determination of a small state to maintain its freedom and independence. This ideal came to be embodied in modern times in that of the nation-state as the symbiotic relationship of a people and a territory. The nation-state thus came to be seen as being an ideal to be espoused in contrast to the universal (imperial) state, which was something to be resisted. As has been seen, those states with universalist pretensions were quick to latch on to the national ideal to further their own aspirations. However, abuse of this sort did not diminish the importance of that national ideal which has made the nation-state the dominant paradigm of the twentieth century.

The existence of this cumulative process in which universal state formation was inhibited and smaller units were favoured over the larger ones has its roots in the unique geography of the Western ecumene. It has been especially in evidence in the peninsular territories of the ecumene, to the west of the Baltic–Black Sea isthmus, where it has been particularly important in influencing relationships between the countries of the core and those of the inner periphery. The nature of Europe as a 'peninsula of peninsulas' has meant that the continent is split into a number of geographical segments each of which has its own particular set of geographical characteristics. It is possible to detect a kind of 'naturalness' about such territorial segments as the Iberian and Italian peninsulas which is not possessed by segments of territory of a similar size embedded in the middle of the Indo-Gangetic plain or the Huanghe basin. In consequence, while the development of unity within one particular segment has been facilitated by its physical circumstances, the extension of power from one to another has proved more difficult. In these circumstances conflict rather than cooperation has been more the norm, and this has centred both on the rivalries among those states having universalist ambitions and on the efforts of the smaller states to resist such attempts and to maintain their independence.

Halford Mackinder saw the complexities of this conflictual situation as resolving themselves into an overall East–West conflict, and he took the wars between the Greeks and the Persians as the starting-point of this. He saw the conflict of 'seamen versus landsmen' as being the most enduring theme throughout European history. In the east lay those large continental states which aspired to dominance over the whole of the continent, while in the west lay a galaxy of smaller states which were jealous of their freedoms and wished to preserve them. The dominant eastern continental state has had many metamorphoses, which have included the Persian, Byzantine, Arab, Ottoman and Russian Empires. Over this long period of time the basic geopolitical thrusts, maintained Mackinder, had remained largely unchanged (Mackinder, 1919).

From the sixteenth century on, the world as a whole began to become a geopolitical entity and a new level began to appear above the levels of the individual ecumenes. What Bryce called the 'World-process' had begun, and it was not to end until the world had become closed. Because it was 'discovered' by the dynamic Europeans, the geopolitical world which began to take shape in the sixteenth century was cast in the European mould. Ptolemy's Mediter-ranean-centred *oikoumene* began to give place to Whittlesey's global ecumene, and the formerly separate 'worlds' came to be influenced by the existence of the one world of which they formed a part. They were increasingly gathered up into a single system which centred on the Western ecumene and was controlled by it. The Western ecumene became the geopolitical prototype for the new global scale of operation, and the conflictual situation which was the norm there was transposed to the global dimension. Thus in the early years of the twentieth century Mackinder's world-view, which had its roots in the wars of the Greeks and the Persians, became the basis for the first geopolitical theory which attempted to make sense of the complex relationships among the diverse component parts of the world's geopolitical space. While it was subsequently to be subject to many modifications and was followed by many alternative world-views, the influence of Mackinder's original proposition has remained a powerful one and one which has resonated down the decades. It has been important in the formulation of other world-views and in the development of the ideas of world systems and world orders which have resurfaced in the post-Cold War years.

During the twentieth century many attempts have been made to interpret the world as a whole from a geopolitical perspective. These can be put into three overall categories, termed the binary, the pluralist and the unitary. Although each of these is founded on a different proposition about the nature of world, all three subscribe to the proposition that, however chaotic and disordered it may appear to be at any particular time, geopolitical order does exist in the world. Although for much of the time this may be only barely discerned, nevertheless, through the complexities of the observable geopolitical forms, it is possible to detect underlying patterns. Each category of world-view will be examined with a view to considering the extent to which it appears to correspond to or diverge from the observable realities of the world scene.

NOTES

1. One of these was the Russian Federation, which, with a half the population and three-quarters of the territory of the Soviet Union, assumed the role of successor state. Russia has inherited the Soviet Union's seat as one of the five permanent members of the Security Council of the United Nations The essential difference is that the Cold War has come to an end and a normality has entered into the relationships between Russia and other major world powers.

2. The old division between the Ottoman Empire and the Holy Roman Empire was regarded as being the division between East and West, and Austria retained the historic function of its predecessor, the Ostmark, as a buttress against eastern invaders. Immediately to the east of Vienna was the *cordon sanitaire* which marked the boundary between what was Western (European) and what was Eastern (Asiatic) (Parker, 1994f: 52–3). The Austrian chancellor Metternich, no doubt with tongue in cheek, considered that the East began at the Landstrasse, the highway leading eastwards out of Vienna.

3. The Straits Question centred on the use of the Sea of Marmora and the Dardanelles, the stretch of water linking the Black Sea and the Mediterranean, by foreign (non-Turkish) vessels. Of particular concern was its use by Russian naval vessels, which could use it to sail from their bases on the Black Sea into the Mediterranean. Once there they were perceived as being a threat to those powers for which the security of the Mediterranean was vital. The Question became all

the more urgent after the opening of the Suez Canal in 1867 when the Mediterranean replaced the Cape of Good Hope as the main route from Europe to the East. This was of especial importance to Great Britain, and so the Straits Question was bound up with Anglo-Russian rivalry.

4. Switzerland came into being as a state in 1384. Correctly named the 'Confédération Helvétique', it originated with the union of the four 'Forest Cantons'. The traditional act of unification was the Oath of the Reutli in which they pledged that they wished to be 'a band of brothers'. The four cantons were subsequently joined by others having the same ideals. Government remained on a cantonal level, and the Swiss Confederation, with its capital in Berne, is responsible only for overall matters such as currency and foreign policy (Pounds, 1963: 173–4).

CHAPTER 7

MIGHTY OPPOSITES:
THE BIPOLAR WORLD

The basic proposition of the bipolar world-view is that, however complex the multilateral relationships among states may be or may become, they eventually resolve themselves into a single bipolar relationship. This takes the form of two dominating states or clusters of states forming two distinct poles of power and then engaging in confrontation with one another.

The most enduring bipolar view has been that which centres on the fundamental duality of Europe and Asia (Chapter 6). The initial West–East duality centred on the lands around the Aegean Sea and Asia Minor (Anatolia), and this was then enlarged into that of the Mediterranean (*Mare Nostrum*) dominated by the Roman Empire and those eastern lands (*Oriens*) dominated by the Persian Empire. In the medieval version of the West–East dichotomy the principal protagonists became Christendom and Islam. Subsequently the massive expansion of geographical knowledge which accompanied the Renaissance revealed with increasing clarity the existence of a previously only vaguely discerned eastern 'world', the outlines of which came into focus beyond the enveloping swathe of Islam. This was at first believed to centre on a group of large islands and peninsulas referred to collectively as 'The Indies', and the initial motivation of the Europeans was the desire to make contact with them. The centre of maritime activity, Europe's Atlantic periphery, from the Iberian peninsula to the British Isles, had until then been the edge of the known world. The pioneering of the new sea routes to the east was to bring about a complete change in geographical values. The periphery was now transformed into the centre of an expanding maritime world which was to unify the oceans and begin the process which was eventually to lead to globalisation. This led to new views of the world and the cosmos, and these had repercussions on the geopolitical world-view. In this the principal danger to the new Eurocentric world was still perceived as being to the East, but now this was a far larger East, and the old fear of Islam was enlarged into a fear of other eastern states as well. At first this new fear was of the 'yellow peril' variety, a vague perception of danger lurking in the distant and the unfamiliar, but during the nineteenth century it came into clearer focus. While the immediate problems facing Europe arose from the rivalries of the great European powers themselves, the greater danger was perceived to lie, as it had always done, in the East.

The most important idea which was based on this thinking postulated the fundamental dichotomy of the 'mighty opposites' of land and sea power (East and Spate, 1961: 419). This concept found particular favour in the Anglo-Saxon countries, especially in Great Britain. In that country Russophobia had been growing ever since the defeat of Napoleon had brought about the rise of Britain and Russia to the status of the first global superpowers. By the late nineteenth century the massive British and Russian Empires appeared to be the twin poles around which world power was coalescing. Britain by sea and Russia by land were gradually extending their tentacles across the globe, much to the dismay of other countries, and they became cast as the main rivals for the world's real estate. This was most in evidence in Asia, where the boundaries of the two great imperial spheres came into contact in a great arc extending eastwards from the Mediterranean and the 'Straits' to the Yellow Sea and the Pacific. 'From the frontiers of Hungary to the heart of Burmah and Nepaul,' thundered *The Times*, 'the Russian fiend has been haunting and troubling the human race, and diligently perpetrating his malignant frauds ... to the vexation of this industrious and essentially pacific empire' (Hopkirk, 1990: 192). This was the essence of the 'Great Game', which was played out in the mountains and deserts of Central Asia, and which took the form of strategic and territorial manoeuvrings aimed at outflanking the enemy and securing a favourable position for one or other of the protagonists. The British fear of Russia centred particularly on South Asia, and the vulnerability of the northern frontiers of the Indian Empire, the 'richest jewel' in the British world empire, was a major concern.[1]

The concern with Russian power was by no means an exclusively British phenomenon. Throughout the whole of peninsular Europe there was apprehension of the enormous Eurasian empire lying immediately to the east which covered one-sixth of the land surface of the globe and the territorial expansion of which was continuing at an alarming rate. From the vantage point of Breslau, on the borders between Germanic and Slav Europe, Joseph Partsch saw 'the Russian colossus' engaged in an 'unceasing expansion' to which *Mitteleuropa* appeared to be particularly vulnerable (Partsch, 1903: 333). The Frenchman Ernest Lavisse compared this Russian expansion to a force of nature. 'The Russian glacier is always gliding onward,' he wrote. and 'at the same time that she increased her territory ... gaining strength'. This territorial expansion threatened a conflict with the sea powers, and this centred on 'the duel between the whale and the white bear' (Lavisse, 1891: 159). After a visit to Russia, de Custine returned with the opinion that 'They wish to rule the world by conquest.' But, he lamented, 'the extension of the power they dream of ... if God grants it to them, will be for the woe of the world'.

The first person to make a clear distinction between sea power and land power, and to analyse their different roles in world history, was Alfred Thayer Mahan (Smith and Nijman, 1994: 156–8). *The Influence of Sea Power upon History*, written by Mahan after extensive research on Anglo-French naval conflict, became one of the most influential books of the late nineteenth century (see Chapter 3), and it presented the first general theory of sea power in modern times (Gooch, 1989). To Mahan, sea power was 'at once an abstraction and a concrete fact' which had been neglected by both historians and political scientists alike in their analyses of the basis of power (*ibid.*: 31). His object was to remedy this neglect and to examine the role of sea power with the aim of 'putting maritime interests in the foreground'. His work led him to the conclusion that sea power was the most important single factor in explaining the success of nations. The elements which made for successful sea power and the principles which derived from them, said Mahan, 'belong to the unchangeable, or unchanging, order of things', and as such they form part of what he termed 'the Order of Nature' (Mahan, 1890: 88). He then went on to apply this thinking to the rise of the United States in the late nineteenth century. He considered sea power to be 'the handmaid of expansion', and its acquisition was essential to America's future success as a world class power (Mahan, 1900: 7). While conscious of the dangers from land-based power, Mahan appeared to have few doubts as to the ultimate effectiveness of sea power in securing world power. 'He recited the glory of Britain's sea power and world dominion.' wrote one biographer, while asserting that the United States' advantageous location 'would give it an opportunity to excel Great Britain at the peak of her greatest power' (Puleston, 1939: 336). His realisation of the overwhelming significance of sea power was something he considered to be 'one of those perceptions that turn inward darkness into light'. He believed it to be the controlling factor so that whoever was master of the seas was master of the situation (Tuchman, 1966: 133).

Halford Mackinder, like Mahan basing his premise on the dichotomy of land and sea power, was, as we have seen, the first geographer to propose a general geopolitical theory. In what he referred to as his 'world outlook' he drew attention to the historical conflicts between the states of the land and those of the sea and the way in which power had oscillated between them. This he considered to have been the most enduring theme running through world history. Writing nearly a decade and a half after Mahan, Mackinder saw the gigantic Russian and British Empires as being the heirs to the long confrontation between land and sea power (Mackinder, 1904). He further developed this theme after World War I, and, despite the tremendous changes which had taken place in the international situation during the intervening period, he argued forcefully for the continued validity of his basic proposition (Mackinder, 1919).

One of the most dramatic results of World War I was the fall of that Russian Empire which had been for so long cast in the role of principal danger. Even if this did not immediately call into question the validity of Mackinder's proposition, it certainly necessitated the explanation of what appeared to be a fundamentally new situation. However, within a decade the Russian Empire had been replaced by the Soviet Union, a successor state which the Western World had to come to terms with. To its Marxist founders it was seen as being the springboard for world revolution, and as such its existence was to be a temporary one until a new communist world order came into being to replace the capitalist one. To those who viewed the prospect of such revolutionary change in a less sanguine manner, the new state represented a new danger to the Western ecumene and, from Mackinder's geopolitical perspective, it could be seen as being the latest of those dangers from the East to menace the Western world. From this perspective the Soviet Union appeared not so much as a new type of state dedicated to the social and geographical redistribution of wealth as an old great power in a new guise. One form of justificatory state ideology had been replaced by another: the Tsar and Holy Russia had been jettisoned in favour of Lenin and communism. What Serge de Chessin called the 'darkness from the East' was revived in a new form (de Chessin, 1930: 2–5).

The behaviour patterns of the Soviet Union soon proved to be very similar to those of its territorial predecessor and, while it claimed to be anti-imperialist, its actions soon belied this claim. The geopolitical structures within which it operated were essentially those of the Russian Empire and these did not substantially change. Like its predecessor, both internal geopolitical structures and the behaviour patterns which were associated with them were compatible with those of states seeking the pursuit of positions of domination (Parker, 1988: 102–29).

The idea that the underlying facts of geography were of greater significance in explaining the behaviour of states than passing beliefs of ideologies was not a monopoly of geographers. To de Chessin the roots of Russian communism were to be found less in Marx's industrial proletariat than in the nomads of the steppes. 'The leaders of the Third International are not Europeans,' he wrote, 'they are Scythians smothered under a Slavonic garb' (de Chessin, 1930: 244). 'In summoning the Scythians to the place of the Varangians,' he went on, they had embarked upon the 'orientalisation' of the country. According to Ladis Kristof, irrespective of which regime was in power, the Russians inherited 'a certain teleological impetus conditioned by history and geography'. He concluded that 'They are the non-nomadic heirs to the nomads; they have rebuilt the Mongol empire from its western end' (Kristof, 1968: 363). Kwanten also emphasised the historical and geographical continuity between the Russian Empire and the earlier steppe empires, a continuity which was basic to the ultimate proposition of the global land power–sea power dichotomy (Kwanten, 1979: 230).

Despite this geopolitical continuum of the Russian Empire–Soviet Union, the reality was that Russia was not inevitably and permanently cast in the role of one of the two competing poles of global power. By the beginning of World War II the Soviet Union's role remained marginal in power of politics, although its presence was a factor which certainly influenced the actions of the more significant players (Edmonds, 1991: 102–13). The origins of the war lay in the same basic situation as had led to World War I, namely the confrontation between the Anglo-French *entente* and a Central European bloc led by Germany. Although that conflict had been initially precipitated by the rivalry between Russia and Austria-Hungary in the Balkans, it had developed into a world war only because of the challenge mounted by the Germans to British maritime power. In World War II, the Anglo-French *entente* was resurrected, but the German-led grouping now centred on the Rome–Berlin axis.[2] Thus initially World War II was a bipolar confrontation within peninsular Europe between the Anglo-French alliance, which upheld the status quo, and the Germans, whose expansionist tendencies were seen as presenting a challenge to their dominant positions. The German strategy was to compensate for the relative weakness of the country's world position by achieving continental hegemony and, by reactivating the idea of the *Drang nach Osten*, securing the *Lebensraum* which it was believed a vigorous people required (Chapter 3).

The European War of 1939–41 culminated in the defeat of France in 1940 and was then widened in 1941 into a global conflict with the entry of Japan on the side of Germany and Italy (the Axis) and of the United States and the Soviet Union on the side of Great Britain (the Allies). The coming together of the allied 'Big Three' into what Roosevelt called 'a harmonious whole moving unitedly for the common good of ourselves and of the world' was facilitated in ideological terms by a temporary and uneasy symbiosis of capitalism and communism (Edmonds, 1991: 30). This Grand Alliance represented the coming together of the historic opponents, land power and sea power, to defeat a hybrid which was threatening them both. To geopoliticians this suggested no less dramatic a development than did its ideological counterpart to economists and politicians. To many who subscribed to the thesis of global dichotomy it presented the very real possibility of an end to that age-old conflict and the dawning of a new era of world harmony (Mackinder, 1943). However, within a few years of the Allied victory the increasing hostility manifested within the Big Three between the Anglo-American and the Soviet camps showed such optimism to have been premature. Following its military victory the Soviet Union projected its power into the centre of Europe, and the whole of the continent east of the Baltic–Adriatic isthmus fell within its extended sphere (Palmer, 1970: 290–320). Russian power had never extended over so large an area, the furthest western boundaries of the Russian Empire in the nineteenth century having followed a line roughly following the Baltic–Black Sea isthmus (Figure 6.2). Thus in the guise of the Soviet Union, Russia moved back into the position which it had temporarily vacated. The Soviet Union, self-proclaimed revolutionary state and harbinger of a new role order, slipped easily and readily into the role of imperial state and pole of land power. The other pole, however, had meanwhile undergone radical change. The British Empire, which had dominated the maritime world for over a century, proved incapable of maintaining its position, and after 1941 the effective centre of power in the maritime world moved across the Atlantic. The nineteenth-century Great Game was resurrected in the form of the Cold War, with the two superpowers, the

United States and the Soviet Union, taking the place of the British and Russian Empires (Dukes, 1970: 121–5).

The global polarisation which then characterised most of the second half of the twentieth century gave a considerable boost to the bipolar thesis. The idea of the dichotomy of land power and sea power also gave a geopolitical dimension to what was otherwise a confrontation dominated by ideology. This put the whole scenario into an altogether wider spatial and chronological context, thus making it less exceptional and more part of Mahan's unchanging order of things. The geopolitical foundations of the distinction between the two superpowers became an important explanatory device in coming to terms with the manifest behavioural and policy differences which existed between them (Parker, 1988). The United States was seen as being a new world power, filling that vacuum left by the older power. MacLeish saw the United States as the bearer of the 'New World', in both the geographical and the political senses, to the centre of the stage. It was the harbinger of 'the free man's image of the earth we live in' (MacLeish, 1943: 10–11). This arose from the fact that the United States was above all a sea power and the sea was 'the great symbol of freedom'. However, the Soviet Union had at first been perceived from a Western perspective as being essentially a regional power with regional interests which need not necessarily conflict with those of the United States. It was 'a land-mass power' whose interests were largely confined to its Eurasian homeland (Tuthill, 1948: 65). Some geographers saw the Soviets as having every right to control and defend a great region which had historically been in the Russian sphere and which was now theirs to develop in the interests of their people (Lattimore, 1948: 262). The expansion of Soviet power and influence during the decade following World War II led to this view being increasingly replaced by that of a menacing 'Soviet bloc' stretching from Eastern Europe to the Far East, the policies of which were directed by the 'Machiavellian hand' of the Kremlin (Lipsky, 1957: 225). The identification of this 'Red imperialism' meant that the Soviet Union was increasingly placed into a geopolitical context which converted it into an old-style power concerned with territorial expansion and dominance.

In this context American political geographers reviewed the relevance of Mackinder's ideas to the Cold War situation in which they found themselves. Edmund Walsh SJ saw the threat posed by the Soviet Union as being of the same order as the historic threat from Russian territorial expansion. To Father Walsh, Soviet ideological penetration was virtually indistinguishable from Lavisse's Russian glacier 'always gliding onward', and he expressed the fear that this could result in a return to what he termed 'the ice age of international relations' (Walsh, 1946: 34). Like Karl Haushofer, whom he had interviewed in prison in 1945 (Korinman, 1990: 324–5), Walsh expressed great admiration for Mackinder, whose 'brilliant hypothesis' illuminated 'an unfolding pattern of Soviet geopolitics' (Walsh, 1951: 156). Hans Weigert also followed Mackinder in viewing the increasing division of the world in terms of land power versus sea power engaged in 'the deadly fight for world domination' (Weigert, 1942: 252). The Mackinder thesis seemed more than ever to conform with reality in the years following World War II when the intensity of the global confrontation meant that, in one way or another, virtually all else came to be subsumed into it.

In the years following the death of Stalin in 1953 the relationship between the two superpowers began to mellow slightly. The continuing hostility was accompanied by an aspiration towards that normalisation of the situation which came to be known by the name of 'peaceful coexistence'.[3] This envisaged a bipolar world given permanence and stablility less by confrontation than by a balance of power. By the 1960s this new situation came to be reflected in modifications in geopolitical thinking. Saul Cohen proposed a global scenario which reflected the diminished intensity of the Cold War and which regarded the extremes of the immediate post-war years as having been exceptional (Cohen, 1964). It was now a 'world divided' and, using the term 'power cores', he saw a world divided into a number of 'geopolitical regions' (ibid.: 62). 'The clear-cut division that existed after the Second World War between the "Free" and the "Iron Curtain" worlds no longer exists,' he maintained. In its place there was 'a state of flux' with 'vast areas shifting from one camp into another' (ibid.: xvii). Nevertheless, Cohen's world-view remained a fundamentally bipolar one since these geopolitical regions were themselves grouped together into two great 'geostrategic regions'. These he called 'the trade-dependent maritime world' and the 'Eurasian continental world', and their core regions were respectively the maritime ring of the United States and the Russian industrial triangle. Cohen also built the dichotomy of land and sea power into their spatial structures. The United States, he maintained, was engaged in 'thrusting its development energies towards its coastal rims' while 'the Soviet Union's development thrust is landward, with its major direction into the Eurasian heartland' (ibid.: 65). In the second edition of Geography and Politics in a World Divided, while Cohen still identified a 'continental world' which he distinguished from the 'maritime realm', he saw both as being loose groups having a 'polycentric nature'. Each of them had two core regions, a situation which he saw as being a better guarantor of 'global equilibrium' than a two-power world could ever have been (Cohen, 1973: 314).

The dichotomy of land and sea power was always a central part of the bipolar theses. In it the maritime and continental states are seen less as being mirror images of one another than as being inherently quite different forms of geopolitical life. Sea power has been the product of maritime states, which have normally been territorially relatively small and whose strength has been built on their commercial wealth. When large entities have arisen in the maritime world these have normally consisted either of alliances or of groupings of geographically proximate states or of maritime empires. These latter have been by nature geographically fragmented and physically diverse, and their discontinuous territories have been bound together by the sea. They possess an inbuilt tendency to disintegrate into smaller units formed out of their geographical components. On the other hand, land power has been founded on territorial expansion and has been brought about by accretion of territory from a single powerful core region. This process has produced large and territorially continuous states. For these, the acquisition of territory has been an end in itself, and their power is based upon it, while for maritime empires territory has normally been only the necessary base for the establishment of successful trading systems. This fundamental difference was considered by Paul Kennedy to have been the underlying cause of the tension which has existed between what he called 'the twin poles of the merchant and warrior states' (Kennedy, 1988: 574).

While Mackinder traced the dichotomy of land power and sea power back to the conflict of the ancient Greeks and Persians, he saw the scale of the dichotomy as having steadily spread out from the Europe–Mediterranean *oikoumene* to encompass the world as a whole. The implications of this produced the Heartland thesis. This can be briefly stated as follows: land powers derive their strength from the land which they occupy and they are strong in proportion to the amount of territory which the occupy. Because Asia is the largest continent it has thus also been home to the largest of the land powers. The ultimate source of their strength lies in the vast centre of the Asiatic continent, and this was what Mackinder originally termed 'the geographical pivot of history' (Mackinder, 1904). He defined this Pivot as being that great expanse of territory in Central Asia to which there was no ready access by sea. This is because it was drained by rivers either flowing into inland seas and lakes, thus having no outlet to the ocean, or draining northwards into the Arctic Ocean, which, being icebound, was to all intents and purposes also an inland sea. Consequently, inferred Mackinder, the power which controlled the Pivot was largely invulnerable to sea power. Latitudinally across this enormous region lies a belt of temperate grassland, the steppe, and it was in this geographical environment that the steppe empires arose. These enormous states were originally the products of nomadic pastoralist societies which relied on the horse both for warfare and mobility (Kwanten, 1979). Their usual response to the geographical and socio-economic difficulties which they have periodically faced was militarism, leading to attacks on the rich maritime societies located around the margins of Asia. The response of the latter was to use their economic strength and mastery of the seas to fend off this aggression from the land. The continual rise of new powers in the heart of Asia necessitated that the maritime states remain constantly on their guard. While in earlier times the power of steppe states had been limited by the harshness of the physical environment, in modern times the great potential of the region was being opened up to exploitation. This meant that for the first time the propensity to territorial expansion was being matched by the acquisition of adequate resources with which to conduct it.

After World War I Mackinder further developed on the Pivot thesis. He

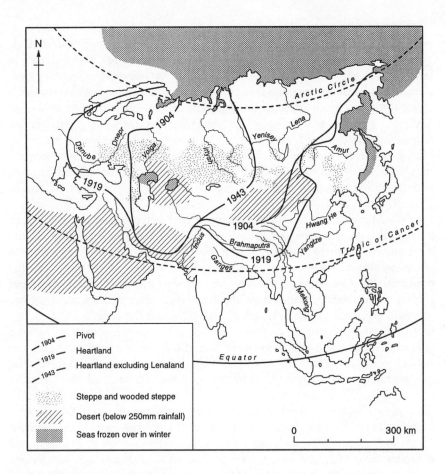

Figure 7.1 Pivot and Heartland

renamed it the 'Heartland' and considerably increased its size (Mackinder, 1919: 135). Like the Pivot, the Heartland consisted basically of those areas which were drained by rivers flowing either into the Arctic Ocean or into the interior. However, to this were added the upper courses of the great Chinese and Indian rivers together with the Baltic and Black Sea drainage basins (Figure 7.1). Mackinder contended that these areas were also largely inaccessible to sea power, a contention which was borne out by the failure of the maritime powers to have made much impact in them. The Crimean War and the subsequent 'Straits' issue — central to the resolution of the 'Eastern Question' — had demonstrated clearly the problems faced by maritime power in extending its control into enclosed seas. As a result the Heartland was deemed to include the whole of that part of Europe lying to the east of a line drawn from Jutland to the Aegean. A substantial part of China, the only significant state to have resisted European imperial domination, also lay within the Heartland, while only Xingjiang and the western areas of Mongolia had been within the Pivot. The Heartland was also a wider concept than the Pivot in terms of the factors which gave it its importance. In addition to its strategic invulnerability, the Heartland possessed immense economic potential for the production of energy, ferrous and non-ferrous metals, raw materials and foodstuffs. This all added up to a region which appeared both to be formidably endowed in almost every respect and also to be protected by its geography from incursion. Mackinder's final proposition, that the Heartland had the potential to become the ultimate centre of world power, arose from this. The principal key to the unlocking of this potential was a modern communications system, and in the early years of the twentieth century this meant the building of railways. In this context it is important to bear in mind that the original 'Pivot' paper had been presented to the Royal Geographical Society in the year after the Trans-Siberian Railway was opened. This great railway crossed through the Heartland from West to East and linked the Russian core region to the Pacific Ocean. This enabled the modern economic development of Siberia to begin in earnest during the years before World War I. Nowhere had the development of railways had such effect, said Mackinder, 'as in the closed heartland of Euro-asia' (Mackinder, 1904). The whole concept of the Pivot-Heartland was thus conceived and developed against a background of rapid change which led Mackinder to his contention that this was where future world power lay. He viewed the rise of the Heartland in the context of his other basic contention that the period during which maritime power had dominated the world, which he called the 'Columbian epoch', was coming to an end. With the realisation of the immense potential of the continental interior the balance was now swinging back from sea power towards land power.

In this context, the Heartland thesis was both a geopolitical statement and a warning about the future of the maritime world. With Britain still the principal maritime power, it was to his own country that Mackinder's warning was clearly directed. He was convinced that the development of land power then taking place posed a threat of greater magnitude to the maritime world than any which had arisen in the past. This was because its centre was in the largest landmass, the potential of which was being released by modern technology. He recalled that 'a victorious Roman General when he entered the City, amid all the head-turning splendour of a "Triumph", had behind him on the chariot a slave who whispered into his ear that he was but mortal' (Mackinder, 1919: 194). Mackinder expressed the opinion that likewise during the deliberations at Versailles 'some airy cherub' should be delegated to whisper from time to time into the ears of the assembled Allied statesmen:

> Who rules East Europe commands the Heartland:
> Who rules the Heartland commands the World-Island:
> Who rules the World-Island commands the World.

Thus, to Mackinder, the possession of East Europe − 'Heartland Europe' − was the principal key to the achievement of world power. At the beginning of the twentieth century the country which possessed the greatest share of this region was Russia, the gigantic empire of which also 'commanded' a large part of the Heartland as a whole. Proof of the Russian desire to extend its 'command' over the rest of the World-Island followed from the continued Russian advance into the Far East, Central Asia and China.

During the decade and a half between 1904 and 1919 dramatic changes had taken place in the international scene. The formidable Russian Empire was replaced by an embattled communist state which at first renounced all claim to the Empire's non-Russian possessions. However, Mackinder had made no necessary correlation between Russia and the Heartland. In fact he referred to Russia as being the current 'tenant' of the Heartland, an expression which implied that in future it was quite possible that there could be different tenants. Indeed, in the past, Turkish, Mongol and Chinese imperial states had been 'tenants' in this sense, and Mackinder considered that both Germany and China could be possible future tenants. Thus, while states came and went, the Heartland was one of those 'immense geographical realities', maintained Mackinder, which 'have conditioned History, and have thus led to the present distribution of population and civilisation' (ibid.: 111). Geopolitically it was thus seen as being a part of Mahan's 'unchangeable, or unchanging, order of nature' rather than being tied to the transitory fortunes of any one particular state.

To the German geopoliticians of the inter-war period the concept of the Heartland was seen as being integrally part of the whole land power–sea power scenario. 'Never have I seen anything greater than these few pages of geographical masterwork,' wrote Haushofer of the 1904 'Pivot' paper (Weigert, 1942). The existence of the Pivot–Heartland then became a central part of his own global explanatory framework (Haushofer, 1931). He envisaged the Heartland as being a gigantic citadel stretching from 'the Elbe to the Amur' which he considered to have been 'the mystical cradle of world conquerors' (Strausz-Hupé, 1942: 60). However, there was a fundamental difference between the geopolitical significance of the Heartland when viewed from Oxford or London, and its significance when viewed from Munich or Berlin. While to Mackinder it presented the greatest threat to the British Empire, to Haushofer it was an immense potential source of physical resources, access to which could give Germany the power to challenge the dominant position of Great Britain. For the German geopoliticians the path to world power lay to the east through the consolidation of the German and Russian Grossraum (ibid.: 59). Germany and Russia, said Walsh, were 'the two titans most concerned with domination of Mackinder's Heartland' (Walsh, 1943: 36).

After 1945 the Heartland came once more to the fore as part of the explanatory framework of the new East–West confrontation, but it now came to be viewed from different perspectives. To those who saw the Soviet Union as representing progress – and in 1945 there were still many who did so – the possession of the Heartland was seen as being an important adjunct to its world role. Providence seemed to have given that state which was the harbinger of the new world order the greatest geographical and geopolitical potential for translating it into reality. 'In the early post-war years', wrote East and Spate, 'the ending of the era of western dominance was hailed as the dawn of the new golden age' (East and Spate, 1961: 356). Owen Lattimore was euphoric about the prospects for the Soviet Union. Fully accepting Mackinder's assertion that the Columbian Age was coming to an end and that a new era of continental power was dawning, he took the view that the age of maritime dominance had been, for a large proportion of humanity, not so much a triumphant one as one of oppression and inequality. The replacement of the Western powers by Asiatic continental states would result in great equality in the distribution of the world's resources. He predicted that with 'the end of the colonial era and the emergence of a new world era' continental power would come fully into its own. This power would centre on 'the inland crossroads of Asia' located between the Soviet Union and China (Lattimore, 1943: 374). With the coming of the air age this would be the natural 'crossroads' of the world's air communications. Thus, unlike Mackinder, he viewed the rise of continental power in a positive light and expressed the opinion that 'A world order that is both stable and progressive must include the concept of large Asiatic states . . . The age in which Asia was penetrated and developed from its fringes towards the center is drawing to an end. A new age is opening out in which the focus of development will lie at or near to the center, and the effect of this development will radiate outwards to the fringes' (ibid.: 394). Half a century earlier, Lattimore's compatriot Mahan had seen the changes taking place in Asia as being a 'problem' for the maritime world (Mahan, 1900), a point of view which was vigorously rejected by Lattimore. 'The age of control is vanishing,' he said. 'Our problem is not how to control this development, but how to adapt ourselves to it.' At the same time Weigert was also stressing the significance of 'the heartland of our century' and of its two principal powers, Russia and China. These powers, he wrote, 'defending the landmasses where a new world is shaping, are chosen by Destiny to make the greatest sacrifices'. Together they were engaged in building the 'new order of the world' (Weigert, 1942: 254–9).

However, while Lattimore, Weigert and even Mackinder himself in his final article (Mackinder, 1943) were welcoming the dawn of a 'new era', other geopoliticians were less sanguine. Edmund Walsh advocated the necessity for geopolitical thinking as part of the armoury of the West when confronted by atheistic communism (Chapter 4). Acknowledging Mackinder's triptych as a 'brilliant hypothesis', he was of the opinion that its validity had been 'modified, but not entirely cancelled out by the coming of the age of air power' (Walsh, 1951: 156). This modification had made it necessary for the Heartland power to seek to extend its control outwards into 'the marginal lands on the rim of the World Island' and there establish military and air bases in close proximity to the principal centres of maritime power. The formula most appropriate to the con- temporary needs of the Kremlin, said Walsh, was 'Who controls the rimlands of

Europe and Asia can protect the Heartland of the World Revolution.' This meant that there was a constant threat to the security of the maritime world. Invoking Mackinder's warnings in the aftermath of that earlier war, Walsh expressed the hope that 'If the airy cherub whom Mackinder summoned to breathe warnings into the ears of the statesmen gathered at Versailles is still in office ... may he keep plucking at the ears of the new negotiators.' He should warn, above all, that 'Moscow lies much nearer to the pulse of Eurasia, India and China than do London and Washington' (*ibid*.: 56–7). The response of the Western world to this new threat from the east had to be to unite and to build up countervailing power.

During the Cold War the concept of the Heartland as the centre of hostile power became an additional evocative image to add to those already in existence. It encapsulated the idea of a massive and hostile 'Soviet bloc' spreading inexorably across Eurasia. This image was by no means always founded on a rational assessment of the real threat which the region posed. Just as in the past geographical terminology had evoked the presence of imagined terrors, so did the concept of 'Heartland' move from the rational into the non-rational. From being a precisely delimited region it became a concept which owed more to ideology than to geography. Hooson maintained that this 'geographically charmed sanctuary' had come to possess 'an almost mystical aura' (Hooson, 1964). Colin Gray warned that the Heartland theory could be misleading since it already allowed for 'the exaggeration of the power of the Heartland states' and as such reinforced and added to the fears already present in the maritime world (Gray and Barnett, 1989: 7). In the imagination, wrote Walters, the Heartland was transformed into a gigantic fortress surrounded and protected by the rampart of the Iron Curtain. Using Kafkaesque imagery, it was the geographical expression of something which was associated with mystery and terror. 'The Silent Castle' was epitomised by the Kremlin itself, which 'loomed overpoweringly in the dark recesses of the mind' (Walters, 1974: 43). Walters went on to demonstrate the extent to which the Cold War geopolitical psychosis was influenced by the Heartland concept (*ibid*.: 50). Legg was equally evocative in his description of the Heartland as filling those who lived beyond its confines with fear and apprehensions (Legg, 1970). Such terms as 'bolshevism' and 'communism' were only the contemporary emotional reinforcements to a much older idea. They represented 'restatements in the contemporary idiom of that fear mingled with wonderment engendered by the great Heartland shining white and enormous in the light of the moon, as Mackinder had visualised it over half a century earlier' (Parker, 1985: 135). Thus, although itself a more clearly identifiable territorial phenomenon than Kennan's 'red flood' and Ambassador Bullitt's 'red amoeba' sweeping across Asia, the Heartland assumed a menacing symbolism (*ibid*.: 169). It became the materialisation of those deep Western psycho-historical fears which sensed the presence of danger and located it in the East. In this respect it gained a certain metaphysical quality as the home of real or imagined terrors much the same as those monsters which had appeared as geographical facts on the medieval *mappa mundi*.

Alongside this emotional approach, which accorded so well with the heightened tensions of the Cold War, there was also new thinking on the real geopolitical significance of the Heartland. Fawcett extended both its size and its long-term significance. While acknowledging that the harshness of the physical conditions in what he termed 'the interior lands of the Old World' were a handicap to development, he maintained that its sheer size and physical resources were bound to confer immense advantages on that power which controlled it (Fawcett, 1949: 98). In a situation where the balance was tilting in favour of land power, he envisaged that the power which controlled the Heartland would eventually become strong enough to break through the vulnerable Mediterranean–Red Sea isthmus, which, since the construction of the Suez Canal, had been the most important axis of communication between Europe, India and the Far East. This would have the effect of extending the Heartland out from the centre of the World-Island, which Fawcett called Mainland, through the Middle East and deep into Africa. If this happened, the balance of land and sea power would be irreversibly tilted in favour of the land (Figure 7.2). An opposite scenario was proposed by D.W. Meinig, who expressed the opinion that the importance of the Heartland had been greatly exaggerated (Meinig, 1956). Using what he termed 'cultural or ... functional criteria' based on 'physical conditions, cultures and nodal location', he proposed a far smaller Heartland extending from the Caspian Sea to Manchuria and including the republics of Soviet Central Asia, Mongolia and the western parts of China. Meinig envisaged his Heartland as being more a strategic than an economic phenomenon, and this made it more Pivot than Heartland (*ibid.*: 560). The epicentre of Meinig's Heartland lay in Xinjiang, a province which Lattimore called 'the Pivot of Asia' in the context of the development of continental power in the post-Columbian age (Lattimore, 1950).

Such Pivot and Heartland concepts as these were all pan-Asiatic in that they transcended state boundaries. In contrast. David Hooson linked the Heartland more specifically with the Soviet Union, and in so doing identified the emergence of what he termed a 'New Soviet Heartland' (Hooson, 1964). Identifying the core of the Soviet state as being in the south of European Russia, he observed a tendency for this to extend latitudinally eastwards from the Volga into Central Asia and Siberia. This Volga–Baikal zone, which he whimsically thought might be either a coffin-shaped or a crib-shaped axis, possessed considerable natural resources, was rapidly urbanising and was held together by the line of the Trans-Siberian railway. By the 1960s it had become a powerful magnet for Soviet economic development, and as a consequence the centre of gravity of the Soviet Union had moved decisively eastwards. Hooson saw the Volga–Baikal zone as having 'the marks of a real continental stronghold'. This new Soviet Heartland was to a large extent coextensive with the steppe lands and its development also linked the Soviet Union with the steppe empires, its predecessors in Central Asia.

Figure 7.2 Heartland extended
Source: Fawcett, C.B. (1947) *Herbertson Memorial Lecture*. London: Geographical Association

While the idea of the Heartland as the centre of continental and eastern power has been built into much bipolar geopolitical thinking during the twentieth century, another binary thesis recalls an earlier West–East dichotomy. This postulates that there are two great centres of world civilisation located on either side of the Eurasian landmass and separated from one another by a vast and lightly populated area. Fawcett termed this the 'Great Divide' of mountains and deserts which lay between the principal centres of the Western and Asiatic worlds (Fawcett, 1949). Febvre considered this to be one of the world's few really 'natural' frontiers, separating the great *mondes* of Europe and Asia

(Febvre, 1932: 296–315). By the beginning of the twentieth century the Far East was the only *monde* in Febvre's sense which had been successful in resisting control by the European powers. The Boxer Rebellion of 1900 had brought together the Western powers in a rare display of unity. The intractability of China, together with such disturbing signs as the rise of Japan to great-power status, contributed to a revival of the idea of a Europe united in the face of such oriental spectres as the 'yellow peril' and the 'rising sun'. This idea gained popularity in Germany in particular, and it fitted in well with German hegemonial aspirations.[4]

Even by the time of Mackinder's Pivot theory in 1904, the joint global hegemony of Britain and Russia, 'the whale and the white bear', was already beginning to become a thing of the past. The Great Game itself was taking on an air of irrelevance as other powers – in particular the United States, Germany and Japan – were flexing their muscles and moving towards the centre of the world stage. Within a year the world was stunned by the conclusive Russian defeat in the Russo-Japanese War of 1904–5, and this precipitated a radical re-evaluation of the power of the Russian Empire in the chancelleries of Europe.[5] While the growing weakness of the 'white bear' had become evident, it was to be some time yet before the growing weakness of the 'whale' became equally evident. At the outset of World War I, the British Empire appeared, on the outside at least, to be more splendid and powerful than it had ever been before.

After World War I, following the acquisition of the former German colonies in Africa and the possessions of the Ottoman Empire in the Middle East, the British and French Empires were larger than ever.[6] However, it was evident to the shrewd observer that Europe's world position as a whole had deteriorated and that Great Britain's hold on world power was becoming precarious. This new situation made Mackinder more convinced that his basic thesis was sound. The Heartland, despite the current disorder within it, appeared to him to be as menacing as ever. It was just that the form which this menace took was different. However, other political geographers were by now reading the signs rather differently. Demangeon, analysing the implications of the changes in the world situation, saw the counterpart of the decline of Europe as being the rise of the East. Organised as it was by Japan and using the vast population and resources of China, Demangeon considered that this region was on course to becoming one of the major centres of future world power (Demangeon, 1923). Karl Haushofer had always been fascinated by Japan and regarded the Japanese experience as being a kind of role model for bringing about an end to the dominant position of Britain. Japanese expansionism had led him to the conclusion that Japan was the power around which the future Asiatic pan-region would be formed (Haushofer, 1913).

In his final contribution to geopolitical thinking, written at the height of World War II, Mackinder outlined a scenario for the post-war world. In it he brought together the two major concepts of 'East' in bipolar geopolitical thinking, the Heartland and the Orient. Mackinder's Heartland of 1943 was much modified in both size and significance. While in the west it included the 1919 extensions from the Pivot, it extended eastwards only as far as the Yenisey River (Mackinder, 1943). This truncated Heartland thus represented a considerable westwards displacement of the two earlier versions (Figure 7.1). No longer did Mackinder see it as being in opposition to the maritime world but rather as linked to it in a new geopolitical region which included the North Atlantic – the 'Midland Ocean'– and North America. This constituted an expanded 'West' which was juxtaposed to an 'East' centring on China and India, the two separated by a great divide of deserts and mountains. This final Mackinder scenario was basically optimistic in the way the previous ones had not been. This was because he saw there being a natural balance of power between the two great world regions which would ensure that world domination by either one of them did not take place. Mackinder's two earlier scenarios had been underlain by acute anxiety for the future of the maritime world, which he saw as being vulnerable to attack from the Heartland. In the last scenario the confrontation of opposites was transformed into a balance between more similar geopolitical entities. Walters was of the opinion that in 1943 Mackinder in fact abandoned the Heartland theory (Walters, 1974: 154). It is certainly true that he abandoned the dichotomy of land power and sea power, inherent in the Heartland thesis, for the very different dichotomy of West and East. He also postulated the possibility that 'balance' would make it possible for confrontation to be replaced by cooperation.

Another explanation of the behaviour of land power is that its fundamental objective is not so much to build up its land base as to bring about the geopolitical conditions to enable it to acquire the strength of the maritime world. In other words, the policy adopted by land power is motivated by the desire to break out from its continental fastnesses and to acquire at least some of the advantages possessed by sea power. Such an interpretation of the motives of land power implies that the perception of the Heartland by those who are inside it looking out is altogether different from the perception of those who are outside looking in. The other facet of the vast size, impenetrability and immense natural resources and strategic location of the Heartland is its remoteness, inaccessibility, environmental harshness and vulnerability to attack over extensive land boundaries. What thus appears from one perspective to be a fortress, from another may appear to be a prison. This accords with the dicta of Mahan and Ratzel that sea power is the essential requirement of those who aspire to world power. 'He who does not share the sea', said Friedrich List, 'is our Lord's stepchild' (Dorpalen, 1942: 66), and his compatriot Ratzel considered that by guaranteeing freedom of movement and thus opening up possibilities 'only the sea can bring out real world powers' (*ibid*.: 68). Land powers, of which Germany was one, were seen as being inhibited from achieving a truly global reach. Their strength and influence were always limited by the constraints of their geographical locations. This Haushofer considered to be *Raumgebundende* (space-constraining), and it stood in marked contrast to the great maritime states, the strength of which derived from their global reach. 'Seapower', wrote Haushofer, 'masters great spaces by leaping lightly from point to point', and it was this which made it *Raumüberwindende* (space-bridging). 'The most decisive of all world-political trends is the drive of a nation towards the sea,' he wrote; '*navigare necesse est*'. Sieward encapsulated this when he maintained that 'The influence of land power ends as a rule at its boundaries, but the influence of sea power may extend across the whole earth' (*ibid.*: 68). This did not mean that either he or Haushofer was against the retention of land power. Of the two it was recognised that because of Germany's location, land power had to take precedence, but the ideal was seen as being a power equally at home in both.

In his analysis of sea power in global politics, George Modelski also concluded that sea power was the principal key to world power. 'It is the fundamental postulate of this analysis,' he wrote, 'that seapower (or, more precisely, ocean power) is the *sine qua non* of action in global politics because it is the necessary condition of operations of global – that is, intercontinental – scope' (Modelski and Thompson, 1988: 13). He posed the question 'Was Portugal the first world power?', and the answer was most decidedly in the affirmative (*ibid.*: 174). Portugal, *fim do mundo*, became the first world power when the sea came to be seen as a means of communication rather than as an impenetrable barrier. Through the great wealth generated by commerce, together with the deployment of strategic naval power which it made possible, it is the maritime rather than the continental states which have been able to assume the global roles (*ibid.*: 151–74).

The idea that the basic objective of the expansion of land power is to transform itself into sea power is also one of the underlying geopolitical explanations of Russian expansion. Denied access to the sea, 'except on the useless frozen North ... the external policy of the country for two centuries has consisted in attempting to reach the open ocean' (Fairgrieve, 1915: 199). Likewise Walsh, quoting Kluchevsky, considered the 'urge to the sea and the constant process of opening up new territories ... as the principal, fundamental factor in Russian history' (Walsh, 1951: 159). According to this interpretation, the theme of the expansion of Russia from its Muscovite core region to encompass the whole of Europe between the Urals and the Baltic–Black Sea isthmus has been the long struggle by a remote and land-locked state to secure access to the sea (Figure 6.2). Since the expansion has been directed particularly towards those seas which could provide warm-water ports, the expansion has tended also to have a strong southerly component. However, it was the westerly drive towards Europe which has been the most powerful one in modern times, and it was in this direction that the country was reoriented in the eighteenth century by Peter the Great. The core region was deliberately moved from the landlocked *Mezhdurechie* to the Gulf of Finland, 'the window on the west'. The Soviet heirs to the Russian Empire returned the capital back to the old core region but the urge to the sea remained. The subsequent move to control the rimlands, maintained Walsh, was motivated not solely by the desire to protect 'the Heartland of the World Revolution' but also to facilitate 'the growth of Soviet sea power, especially submarines' (ibid.: 157). This gives added weight to the final assertion of Mackinder's triptych that 'Who rules the World-Island commands the world.'

Binary thinking need not necessarily imply the existence of two great 'poles' of power locked together in 'eyeball to eyeball' confrontation. A frequent situation historically has been one in which a single large state, bidding for a position of dominance, has been confronted by an *ad hoc* alliance of smaller states which oppose the ambitions of the would-be dominator. Indeed, this had been the Greek–Persian situation which Mackinder took as his starting-point in the development of the Heartland thesis. In the subsequent history of Europe similar alliances have frequently been formed to combat the perceived danger from a powerful and menacing Eastern state. Besides obvious differences in geographical size, the structural characteristics of the would-be dominator are very different from those of the smaller states, and particular structural factors can be detected in those states which have bid with some success for positions of dominance in the Western ecumene (Parker, 1988: 64–75). Spykman saw the growth of what he called 'the hegemonic power of the period' as resulting from steady accretions of territory so that it eventually became so powerful that the smaller states were no longer able to resist it (Spykman, 1942: 25). Nevertheless, in the Western ecumene, despite the powerful expansionist drives exhibited by the would-be dominant state, the alliances of smaller states have been successful in preventing the achievement of complete domination. It has become a binary confrontation between a single state and a grouping of smaller states. This situation has then resolved itself with the eventual disintegration of the would-be dominant state as a result of internal and external pressures and a return to a more complex geopolitical pattern of relationships. Since the Western ecumene has been the motor for the process of globalisation there has been a strong tendency for the replication on a global scale of the pattern of geopolitical relationships in this region.

Just as binary thinking has been associated with the existence of two great centres of power, so also it has been associated with confrontation and conflict. However, these also need not be considered as being necessarily a part of it. Even Mahan, the great advocate of sea power and expansion, did not consider conflict to be inevitable. 'It is a mistake, and a deplorable mistake,' he observed, 'when recognising conditions of conflicting interests ... to see in them only grounds for opposition and hostility' (Mahan, 1900: 45). While Mahan emphasised 'expansion' and 'conflicting interests', he also expressed the opinion that a state of equilibrium was far preferable to one of conflict. When he asserted that this could best be reached by 'natural selection' he was using the biological terminology which was favoured at the time. He hastened to make the qualification that while the phrase 'natural selection' implies 'conflict and suffering' this could be avoided 'by the rational process of estimating the forces at work, and approximating to the natural adjustment by the artificial methods of counsel and agreement'. In this way a state of equilibrium could be reached 'by free self-assertion, allowing each to find its proper place'. Such methods, he concluded, 'seem somewhat more suitable to the present day' (ibid.: 46).

Likewise, another imperialist of the time, Lord Curzon, also advocated peaceful solutions to disputes which in the territorially finite world of the twentieth century could otherwise result in violent conflicts. 'As the habitable world shrinks,' he wrote, 'the interests or ambitions of one state come into sharp and irreconcilable collision with those of another' (Curzon, 1908: 5). To Curzon the key to peaceful solutions was to be found on the frontiers. They are 'the razor's edge on which hang suspended the modern issues of war and peace', but their delimitation had been in the hands of 'a few silent men ... engaged in tracing lines upon the unknown areas of the earth' (ibid.: 5). Curzon's prime concern was with the Anglo-Russian confrontation in Central Asia and particularly with the vulnerability of the Indian Empire to invasion from the north. His solution to this problem was the advocacy of 'buffer zones' separating the spheres of influence of the great powers and so preventing 'irreconcilable collision' from taking place. Curzon saw these buffer zones as being 'on the outskirts of empire' ruled by 'twentieth century marcher lords' (ibid.: 57). Despite his advocacy, in practice no such zone ever came into existence between the British and Russian Empires although there were places, such as Afghanistan, the small Himalayan states and Tibet which managed to sustain a fragile independence between the spheres of the two great protagonists.[7] However, they generated much suspicion and, when the Great Game did come to an end, it was because of a fundamental change in the whole world situation rather than the establishment of agreed no-go areas. The 'buffer zone' idea was developed further by Curzon after World War I when, as Great Britain's Foreign Secretary, he was involved in the drafting of the peace treaties. He firmly believed that such a zone was necessary to separate the German and Russian spheres, and the mosaic of small states between the two was intended to be a buffer of this sort. 'The shape of Europe as it finally emerged from the council rooms of Versailles, Trianon and St. Germain,' wrote Strausz-Hupé, 'unmistakably bears the stamp of the Curzonian school of thought' (Strausz-Hupé, 1942: 208). Curzon believed that 'scientific knowledge had precedence over ignorance', and this now made frontiers 'capable of being converted into the instruments and evidences of peace' (Curzon 1908: 54). The concept of the buffer zone is also to be found in Fairgrieve's work, but to him it was 'a crush zone of small states' which, although separating land and sea power, was itself in a precarious position (Fairgrieve, 1932: 330). In the opinion of Stausz-Hupé, the concept of the buffer zone was never a really satisfactory answer to the problem of frontiers, and contemporary geographers have tended to agree with this judgement (O'Sullivan, 1994: 32–3). The Curzonian-type buffer zone, although dressed up as an area of peace, is in reality still a zone of confrontation. Strausz-Hupé maintained that the interests and ambitions of the states which it separated were not radically altered by its existence. Rather 'It is [that] frontier that facilitates intercourse between nations' which is 'the frontier par excellence of a stable world order' (Strausz-Hupé, 1942: 240). Quoting Lyde, he saw the ideal frontier as being one 'with geographical features conducive to peaceful intercourse' rather than one which prevented or discouraged it (Lyde, 1915). These were exactly the points which were made by Demangeon and Febvre (1935) and Ancel (1938) about the role of frontiers in the specifically European context.

Nicholas Spykman also considered that peaceful solutions were possible, but rather than Mahan's 'rational process' or Curzon's 'scientific knowledge' he advocated the buildup of sufficient countervailing force as being the best deterrent to aggression. What he termed 'the extended and offensive world strategy of the opponents required an equally extended and not less offensive counterstrategy' (Spykman, 1944: 255). Rejecting *Idealpolitik* for *Realpolitik*, he maintained that it is only when states realise that they no longer have the power to enforce their will that they become reasonable and will be prepared to engage in peaceful dialogue (*ibid.*).

When put into such evocative terms as 'Yellow Peril', 'Rising Sun' and 'Heartland', the bipolarity of West and East has slipped into a confrontational mode. However, by 1943 Mackinder had ceased to see it in this way. It was the dichotomy of land power and sea power which he had always seen as being inherently confrontational, but the dichotomy of Occident and Orient appeared to him to have the possibility of bringing all this to an end. He envisaged a balance being struck between the two great worlds which 'Thus balanced would therefore be free' (Mackinder, 1943). This idea was also present in the thinking of Fawcett, Curzon, Febvre and others. While 'buffers' and 'crush zones' were rejected as being inherently unstable, the great swathe of mountain and desert separating the two worlds was identified as being as 'natural' a frontier as could be hoped for.

Saul Cohen took a similar view of the balance between the world's two great geostrategic regions, but to make it effective it was necessary to have the machinery in place to facilitate both internal and external changes. He went on to propose a scenario in which there was an 'isostatic balance of power' which would lead to the establishment of a condition of 'geopolitical equilibrium'. Cohen's terminology echoes that of Mahan, who nearly a century earlier had also looked for 'equilibrium' but in so doing had used a very different terminology. Whereas Mahon's 'natural selection' used the terminology of biology, Cohen's 'isostatic balance' drew rather on the terminology of geology. Each emphasised the necessity of 'approximating to the natural adjustment' using a terminology which reflected the wider thinking of their times (Cohen, 1991).

In conclusion, it can be seen that binarism has taken many different forms over the years. In the opposition of land power and sea power, the differences between them spring from the fundamentally different geographical conditions of their origins and development. While the complexities of the world's geopolitical surface have been periodically 'resolved' through their bipolarity there has also been another bipolarity founded on the older idea of the differences between the 'two halves' of the world. This bipolarity is one which has proved more amenable to more constructive thinking about non-confrontational methods of solving problems. The links between the two may lead towards another form of binarism, but they may also lead towards an entirely different geopolitical world-view.

NOTES

1. While the true inventor of the term 'Great Game' appears to have been a Captain Connolly, an active participant in the 'fact-finding' espionage which went on constantly in Central Asia during the nineteenth century, the populariser of the term was Rudyard Kipling. In *Kim* the 'North' was a barely civilised and highly dangerous place into which only the most intrepid were prepared to venture. Kim was clearly in this category when he announced, 'Now I shall go far and far into the North, playing the Great Game' (R. Kipling, *Kim*, 1901). This all formed part of that culture of imperialism which built up during the second half of the nineteenth century (Said, 1993) and which produced the 'orientalism' inherent in *Kim* (Williams, 1993). To Hopkirk, *Kim* incarnated the whole psychology of the Great Game and its role in the great power rivalries of the period (Hopkirk, 1996). It helped set the tone for that *Boys' Own Paper* sense of excitement and adventure which underlay the whole imperial enterprise from a British perspective.

2. 'Axis' was the name given to the collaboration of Nazi Germany and Fascist Italy in the years leading up to and during World War II. The term was first used by Mussolini with reference to a treaty signed between the two countries in November 1936. A closer alliance was signed in May 1939 and it was this 'Pact of Steel' which brought Italy into the war on the side of Germany. The alliance between Germany, Italy and Japan was then consolidated in the Tripartite Pact of September 1940. The term 'Axis Powers' was used during World War II for Germany, Italy and Japan and their Balkan allies.

3. Peaceful coexistence was a term associated particularly with the Soviet leader Nikita Khrushchev (1891–1971), who attempted to promote an atmosphere of *détente* after the nadir to which East–West relations had sunk during the later Stalin period. It became central to Soviet thinking for the rest of the Cold War until the thaw of the Gorbachev era (Arbatov, 1971).

4. The term 'Yellow Peril' was one of those which had been much favoured by the Kaiser Wilhelm II. It was part of the idea of alerting the Europeans to the dangers which were perceived as lying to the east. Needless to say, the Kaiser saw Germany as taking the leading role in this new European consciousness. The temporary unity of the European powers when confronted with the Boxer rebels in China gave some indication that the sense of common danger from outside could have the effect of at last bringing the Europeans together.

5. Looked at from a geopolitical perspective, the Russo-Japanese war was a

confrontation of land power and sea power. It was the attempt by a great land power (Russia) to deploy its power at sea and by an emerging sea power (Japan) to project itself on to the adjacent continent. The Russian fleet sailed to the Far East from its naval base at Kronstadt on the Gulf of Finland. It was forced to take the long route around the Cape of Good Hope since the Suez Canal was denied to it by Great Britain, its arch-rival for global power and Japan's principal ally at the time. After a journey of some 12,000 miles which took eight months, the exhausted Russians were confronted by the Japanese fleet lying in wait in the Straits of Tsushima between Japan and Korea. In the Battle of Tsushima the Russian fleet was all but annihilated. It was one of the most comprehensive defeats in naval history and put paid to Russia's attempts to extend its position in the Far East at the expense of China. Japan's rise as a major world power dates from this battle. In 1908 Korea was annexed and the process of Japanese penetration on to the Asian mainland began.

6. In 1919 the British Empire was larger in both territory and population than it had ever been before. With an area of 13.7 million square miles and a population of 275 millions it was the largest empire which had ever existed. Just over a decade later the Statute of Westminster (1931) inaugurated the transformation of the Empire into the Commonwealth. By confirming the status of the dominions as 'autonomous communities ... equal in status' this statute in effect began the process of imperial disintegration.

7. Tibet was legally a part of China but by the late nineteenth century it was autonomous and in many ways was acting as an independent state. The British attempted to shift it increasingly into their own sphere but its theocratic ruler, the Dalai Lama, was able to maintain a precarious position of neutrality in the Great Game.

CHAPTER 8

GREAT SPHERES:
THE MULTIPOLAR WORLD

In contrast to the 'mighty opposites' of the bipolar world, the multipolar view hinges on the idea that the complexities of the geopolitical world resolve themselves into more than two parts. The idea that the world is fundamentally pluralist in this sense dates geopolitically from the approaching end of what Mackinder termed the 'Columbian epoch'. During this period the world had come to be seen by the Europeans as being firmly Eurocentric, the other continents being relegated to that 'dark Egyptian night' of which Kipling wrote.[1] By the early years of the twentieth century new world powers, notably the United States and Japan, were emerging on the scene and the fact that there were other potential centres of power was becoming clear. By then it was at last being recognised that there were other civilisations which in the past had themselves been major centres of power.

That particular form of pluralism which presented the most important challenge to the bipolar views of Mahan and Mackinder was the one which contended that the world's geopolitical surface resolved itself into three 'great spheres'. A basic feature of the world map in both ancient and medieval times was the threefold division of the world into the continents of Europe, Asia and Africa, and until the Renaissance this remained the central feature of the European world-view. While subsequently the increasingly dominant position of Europe had the effect of relegating most of the rest of the world to obscurity, post-Renaissance Europe became, as has been seen, a geopolitical patchwork quilt dominated by the great powers. These powers maintained a *modus vivendi* based on an uneasy balance of power, and a geopolitical scene change, reflecting the changes in this balance, was periodically brought about by war. Alliances among these powers were arranged and rearranged in accordance with the shifts of political expediency.

It was not until the second half of the nineteenth century that the pragmatic alliances among the European powers began to harden into more solid groupings. These groupings centred respectively on the powers of the west, the centre and the east of the continent. This threefold division became the basis of those alliances which went to war with one another in 1914 and again in 1939–41. While the subsequent Cold War was firmly between two 'worlds', the idea of there being a third such 'world' had been present from the outset. As the intensity of the bipolar confrontation began to diminish in the 1960s so Europe began to emerge as a third potential player.

As has been seen, underlying geopolitical thinking in the early twentieth century was a strong sense of foreboding. Kjellén himself was tormented by his conviction that the fragile balance of power was breaking down and that the nations were drifting inexorably towards war. Confrontation was in the air, and the most basic was that between Russia and Britain, the great powers of land and sea. While from a maritime perspective this confrontation renewed in global form the threat posed throughout history by the Asiatic empires, from the perspective of continental Europe it posed quite a different kind of threat: that of being crushed between Lavisse's whale and white bear. In maritime, and particularly British, thinking the lands stretching eastwards from the centre of Europe through the Balkans to the Middle East were essentially part of a great shatter belt between the spheres of maritime and continental power which then extended on into Asia. This was Curzon's buffer zone 'on the outskirts of empire' (Curzon, 1908), and also Fairgrieve's crush zone consisting of 'buffer states, precariously independent politically, and more surely dependent economically' stretching from Eastern Europe to Southern Asia (Fairgrieve, 1932: 330). 'This zone of states,' went on Fairgrieve, 'has varied in position ... with changing conditions, but it has included at various times Finland, Sweden, Norway, Denmark, Holland, Belgium, Luxembourg, Switzerland, Poland, the Balkan States, Persia, Afghanistan, Siam and Korea'. Most significantly he asserted that 'Germany and even China belong to this belt. Central Europe, unorganised and broken into small and antagonistic communities, essentially belongs to the crush zone, but organised and powerful, is in a very different position' (ibid.). To make Central Europe 'organised and powerful' was the fundamental purpose lying behind the rise of geopolitical thinking in Germany. Following the unification of Kleindeutschland ('little Germany') into the German Empire in 1871, an important element in German foreign policy had been to forge tighter bonds among the lands of Grossdeutschland ('greater Germany'), which centred on the German and Austro-Hungarian Empires. The proposition underlying this was that, given the vulnerability of its geopolitical situation, Germany could be secure only as part of a grouping of Central European states. This was the basis of the doctrine of Mitteleuropa, a strong and cohesive geopolitical region in the heart of the continent able to resist domination by the maritime and continental powers. This was advocated by a number of geopolitical thinkers in the years before World War I, notable among whom were Joseph Partsch and Friedrich Naumann (Chapter 2). Partsch envisaged the grim possibility of 'the colossal empires of Great Britain and Russia' being in a position to 'subjugate or absolutely to absorb the less spacious powers of Central Europe'. Observing that in the past Central Europe had been 'the battlefield of all nations,' he concluded that 'The course of the world's history does but warn the Central European states to draw socially closer together, and to subordinate lesser dividing political interests to the greater aims of maintaining to the full their independence' (Partsch, 1903: 5). The actual boundaries of the proposed *Mitteleuropa* varied enormously, and in Partsch's definition it stretched eastwards from the Vosges to the Baltic–Black Sea isthmus (Figure 8.1). It thus consisted of virtually all those lands lying between the eastern frontiers of France and the western frontiers of the Russian Empire. Its population of 130 million and its considerable and varied natural resources made it potentially a most formidable power. Germany was deemed to be its natural centre and the only power capable of providing the necessary organisation to unify it.

Mitteleuropa had initially been conceived of as being a counter to the threat to the new German Empire from the other European powers which surrounded it in menacing fashion, but its effectiveness necessitated the expansion of its influence, and this included the acquisition of more of the *Lebensraum* which a highly populated country like Germany was deemed to require. This has to be seen in the context of the early-twentieth-century belief that overpopulation was one of the major problems facing Europe. To Ratzel and his followers there was an inextricable relationship between national development and the possession of adequate *Raum*, and territorial expansion in Europe was considered to be the only way in which this could be achieved. It was something which the British and other maritime empires had been able to do by means of overseas colonisation. For Germany to obtain the necessary *Lebensraum*, as well as resources and markets, it was argued, it was necessary for Germans to look eastwards. This became the policy of *Drang nach Osten*, which took German political and economic influence eastwards across the Balkans to the Dardanelles and beyond. Naumann, writing during World War I, extended Partsch's boundaries of *Mitteleuropa* to encompass both Scandinavia and Turkey. This 'greater' *Mitteleuropa* he saw as being one of the great world powers of the future. 'Mid-Europe is the fruit of war,' he wrote. 'We shall emerge from the war as Mid-Europeans (*Mitteleuropaer*)'. (Naumann, 1916: 287). He envisaged the *Mitteleuropa* of the future as being one of the great *Weltwirtschaftskorper* (world economic groupings) (*ibid.*: 190).

Naumann's dream was not to be realised, and in the wake of Germany's traumatic defeat, *Geopolitik* emerged as heir to the ideas of Ratzel and, in particular, to the *Mitteleuropa* doctrine (Chapter 3). Haushofer's answer to what had gone wrong was that *Mitteleuropa* on its own had not been sufficient. Germany had not encountered the conflict of the land and sea powers, as might have been anticipated, but an unexpected alliance between them. The motivations of the temporary cooperation of what Haushofer called 'the pirates of the sea and the pirates of the steppe' had to be understood, 'for we must know what such alliances entail for us who are being caught between them' (Dorpalen, 1942: 320). In these circumstances Haushofer maintained that in order for Germany to become really secure and successful, it had to become a power with a global, and not merely a European, reach. In order to attain this it was necessary to achieve mastery on both sea and land. This was something

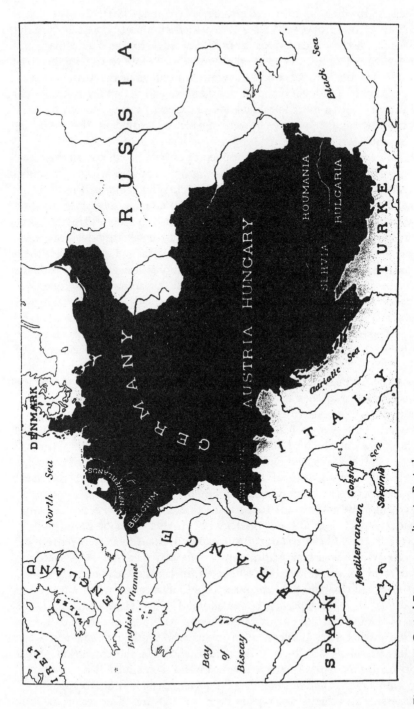

Figure 8.1 Central Europe according to Partsch
Source: Partsch, J. (1904) *Central Europe*. London: Heinemann

which neither the great powers of the sea nor those of the land had been able to accomplish. 'This short-sightedness on the part of both continental and maritime nations', he asserted, 'is world history's war-geographical *Leitmotif'* (*ibid.*: 309). 'The pirates of the steppe and the pirates of the sea' had achieved dominance only within their own particular elements. The disadvantages of Germany's central position could be turned to the country's advantage since, with its continental and maritime frontages, Germany possessed the potential to acquire the advantages of both and thus to use the resources of both the maritime and continental worlds. Both the land and the sea, the Heartland and the oceans, were open to penetration, and this was to be the basis of that *Raumüberwindende* which would give Germany the real world power which was so desired.

The geopoliticians thus advocated that a German-organised *Mitteleuropa* should be both a land and a sea power. The actual boundaries of this German *Grossraum* were much debated, but it was generally agreed that the *Drang nach Osten* was its natural orientation and that *Lebensraum* was to be sought in the east. Haushofer went on to develop the *Panideen*, the global pan-regions each of which would be dominated by one of the great world powers of the future. Following the achievement of continental dominance in the Northern Hemisphere these powers would then extend their spheres of influence into the inter-tropical regions. Initially Haushofer envisaged three great pan-regions: that of the Far East, dominated by Japan; that of the Western Hemisphere, dominated by the United States; and that of Europe and Africa, dominated by Germany. It was the expansion made possible by mastery of the land and sea by the new *Raumüberwindende* states of the world, which Haushofer saw as being the basis of the unity of the great continental masses. In this way those lands which had been dismissed as being part of the 'shatter belt' or 'buffer zone' between land and sea power would be transformed into the centres of new giant states. An entirely new structure of world power would then replace that controlled by the maritime powers. While initially this was a tripolar structure, Haushofer was not wedded to the idea of there being three centres of world power, and in some later versions the Soviet Union was given the status of a pan-region.

During World War II a re-evaluation of the world geopolitical scene took place in the Allied countries, and particularly in the United States after its entry into the war. This was to a large extent a response to the implications of German *Geopolitik*. Nicholas Spykman undertook an examination of 'the territorial relations of states in a geographical sense'. He expressed the view that 'The basis of world planning for peace must be world geography' and that 'the unit area for analysis must be coextensive with the surface of the earth' (Spykman, 1944: 6). While he connected the thinking of the German geopoliticians with that of Mackinder, the conclusions which he drew were different from theirs. Spykman argued that what he termed 'the centres of power in the world' lay neither in the maritime nor in the continental worlds but in the lands between them. These he named the 'Rimland' of Eurasia, which centred on what he called 'the European littoral', the Indian subcontinent and the Far East (Figure 8.2). It had been the historical objective of both the maritime and continental powers to secure control of the Rimland and to consolidate their power within it. While this had frequently been accomplished for individual parts of the Rimland, the most usual situation within it had been one of conflict. However, contended Spykman, it was possible that a future great power could come to dominate the whole of the Rimland. 'The girdle of maritime seas' provided a 'maritime highway' from the Baltic Sea to the Sea of Okhotsk, and this now made communications within and around the Rimland both cheap and easy (ibid.: 24). A united 'Eurasian Rimland' would thus be a formidable power which would have the strength to upset the existing balance and to dominate the world. Spykman saw the United States alongside Great Britain, as being an integral part of the maritime world, and, together with the principal land power, the Soviet Union, they had a common interest in preventing 'the unification of the Old World centres of power', that is to say the Rimland. This was Spykman's geopolitical explanation of that alliance of land and sea power which characterised both world wars. However, unlike the German geopoliticians, Spykman saw the mastery of one element as being a distinct advantage. The power of the 'amphibian Rimland' had historically been held in check by the alternating pressures from land and sea (ibid.: 54). He considered that waging war 'on two fronts and in two elements at the same time' was what had irrevocably weakened the enemy powers in World War I.

Thus in Spykman's world-view, there were three principal centres of world power: the maritime world; the continental world (centring on the Heartland); and, between the two, the Rimland. Spykman maintained that it was this latter – and not the Heartland – which possessed the greatest potential for world domination, and this could be prevented only by joint action by the other two centres of power.

After World War II, addressing the whole question of Heartland versus Rimland, Meinig (1956), came down on the side of the latter. He diminished both the size and importance of the Heartland and at the same time emphasised the importance of the Rimland. He divided it into two parts, which he called respectively 'extrainsular' and 'intrainsular'. The former looked outwards towards the maritime world, while the latter looked inwards towards the continent. The exact dividing line between the two oscillated in accordance with the relative strength of the power of the maritime and continental worlds at any particular time. Like Spykman, Meinig believed that the real centre of power lay in the Rimland, not in the Heartland, and it was in the interests of both the maritime and continental powers to consolidate their strength by achieving and maintaining control over it.

The whole concept of the Rimland as the principal centre of world power was based on the premise that the World-Island was the centre and heart of the destiny of mankind and that the United States was a part of what Mackinder

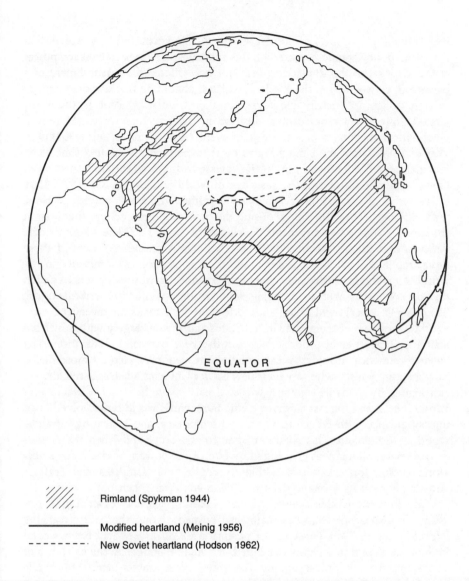

EQUATOR

/////   Rimland (Spykman 1944)

———————   Modified heartland (Meinig 1956)

- - - - - - - -   New Soviet heartland (Hodson 1962)

Figure 8.2 From Heartland to Rimland

had termed the Outer or Insular Crescent. Spykman had contended that American policy should be based on this awareness and seek to limit the power at the disposal of the Rimland states. This necessitated the establishment of a balance of power within the Rimland which it should be the task of American foreign policy to sustain. However, another tripolar concept elevated the United States to a more central position in the structures of world power. Geopolitical thinking along these lines went back to the Spanish–American War of 1898, when the United States came to be seen for the first time as an imperial power in its own right. While Lavisse had viewed the confrontation of Great Britain and Russia as the basic fact of world politics (Lavisse, 1891: 159), a quarter of a century later Naumann identified the pre-eminence of three 'World States'. These he called – using the biological terminology favoured at the time – 'three great organisms which are relatively complete: Great Britain, America and Russia' (Naumann, 1916: 182). The size and resources of these three 'super-national Great States' gave them a position of dominance in the world. As with Haushofer later, Naumann did not regard this triple domination as being a permanent feature. He foresaw the possibility of Mitteleuropa becoming also a 'World State' and so joining their ranks. In the event, after World War I two of them, the United States and Russia, largely withdrew from active participation in world affairs for the best part of a generation. The 'Fortress America' attitudes of the isolationists were paralleled by those of the Russian communists, who saw their new Soviet Union as a beleaguered fortress surrounded by a hostile capitalist world. Great Britain, the third of Naumann's World States, and the last survivor of the Eurocentric world order, joined in an uneasy alliance with France to exercise a temporary, and increasingly fragile, world condominium. This situation came to an abrupt end when the Anglo-French condominium was challenged by two of the powers of Haushofer's new world order. Fortress Russia within its continental fastnesses and Fortress America behind its 'oceanic defensive perimeter' were then both definitively brought into the world scene (Spykman, 1942: 5). The victorious 'Big Three' alliance consisted of what Naumann had termed, during the earlier war, the World States, and the challenge of Naumann's Mitteleuropa had for a second time failed. World peace now depended, asserted Spykman, on the existence of 'an equilibrium of power among the three great states' (ibid.: 58). While accepting this tripolar assessment, Gyorgy saw the United States as being in the more vulnerable position of 'a continental island between Europe and Asia' (Gyorgy, 1944: 353).

George Cressey was more euphoric in his estimation of American power. While recognising the emergence in Asia of a new centre of power in the world, he questioned the role of the Heartland. 'If there is anywhere a world citadel or Heartland,' he wrote, 'it may well lie in North America rather than Asia' (Cressey, 1945: 245). He concluded prophetically that 'no world war can be won without the aid of the United States'. In a post-war critique of Soviet power, and of the Heartland in particular, he identified the geopolitical weaknesses of the Soviet position (Cressey, 1945: 237–42). On the other hand, he saw what he called 'this New World Continent' as having the greatest potential of all the great centres of world power and of being, in a sense, itself a 'heartland'.

Thus while the 'Big Three' of the 1940s recalled Naumann's 'Great States', the phrase also looked forward to the years following the Greek crisis of 1947, when it became clear that the world was becoming increasingly bipolar. Although Spykman had himself used the term 'the three superpowers', it became all too clear that Great Britain was not in the same league as the other two and was really a survivor of the nineteenth-century world order rather than a major player in that of the second half of the twentieth century. Out of this realisation came the idea of Britain as being a 'third force' between the 'mighty opposites' of the two real superpowers. This was the geopolitical dimension of one aspect of British foreign policy in the immediate post-war years. It was proposed that Britain and France should pool their resources as the basis for a new 'third force'. The Big Three having become, nominally at least, the 'Big Four' with the addition of France, the British Foreign Secretary, Ernest Bevin, proposed developing on the *Entente* and, together with their Afro-Asian Empires, building what had the potential to become a formidable power bloc (Bullock, 1983: 193–4). This he referred to as the 'three great Monroes', consisting of the United States, the Soviet Union and the Anglo-French alliance.[2] The United States hegemony over the New World and Soviet hegemony over Eurasia would be balanced by an Anglo-French condominium over Afro-Asia. In this way the Eurocentric world of the nineteenth century would be able to adapt to — and become part of — the new world system. Despite its promotion at the highest levels in both countries, the idea of an Anglo-French 'third force' was never to become a reality.[3] Its effectiveness on a global scale was dependent upon the strength of the overseas empires of the two powers, and it was becoming all too clear that these were built on shifting sands. However, it was Spykman's 'European littoral', one of the three major centres of Rimland power, rather than the Anglo-French joint sphere, which emerged in the 1950s and 1960s as the potential 'third force'. As the empires crumbled away, the idea of a United Europe arose — phoenix-like — from their ashes, and it took the form of the European Community.

The new geopolitical entity was based on ideas which had been generated as early as World War I. Demangeon's *Le Déclin de l'Europe* (Demangeon, 1920) appeared a few years after Naumann's *Mitteleuropa* (Naumann, 1916), and very soon after Mackinder had transformed and enlarged the Pivot into the Heartland (Mackinder, 1919). Naumann advocated a strengthening of the ties among the countries of Central Europe while Mackinder advocated a strengthening of the ties among the maritime powers, foreseeing Bevin's 'Monroes' of the 1950s. However, Demangeon's thesis was essentially different from that of the other two. He was concerned with the implications of the decline of Europe and, using such terms as 'grouping', 'linkage', 'community' and 'bloc' he proposed unification as the answer to the problem. Developing ideas which had originated with Vidal de la Blache, Demangeon was one of the first geographers to advocate European unity and to employ a geopolitical terminology to describe it (Parker, 1987a: 15–16). The decline of Europe meant the end of the Eurocentric world, and he saw the United States and Japan as being the emerging great powers of the future. In these circumstances, he maintained, it was essential for Europe to unite if 'le vieux continent' was to continue to play a global role. Demangeon's world-view was thus also a tripolar one, and it bore many resemblances to that later developed by Haushofer, but there were essential differences between the approaches of the French and the German geographers. Demangeon's proposal was for the creation of a European federal state which would secure unity without dominance. The idea of European union was discussed widely during the 1920s and became a central element in the strategy for bringing about greater security in Europe. Leading French political figures of the time, such as Georges Herriot and Aristide Briand, took up the idea, and it reached its high point with Briand's 1932 proposal for the creation of a 'United States of Europe'.[4] It is significant that while Demangeon's ideas became closely linked with internationalism and the League of Nations, those of Haushofer became linked to Hitler and the Third Reich. While the idea of *Reich* (Empire) collapsed in ruins in 1945, the idea of *union* went on to become the basis of the post-war European Community. This Community evolved into the concept of a geopolitical entity, as opposed to the more limited economic and defence entities represented by OEEC (the Organisation for European Economic Co-operation, now the Organisation for Economic Co-operation and Development) and NATO (Parker, 1983: 51–61). It was this fledgling European geopolitical identity which was the basis of the idea of Europe as a 'third force' in the bipolar world (*ibid.*: 90–101).

By this time another idea was consolidating itself as a counter to the bipolarity of the Cold War world. This was that of a 'Third World' which had quite different characteristics from the 'First' and 'Second' Worlds and which encapsulated a vision of a different world order. Like the European Community, it arose out of the ashes of the European empires, but it came from their subject peoples rather than from the former imperial powers themselves. Coming into existence in 1955 at the Bandung Conference of states from the African and Asian continents, it presented a vision of both a united front against the continued domination of the former imperial powers and also a global alternative to the confrontation of the 'northern civil war'.[5] Although the Third World movement initially centred on Southeast Asia, and particularly on Indonesia, one of the first new states to emerge out of the disintegration of the colonial empires, it was India which subsequently took the lead (Brecher, 1963: 42–6). The ideas lying behind it were refined and developed by Krishna Menon and Jawaharlal Nehru, who saw India, the largest and most powerful of the new states, as being the key to its success (Brecher, 1968: 295).

The role of India in the world was seen in quite a different light by Saul

Cohen. Viewing it less as the leader of a grouping of relatively weak countries, he elevated the subcontinent to being a potential third geostrategic region lying between the other two (Cohen, 1964). 'India is the pivot of South Asia,' he wrote, possessing 'tremendous geopolitical significance in the maintenance of an effective balance of power in Asia' (ibid.: 220). Menon and Nehru may have agreed about the power, but they envisaged its use in quite a different way. The Third World of which India was to be firmly a part was seen by them not so much as a third centre of power in the traditional sense but as offering an alternative world vision which was cooperative rather than confrontational in stance. Menon firmly opposed the global domination of the great powers but no less firmly rejected the idea of a 'third bloc' (Brecher, 1968: 8). Using such terms as 'non-aligned' and 'area of peace', he invoked Gandhi's ideas as being more appropriate to countries which did not possess the physical power to oppose the established world order in any other way. As more new states emerged on the world scene during the 1960s the geographical area of the Third World was extended to cover a large part of the inter-tropical world (Figure 8.3). It consisted of a large and diverse collection of mainly new countries, but it concretised on the Afro-Asian world as a geopolitical entity. Focusing on the Indian Ocean, this was initially unified only by its relative underdevelopment and its opposition to the economic and political dominance of the great powers of the Northern Hemisphere. The Indian Ocean had been a 'realm' in the geopolitical sense in the past, and now it re-emerged in this new form.[6]

By the late 1970s, with the Cold War growing ever more stale and sterile, the idea of the Third World as alternative came to be pursued by radical geographers (Blaut, 1978: 309–13). If the bipolar confrontation was perceived in many ways as being a kind of 'cold civil war' taking place within the Northern Hemisphere, the growing problems of the rest of the world were being neglected. These centred on development and the way in which the world's resources were being used overwhelmingly for the enrichment of relatively few countries (Blaikie, 1989: 125–51). There was 'another' world, the countries of which had been considered as pawns in the conflict, whose real interests were seldom addressed at all. Walters identified the division between 'advanced countries and less developed countries', and he observed that 'in so far as it has a general geographical line it is more a North–South division' (Walters, 1974: 198). In this way 'South' made its first appearance as something more than a directional concept. The perception of the global dichotomy of East and West came to be challenged by a new dichotomy of North and South (Brandt, 1980). From then until the fall of the Soviet Union the world had become firmly trinary, if not tripolar, and the problems of the South came increasingly to be seen as being the problems of the globe as a whole.[7]

The trinary idea represents a special form of pluralism since it rests on the idea of there being a 'third' entity – whether conceived of as being a 'third force', a 'third world', a 'third zone' or a third 'Monroe' – interposed between a:

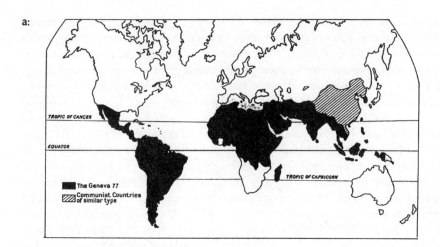

b:

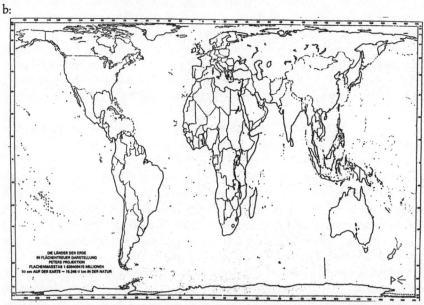

Figure 8.3 (a) The Third World in the 1960s. The 'Geneva 77' consisted of those countries which attended the United Nations Conference on Trade and Development (UNCTAD) held in Geneva in 1964. This gives a good indication of those countries which could then be considered to be members of the Third World. (b) The Peters projection. Arno Peters's decimal grid divides the surface of the earth into 100 longitudinal fields of equal width and 100 latitudinal fields of equal height. The map is then built up from the equator, so showing the world as viewed from a 'Southern' perspective.

Source of (b): Dr Arno Peters

the two 'mighty opposites'. This is brought about by the existence of an alternative to the major protagonists, and it presents the possibility of the replacement of one or other of them. If, on the other hand, there is a fourth, fifth or sixth large entity in the world, then it is less a question of there being an alternative within the existing system as of different presumptions being necessary about the nature of the world system itself.

Fairgrieve identified the three 'ancient settled civilisations' of what he called the 'Old World Parallelogram', and to these he added the United States in the New World. Each of them constituted a distinct human region and a historic centre of power, but it was only the United States which was at the time a world power in its own right (Fairgrieve, 1932: 334). Fairgrieve considered China, which he saw as being 'a world in itself ... far too great and homogeneous to be crushed' as being archetypal of the genre, but the others also possessed, in varying degrees, the same basic set of geopolitical characteristics. In Fairgrieve's world-view the four were joined together by 'a continuous route', which he called the 'Northern Belt of Settlement and Movement' and which held them together like a chain around the globe (*ibid.*: 338) (Figure 8.4).

In the year of the outbreak of World War II, Derwent Whittlesey referred to what he called 'the earth's largest political entities'. These were Russia, China, India and the United States, and the combination of their great size with their immense physical and human resources put them into a special category of world power (Whittlesey, 1939: 11). To these Whittlesey added Brazil, Canada and Australia as states possessing immense potential to become future centres of world power. He stressed that the size and power of a state were far from being synonymous even if they were regarded only in terms of potentials. Ultimately it was what he called the 'geographical maturity' of the state which determined the extent to which resources were transformed into effective power. He considered that at the time of the outbreak of World War II only one of these very large states had attained the necessary geopolitical maturity, and that was the United States. A gaping chasm thus existed between potential and achievement, and the actual distribution of world power had to be explained by other factors. Like Fairgrieve, Whittlesey thus recognised that the great centres of civilisation are not necessarily – or even probably – themselves states, and both drew attention to the divisions within Europe as being proof of this.

Spykman pointed to a close correlation between geopolitical pluralism and the breakdown of the great imperial systems. Echoing Mackinder's comments on the end of the Columbian epoch, he maintained that 'an epoch in the world's history has come to an end' and, as a result of this, 'The center of world power has left western Europe; or rather there is no longer a center of world power.' In its place there was 'the decentralisation of power and the creation of great spheres dominated from different centres'. These he identified as being the Americas, the Far East, 'the Heartland of Eurasia', the Eastern

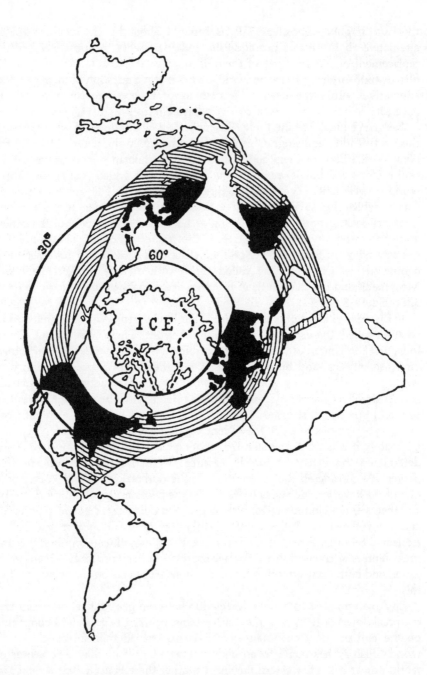

Figure 8.4 The northern belt of settlement and movement
Source: Fairgrieve, J. (1932) *Geography and World Power*. London: University of London
Press

Atlantic and the Indian Ocean (Spykman, 1938: 45). Each of these was dominated at the time by a single great power, these being respectively the United States, Japan, Russia/Soviet Union, Germany and Great Britain. While the great centres of civilisation change only slowly, world powers rise and fall with far greater rapidity, and this led Spykman to make a clear distinction between a 'civilisation' and a 'power' (ibid.: 44). While he saw it as being the norm for each 'great sphere' to be dominated and organised by a single great power, globally he thought of there being a necessary balance of power among them so as to prevent a dominating position being achieved by any one to the detriment of the others.

Both Haushofer and Spykman envisaged the domination of each civilisation by one single power, so producing a world consisting basically of great powers each with its own regional power base. However, Vidal de la Blache had proposed an alternative model of the process of unity arising not from domination by one single power but by the coming together of the constituent political units to form a larger unit. This is the process of groupement, leading to a communauté of the nations, which, as has been seen, became the basis of Demangeon's proposals for the unity of Europe. Although Demangeon's new scenario was in the first instance tripolar, tripolarity was not an essential condition of it. Demangeon envisaged the continued existence of the British Empire in some form or another and, like Vidal before him, he saw India as being the keystone upon which British world power rested (Demangeon, 1923: 236–61).

In the complex and fluid world of the years immediately following World War II, both power and agreement were used in the process of consolidation. While each of the superpowers had its own 'great sphere', lesser powers began to reach out towards the formation of groupings. This process was led by the former European great powers, which sought to compensate for their diminished world status by the creation of a new geopolitical identity within which they would collectively regain some of that power and world influence which individually they had lost. While organisations such as the OEEC, NATO and the Council of Europe became models for the development of similar organisations in other parts of the world, it was the European Union which developed the strongest dynamic based on the emergence of a new transnational geopolitical structure (Parker, 1983).

The emergence of this new organisational structure in the 1950s and 1960s coincided with an increased emphasis on multipolar explanation in geopolitics. De Blij proclaimed that 'the time of the blocs ... has arrived' and, despite all the problems and reverses, the trend appeared to be a permanent one. As a result of this, 'a new politicogeographical map is indeed being forged' (de Blij, 1973: 446). G.R. Crone saw the new groupings as being the most important feature of the post-war world, and went on to identify 'at least ten large political groups of countries'. While the actual degree of integration within each of these groups varied considerably, Crone considered them to be 'regions which themselves

[have] an historical justification and a cultural basis'. They could be geographically consolidated into blocs of contiguous countries or they could also consist of groups of territorially discontinuous maritime states. Among them were what he identified as 'four groups of world status', these being the communist bloc, India, Africa and the West (Crone, 1969: 234). Hugh Tinker, evaluating the position of India in the world of the 1960s, considered what he termed 'the family of continental nations' as consisting of China, Brazil, the USSR and India (Tinker, 1963a: 259).

In the 1970s East and Prescott waxed poetic, using Walter de la Mare's 'All is flux, nor stays but changes on' to describe what they called 'those restless forces that operate on the international stage of a dynamic world' (East and Prescott, 1975: 235). They drew a picture of a 'a markedly different international scene' from that of the past, the main characteristic of which was its fragmentation (ibid.). But while the principal theme of East and Prescott was 'a world fragmented' – evocatively represented by a shattered glass – the most important development which they saw taking place was international grouping (ibid.: 211). 'Certainly the marked trend towards wider political association which has manifested itself since 1945', they said, 'expresses ... fresh efforts of progressive thinking' (ibid.: 212). What Hartshorne had referred to as 'political organisations at higher ranks', East and Prescott shortened to 'international blocs'. These they saw as 'looking forward towards the effacement of the concept, as some would think outworn, of national sovereignty. Here, indeed, a revolutionary note is struck in favour of a large, well-ordered, multi-national society' (ibid.: 213). In this the European Community was an organisation of wider geopolitical significance which 'offers the world a model for regional cooperation'. Russett went further by developing a model for regional cooperation (Russett, 1974). He examined those factors which had to be present in order that regional groupings of states should be stable and successful in a diverse and 'variegated' world. In this he identified the necessity for congruence in socio-cultural homogeneity and political and economic independence. While as yet 'the regional subsystems of the world are far less well delineated than the boundaries of national systems', he predicted that there would be further integration at regional levels (ibid.: 282–90).

Thinking along these lines reflected a widespread view that regional cooperation was bound to be a good thing since the alternative was conflict as in the past.[8] However, there was less inclination to address the question of the relationships among such regional groupings. In view of the antagonism of the regional groupings of the West and East, there was on the face of it little reason for supposing that similar hostility would not also be a feature of other regional groupings. East and Prescott had observed that the very success of the European Community had contributed to the 'persistence of the division of Europe'. The overall effects of regional integration need not necessarily be peaceful, observed Russett, since conflicts could as easily develop among regions as among countries. It was therefore necessary to address the whole question of the relationship of the emerging regional blocs in the context of global cooperation. In this way it would be possible to 'determine whether the regional blocs will build a stable political edifice for man, or merely a shaky temple he can pull down upon his head' (Muir, 1975: 200).

In the 1960s Saul Cohen had seen 'a world divided', but this world-view was produced at a time when the Cold War confrontation continued to dominate the scene and the two great blocs still appeared to be relatively monolithic. In the nuclear age, said Cohen, the notion of the achievement of supremacy and dominance had become quite inappropriate. Likewise ideas of containment and of the shoring up of the perimeter were now rendered out of date. Heartland–Rimland thinking had made the United States accept obligations too widely. 'The Free World has become the victim of a myth,' asserted Cohen, 'the myth of the inherent unity of the World-Island, given the unity of the Heartland in combination with part of the Rimland. An adjunct of the myth is that the sea-based powers cannot maintain their position unless their complete command over all parts of the Eurasian littoral is maintained. This is the myth that stems from Mackinder's earlier writings and Spykman's rejoinders' (Cohen, 1964: 56). In his Parthian shot on this subject Cohen again returned to Mackinder. 'It is especially ironic that so little attention was paid to Mackinder in 1943,' he said, 'when he suggested that the maritime world was ultimately divisible into three units' (ibid.: 58). Cohen's own rejoinder was that the whole Heartland–Rimland thesis and the 'falling-domino theory' based upon it should be abandoned and replaced by a tighter regional construct. Conceding an overall bipolar framework, he envisaged the partial disintegration of the blocs and the emergence of regional groupings. These were 'larger territorial frameworks' than those provided by states. 'These regional processes are strongest within the geopolitically more mature parts of the world. The national processes are strongest in the underdeveloped regions' (ibid.: xvii). The new regionalism was seen as being more conducive to necessary change than the rigidities of the bipolar system. The world system was naturally dynamic rather than static, and his objective was 'to present a framework that anticipates the geographic dynamics of our times' (ibid.: 286). In doing this he linked the multipolar system with the bipolar one, seeing them as being complementary to one another rather than representing mutually exclusive world systems. At a time when the persistence of the Cold War appeared to reinforce the views of those who believed that the bi-polar system was now virtually permanent, Cohen observed that within the overall framework of the two great 'geostrategic' regions new 'geopolitical' regions were already in course of emerging. These were North America, Western Europe, the Soviet Union and China, and their distinguishing marks were 'contiguity of location and complementarity of resources'. In this way, within the overall bipolar framework 'multiple power nodes' were emerging (Figure 8.5). Developing further on this theme, in 1973 Cohen stated that 'The major premise of [this] work is that the dynamic balance

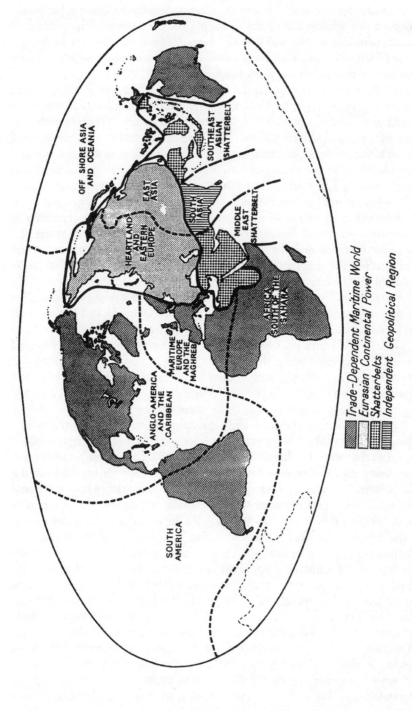

Figure 8.5 The world's geostrategic regions and their geopolitical subdivisions
Source: Cohen, S.B. (1964) *Geography and Politics in a Divided World*. London: Methuen

that characterises the relations among states and larger regions is inherent in the ecology of the global political system' (Cohen, 1973: vi). He asserted 'the polycentric nature of global power' and the prime importance of the four great 'power nodes'. The principal characteristics of the world system as envisaged by Cohen were thus that it was polycentric and also hierarchical, and that its component parts existed in a state of dynamic 'geopolitical equilibrium' produced by 'an isostatic balance of power'. Isostatic forces would lead to the creation of a 'dynamic macro-regionalism'. The capacity for change was 'an essential feature of geopolitical life' (ibid.: 288). Rigidity led to the perpetuation of unsatisfactory systems based on outmoded ideas, and this gave rise to instability and the use of violence in seeking solutions to problems. The polycentric world was thus a far better guarantee of global peace than the bipolar world could ever be (ibid.: 314).

The polycentric world-view can be summed up as being one in which the norm is considered to be the existence of a number of centres of power. The tricentric world is a specific variant on this which interposes a third entity into the bipolar conflict. Far from being a 'fragmented' world, which implies the breakup of something which should be whole, or a 'divided' world, which also implies deviation from a desired unity, the polycentric norm is a 'balanced' world in which a number of separate centres of power counterbalance one another. As Cohen put it 'Spheres of influence are essential to the preservation of national and regional expression ... the alternative is either a monolithic world system or utter chaos' (Cohen, 1973: viii). This is less a state of global harmony, as had been envisaged by Whittlesey, then one of controlled power. When the balance is working properly it prevents any one of the component units from becoming too powerful and thus attaining a position of dominance. In this concept that 'balance of power' which has been the essential feature of the European international scene in modern times is transposed to the global level. The balance must of necessity be a dynamic one which allows for change taking place in the realities of power. This polycentric view relegates the bipolar world to that of being an unusual and temporary occurrence, characteristic of specific circumstances. Viewed in this way it may also be seen as being a safeguard against that kind of dominance which is inherent in the third of the major world views.

NOTES

1. America was, of course, an exception to this 'Egyptian night'. The phrase comes in the poem 'The White Man's Burden', which Kipling wrote after the Spanish–American War of 1898. In the poem, the United States is encouraged to 'Take up the white man's burden', something which Kipling saw in rather idealistic terms. Although the United States did not choose to take up the burden in quite the way Kipling envisaged, it certainly entered the ranks of the great powers and proved

so effective a power that within half a century it had replaced Great Britain as the major world power.

2. The Monroe Doctrine, named after the American President James Monroe, was issued by the White House in 1823. It stated that any incursions by European powers in the American continent – North or South – were considered dangerous to the peace and safety of the United States and as such would be regarded as being unfriendly acts. The doctrine was an early assertion of the hegemony of the United States in the Western Hemisphere. In recent times it has been identified with a major power holding a hegemonic position in a particular region (O'Loughlin, 1994b: 166–8).

3. The *Entente Cordiale* of 1904 was seen by many at the time as being the first stage in the further improvement of relations between Great Britain and France. Although itself basically a colonial agreement, it provided the framework for the Anglo-French alliance in two world wars. In 1940, only weeks before the fall of France, the beleaguered French government proposed a full union between the two countries. This was an idea which had considerable appeal for Prime Minister Winston Churchill, but the circumstances of the time clearly made it impracticable even if the British government had been prepared to accept it. After World War II the Treaty of Dunkirk (1947) pledged the two countries to close cooperation. It signified a recognition by Britain of the return of France to the ranks of the great powers, something which Britain had fought to bring about. As a result of British pressure the 'Big Three' became the 'Big Four' and then the 'Big Five' with the inclusion of China. These five powers then went on to become the permanent members of the Security Council of the United Nations (Edmonds, 1991: 436–7). In 1951 the French government proposed the establishment of a 'community' of European nations, and at first it envisaged that Britain and France should jointly take the lead in its formation. Britain proved to be far less inclined towards cooperation with France in a European context than it had been in the global context and, as a result of France's insistence on pushing ahead with the scheme, relations between the two powers cooled.

4. The 1920s was a time of high hopes for internationalism. These centred on the League of Nations in Geneva, where the leading European statesmen met regularly to discuss closer cooperation. Important among them were the German and French foreign ministers, Gustav Stresemann and Aristide Briand, who worked together tirelessly for a permanent reconciliation between their two countries and shared the Nobel Prize for Peace in 1926. The close relationship between Germany and France which was built up at this period was damaged by the death of Stresemann in 1929 and then brought to an end in 1933 following the coming to power of the Nazis.

5. The Bandung Conference of 1955 was hosted by President Sukarno of Indonesia in order to bring about an alignment of the policies of the Afro-Asian countries in regard to world issues. Altogether 29 countries, including China, sent representatives to the Conference, and representatives of the African National Congress also took part. The central theme of the Conference was non-alignment in the Cold War, but as the non-aligned movement developed it was not confined to the Afro-Asian countries. Subsequent conferences were held in Belgrade (1961) and Cairo (1964).

6. The geopolitical unity of the Indian Ocean had been achieved by the Portuguese, who wrested it from the Arabs in the early sixteenth century. It subsequently became commercially, strategically and even politically the centre of British world power. Since the 1960s this role in the Indian Ocean region has in many ways been increasingly assumed by India.

7. The Brandt Report (1980) was a landmark in Western thinking on issues concerning the Third World. Produced by a distinguished international group and chaired by the former German Chancellor, Willy Brandt, the report highlighted the problems of the developing countries. It sought to demonstrate that the best interests of the West, and of the world as a whole, lay in the solution of these problems.

8. An example of regional cooperation along federal lines was the Central African Federation of Northern and Southern Rhodesia and Nyasaland (1953–63). It was embarked upon by the British government during the independence process in what it considered to be the best way of moving forward in the wider regional interest. The emerging sense of 'national' identity within the member countries of the federation proved to be too strong, and it was unsuccessful in its objectives. Northern Rhodesia and Nyasaland became independent as Zambia and Malawi in 1964 but, as a result of the reluctance of the white minority to concede majority government, the independence of Southern Rhodesia was considerably delayed. It did not finally become an independent state until 1980, when it took the name of Zimbabwe.

CHAPTER 9

CONFUTING THE BLIND GEOGRAPHERS? THE CENTRE–PERIPHERY WORLD

I will confute those blind geographers
That make a triple region in the world,
Here at Damascus I will make the Point
That shall begin the Perpendicular.

Christopher Marlowe, *Tamburlaine the Great* Pt 1. IV. iv

The principle of centrality has frequently been a feature of those geopolitical world-views which we have so far examined. It is founded on the proposition that, however complex the patterns of international relationships may become, there is always a 'central place' which enjoys a position of particular significance. Such pre-eminence need not necessarily be exclusively political: it may include political, commercial, technological, cultural, demographic or military elements in various combinations. A place endowed with such qualities can be a city, a nation or a region, and in geopolitical terminology it can be variously described as a core region, a zone, a belt, a centre of gravity or a heartland.[1] While the actual locations which have been deemed as fulfilling this role have changed considerably over time, the basic idea of there being a 'centre' within a particular state, region or the world as a whole has remained.[2] In the medieval *mappa mundi* it had been Jerusalem, and in modern times there have been many 'points' through which the 'Perpendicular' has been drawn.[3]

The corollary of the existence of a world centre is bound to be that of the existence of a world periphery, an edge, which is in all ways its opposite. While the centre is that place where power in many different forms is concentrated, the periphery is the area which is, by definition, powerless. Between these two extremes there is a gradation from absolute centrality to absolute peripherality. It is in this grey area between the middle and the edge that the complex relationships and rivalries of the geopolitical world have been played out and where those aspiring to future power have lain in wait (Parker, 1988: 64–75).

The fact that the centrist view is present in the other views may stem, in part at least, from the exaggerated importance invariably accorded to any particular place by those who live in it. By virtue of their close terrestrial relationship to it, it becomes the ultimate geographical reality and the principal focus of their environmental experience. There is thus a built-in bias in favour of the homeland which results in a topological transformation that gives the point of observation an importance far above that which could possibly be accorded to it by any objective assessment of its significance (Figure 9.1). The countries of those geographers who have been responsible for producing the most influential world-views have invariably been accorded an especial significance in their theories of world power. In 1868, over three decades before Mackinder's 'Pivot', Charles Dilke pondered the changing centre of gravity in the English-speaking world – to which he gave the name 'Greater Britain' – and related this to the subjectivity of world maps on the matter of centres. These he collectively named after the *omphalos* (navel) at Delphi, the point which the ancient Greeks had thought of as being the centre of the *oikoumene*, the inhabited world. 'Herodotus held that Greece was the very middle of the world,' observed Dilke, 'and that the unhappy Orientals were frozen, and the yet more unfortunate Indians baked every afternoon of their poor lives in order that the sun might shine on Greece at noon' (Dilke, 1890: 70–3). Two thousand years on and 'London plumes herself on being the "centre of the terrestrial globe"'. Such 'omphalism', observed Dilke, inevitably produces world-views which are subjective and which therefore represent distortions of reality. He commented that now Fort Riley in Kansas had taken over from Independence in Missouri as ' the centre of the world ... the Hyde Park Corner from which continents measure their miles' (*ibid.*).

To perceive the world only 'from a certain vantage point', said Braudel, 'is to favour from the start a one-sided form of explanation' (Braudel, 1984: 19). From the earliest times world maps based upon such subjective perceptions of geographical reality have been used to justify assertions of power and pre-eminence. Just as Eratosthenes gave Greece a pivotal location at the centre of the *oikoumene*, near the very point where the three continents met, so likewise Mackinder observed that the British Isles lay at the very centre of the world's land hemisphere (Mackinder, 1902: 40) (Figure 9.1). Both were using the 'facts' of geography as they knew them to justify the 'natural' pre-eminence of their own country. In the early twentieth century British geography textbooks employed both cartography and geometry to demonstrate the centrality and the global power of Britain (Figure 9.2). The new polychromatic political atlases available throughout Europe, although highlighting different imperial posses-sions and displaying a kaleidoscope of imperial colours, subscribed to what was basically the same world-view. They were all Eurocentric, and represented chromatic topological transformations of the same basic centre–periphery world image.[4]

The biggest and most emotionally charged of these was the British world image, represented by the map of the British Empire, using the Mercator projection and coloured in strident pink glowing triumphantly out from an otherwise dull grey world. The perception of Great Britain as 'Top Nation' gained widespread acceptance even among those who did not necessarily subscribe to the associated idea that this was, in another of Sellar and Yeatman's

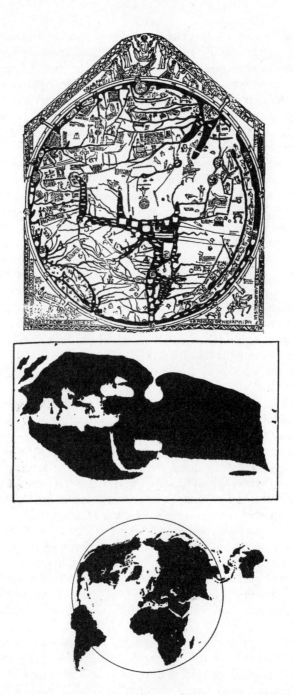

Figure 9.1 Changing centres and peripheries: Britain in the world
Source: Mackinder, H.J. (1902) *Britain and the British Seas*. Oxford: Clarendon Press

Lesson 1.—The British Empire, 1.

1. The British Empire is the largest empire on the face of the globe.

(i) The sun never sets on the British Empire, and never rises.

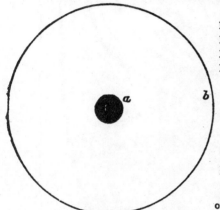

(ii) The British Empire is one hundred times as large as Great Britain. In this diagram, *a* is Great Britain ; *b* represents the size of the British Empire.

2. It has an area of over 13,000,000 square miles.

(i) The British Empire is larger than the Russian Empire by above 4 millions of square miles.

(ii) The British Empire has about one-fourth of all the land on the globe.

3. It has a population of about 434,000,000.

(i) The British Empire has about one-fourth of all the people in the world.

(ii) The most thickly peopled part of it is the Valley of the Ganges.

Figure 9.2 The geometry of Empire
Source: Meiklejohn, J.M.D. (1913) *A Short Geography*. London: Meiklejohn

immortal phrases, 'A Good Thing'. In geopolitical world perceptions the 'is' is thus something quite different from the 'ought to be'. While to its friends Great Britain was the kindly and humane mistress of the world, to the country's enemies Britain was seen as exerting a stranglehold upon it. To Haushofer Britain was an enormous octopus clutching the world in its tentacles (Figure 9.3). It was British power in particular, rather than the idea of the Eurocentric world, which was challenged by German *Weltpolitik*. The German geopoliticians simply wanted to substitute a German octopus for the British one. Similarly, while the Monroe Doctrine of the early nineteenth century sought to justify American guardianship of the New World, by the end of the century the phrase 'New World' had also taken on what Dilke termed 'a less physical than moral' connotation. The contrast with the 'Old World' had been transformed into something more than a matter of hemispheres. This vision came to be

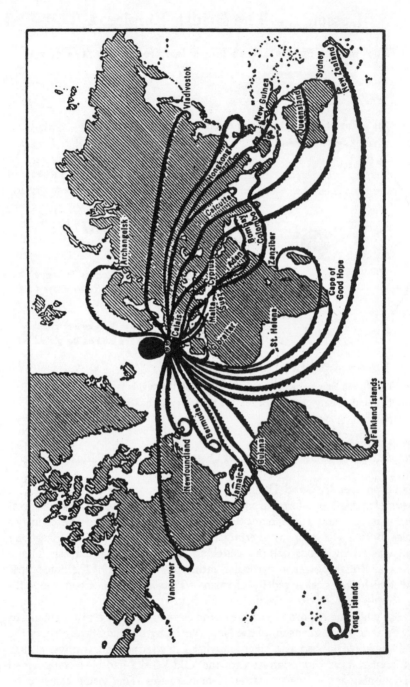

Figure 9.3 Haushofer's map of the British Empire
Source: Dorpalen, A. (1942) *The World of General Haushofer.* New York: Farrar & Rinehart

expressed cartographically in new maps depicting the centrality of America, and what Henrikson termed the American *Insula Fortunata* was depicted as being engirdled by a swathe of oceans (Henrikson, 1980: 506). Spykman's fragmentation of the World-Island so that America might remain whole recalls Dilke's observation about the 'centre of the world' (Parker, 1996: 75). The continents of the World-Island surrounding the *Insula Fortunata* were imbued with the same kind of cartographic menace in Spykman's maps (Spykman, 1944) as the Heartland later came to possess during the Cold War.

To that Northern world which centred omphalistically on Europe and America, James Fairgrieve added the great powers and the historic civilisations of Eurasia. In so doing he widened the whole geopolitical spectrum, seeing the whole as constituting a 'Northern Belt of Settlement and Movement' (Figure 8.4). This historic locus of civilisation and power was firmly centred on the temperate lands of the Northern Hemisphere, and within it lay all the great powers together with their major dependencies (Fairgrieve, 1932: 338). Both the two World Wars and the Cold War, which together took up the greater part of the twentieth century, reflected the fact that, despite that 'movement' which Fairgrieve saw as giving it an overall unity, politically the 'Northern Belt' was highly divided. While this division had begun as multipolar great-power confrontation, in its ultimate stages it had resolved itself into a bipolar one.

During the 1970s, as the bipolar world which had existed for a quarter of a century began to unravel, its geopolitical justification came to be challenged. Other world-views, until then frozen out by the Cold War, began to reappear, and the most influential of these was the centre–periphery view (Gottmann, 1980). The most significant new contribution to the centrist contention was world systems analysis. From the 1980s this came to be particularly associated with the work of George Modelski and Immanuel Wallerstein. Viewing the world as a 'system' with a basically centre–periphery structure, they proposed a totally different global scenario from that of the Cold War. This new centrism was part of what can best be described as 'planet earth' thinking which arose from an increasing realisation that the most important contemporary issues were those which confronted humanity as a whole and were too large for any one country and too complex for any one ideology to tackle successfully. They were interlinked and related in a variety of ways to the relationship of mankind to the world as a whole and, in this context, terms such as 'natural' and 'organic', which had been current in the early part of the century, began to creep back. Important among the issues which now came up for examination was the rapid depletion of the world's finite resources and the very real possibility of the exhaustion of many of them within the foreseeable future. This led on to the question of the inordinately large share of these resources being used up by the countries of the developed world, which in turn pointed to the extremes of global wealth and poverty that continued to exist a generation after the European empires had been replaced by the independent states in Africa and Asia.

It has been demonstrated that during this period global economic inequality had increased rather than diminished and this had produced what Braudel termed 'a discriminatory geography' (Braudel, 1984: 39). With the increased integration of the planet 'the most advanced are dependent on the most backward and vice versa: development is the reverse side of underdevelopment' (*ibid.*: 70). Consequently a large section of the globe, containing the majority of its people, was relegated to the periphery of a system which was designed to channel the greater part of the world's wealth towards the centre. By the 1970s this was seen to be hardening into a pattern of development and underdevelopment which split mankind into haves and have-nots on a global scale (Sweezy, 1974: 143). The realisation of this imbalance was one of the prime causes of the beginnings of the geopolitical paradigm shift from the perception of a world divided by ideological confrontation to that of a world divided by differences of wealth. Peter Taylor saw the effect of Wallerstein's approach as putting the North versus South conflict 'at the centre of the stage' in place of the East versus West conflict (Taylor, 1981: 166).

In the light of the dawning realisation that one of the most fundamental problems was global inequality, the Cold War confrontation came increasingly to be seen as not only an irrelevance but, as a result of the arms race which it had encouraged, a profligate waster of valuable resources. Scientific research was beginning to identify the use of raw materials such as fossil fuels as a major cause of damage to the environment. This came into focus on overarching themes such as that of 'global warming' which encapsulated the twin issues of the waste of resources and the irreversible damage to the environment which was beginning to take place.

With the questioning of the assumptions underlying the Cold War came also a questioning of the assumptions underlying the nature of that geopolitical world produced by it. These were based on the belief that there existed an irrevocable and permanent split between two great centres of power each holding to an ideology which was incompatible with the other. The differences between the two in a great variety of ways was judged to be so great that the term 'worlds' had been invoked to describe them. The term 'world', much used in the past to describe those geographical regions remote from the Western ecumene, had been transferred to the great ideologies, which were seen as being virtually geographical phenomena possessing the kind of permanence associated with the physical features of the world's surface. Even those, like Cohen, who appreciated its dangerous and stultifying effects were not able to shake it off. Despite the new perception of a more fluid international situation, the ghost of the two worlds remained in concepts such as 'geostrategic regions' and 'blocs' .

In order to be effective in addressing the new set of issues, peri- and post-Cold War thinking needed to free itself from the 'two worlds' ideological baggage. This came about through the interdependence within a finite space implied in 'planet earth' ideas and the scotching of the Cold War myth of the 'mighty opposites' in a divided planet. The truth was increasingly seen to be otherwise. The USA and the USSR had never been equals, said Agnew, and the USA had been 'the one true superpower of the post-World War II geopolitical world order' (Agnew, 1993: 210). The Soviet Union's economy had always been far smaller and far less technologically advanced than that of the United States and the other major Western powers; the same imbalance also applied to the overall power and resources of the two blocs. The weakness of the Soviet bloc had been masked by its huge military expenditure and the inordinately large share of its overall resources which was channelled into its military–industrial complex. As the balance of terror began to abate, the underlying superiority of the West became ever more evident, and this pointed increasingly towards the existence less of 'mighty opposites' than of a single world centre. The rationalisation of this took the form of world-systems analysis.

A system can be defined as being a grouping of related elements organised for a purpose. The systems approach consists in the analysis of physical and social systems with a view to understanding the workings of complex and dynamic situations in broad outline. In *Explanation in Geography* David Harvey judged systems analysis to be 'a convenient calculus for examining geographical problems' (Harvey, 1969: 142). By the 1970s the systems approach in the social sciences was being applied to the field of international relations. Among the most important pioneers of this were Harold and Margaret Sprout, who explored the role of what they called the 'milieu' (environment) in international politics and advocated a more holistic approach to international relations through the linking together of economic, political, international and geographical factors (Nijman, 1994: 221–2). This approach centred on the 'ecological triad' based on the actor–environment relationship which derived from 'opportunity' (possibilities) and 'willingness' (capabilities). Based on the principle of systemic interdependence, this was grounded in an ecological view of the natural and human world as consisting of a single functioning whole.

While systems analysis has a wide application in geopolitics and political geography, the main objective of this chapter is to assess its importance in the development of the contemporary centre–periphery world-view. The basic proposition of world systems analysis is that there is indeed a world system which operates as a functioning whole. This system dates from the opening up of the world by the Europeans in the sixteenth century and the great economic and political expansion which then followed from this. This expansion resulted in the creation of that European 'world-economy' which from then on dominated all the other 'world-economies', increasingly absorbing them, or parts of them, into its extended sphere. The most fundamental spatial characteristic of the new situation was that it was based on a centre–periphery structure. Braudel demonstrated how in the sixteenth century the conflicts within the European world entered a larger dimension, and the North Atlantic became the centre of the power struggle for hegemony on a global scale. 'The Atlantic Ocean,' asserted Braudel, had become 'the new centre of gravity of the world' (Braudel, 1972: 678). The power of this particular region subsequently became entrenched into a global hegemony which developed successively into the focus of the world's commerce, industry, imperial power and, finally, of the globalisation process itself.

While both Modelski and Wallerstein have engaged in world-systems analysis, and Braudel's historical survey of *le temps du monde* (the world perspective) has been systems-based, there have been significant differences in the conclusions which each of them has reached.

Modelski approached the whole question from an international relations perspective and in so doing 'discovered a symmetry to international politics that is the very antithesis of anarchy' (Taylor, 1993a: 65). His proposition is that there is a global political system which is autonomous of other systems. It is subject to constant change, and this manifests itself as 'a recurrent pattern' (Modelski, 1978: 214). Since the global system came into being in the sixteenth century it has taken the form of a succession of 'long cycles', and from then on it has become possible to talk of world power as opposed to the more geographically limited power of earlier times (Modelski and Thompson, 1988: 97–132). The cycles have centred on a succession of states which have been 'entities uniquely dominant in the global system' and which have acted as the motors for change within it. Modelski called these 'world powers', and he regarded the urge to create a world order as arising from an innate will to power (*ibid.*). As the global connections were brought into being by the use of the sea and by the deployment of sea power, world powers are essentially maritime powers. He distinguished between global powers, which had a wide maritime reach beyond Europe, and true world powers which attained at a given time a commanding position within the system (Table 9.1). According to Modelski, there have been four such powers: Portugal, the Netherlands, Great Britain and the United States. Modelski and Thompson contended that Spain was never a real world power in this sense and France was prevented by Britain from developing a world role and had to settle eventually for a regional pre-eminence limited to North and West Africa.[5] The fact that France, despite its considerable resources, was not able to achieve global pre-eminence was attributed in part to the oscillations in French regional and global priorities, and France is thus considered to be a global power whose 'drives wobbled' (*ibid.*: 246). The rise and fall of the world powers is attributable to intra-systemic changes in patterns of trade, industrial development and technological advance. Observing that 'In every known system order is continually lost', Modelski demonstrated that structures run down and have to be reconstructed, and this reconstruction takes the form of cyclic change (Modelski, 1978: 225). He maintained that 'The essence of global power ... is functional network control.' As the world order of a particular cycle breaks down it will be followed by a period of disorder and conflict which will eventually give birth to a new world

Table 9.1 World powers and global powers: the long cycles of conflict

Long cycle	Global war	Participating powers
1	Italian and Indian Ocean Wars, 1494–1516	**Portugal**; Spain; England; France
2	Dutch and Spanish Wars, 1580–1608	**Netherlands**; England; France; Spain
3	Wars of Louis XIV, 1688–1713	**Britain**; Netherlands; France; Spain; Russia
4	Napoleonic Wars, 1792–1815	**Britain**; Russia; France; Netherlands; Spain
5	World Wars I and II, 1914–45	**United States**; Britain; France; Russia; Germany; Japan

Note: World powers are printed in bold type
Source: Based on 'Long cycles and global wars', in Modelski, G. and Thompson, W.R. (1988) *Seapower in Global Politics, 1494–1993*. London: Macmillan.

order built around a new world power (*ibid.*). The 'long cycle' is the period associated with the dominant position of one particular power, each normally lasting for around a century, after which control is increasingly lost and a new cycle will then begin. Justifying this time-scale, Modelski asserted that 'A century is the life of about three generations, and if we were to look within each cycle for evidence of a Buddenbrooks syndrome we might say that one generation builds, the next consolidates and the third loses control' (*ibid.*: 232).

While Modelski emphasises political factors and in particular the state as the essential driving force within the world system, Wallerstein places the emphasis on economic factors, and in particular on the 'capitalist world-economy' (Wallerstein, 1984). The state is perceived as being a result rather than a cause, and it is the 'world-economy' which is responsible for the nature of the world order, and for the cycles to which it is subject at any given time. A world-economy is here defined as being an economically autonomous area of the world which is able to provide for the greater part of its needs. Composed of a hierarchy of zones each with its own particular economy, it possesses a unity which extends across political frontiers. It has a core–periphery structure, and one overarching economy dominates the whole. Core–periphery analysis seeks to explain the inequality within it and the 'the suction and force of attraction of the poles of growth' (Emmanuel, 1972: 43). Wallerstein saw the European world-economy as being the matrix of capitalism. Using the term 'hegemony' to describe that power which was at the centre at any particular time, he sees this position as being firmly based on economic supremacy. The 'hegemonic urge' related to successive waves of the world-economy. According to Wallerstein the first world power was the Netherlands rather than Portugal, and a true world-economy did not really come into being until the twentieth century. He referred to the 'hegemonic cycles' of the Dutch, British and

Americans, which related to 'three logistic waves of the world-economy'
(Taylor, 1993a: 69). His 'world-systems project' is conceived of as being an
alternative to the Marxist world-view. He did not conceive of capitalism as
being a stage in an ordered process. 'Order', he maintained, 'is not a final
outcome of the system' (Taylor, 1989: 339). Like Marx, he saw the necessity of
moving away from the capitalist mode of production but differed from Marx as
to the methods to be used in achieving this.

Taking Wallerstein's perspective as a basis, Peter Taylor asserted that 'In
world-systems analysis geopolitics is about rivalry (until very recently East
versus West) in the core for domination of the periphery by imperialism
(currently North over South)' (Taylor, 1993a: 52). He conceived of 'the world-
systems project' as being 'a history of our modern world in the "great tradition"
leading towards a kind of post-Marxist radical progressive world-view. This
presents a challenge on all fronts to capitalism, Marxism and Mackinder'
(Taylor, 1989). This also challenges that 'progressive myth' − or 'progress-
organising myth' − which underlies Western capitalism but which has failed to
tackle the question of inequality or to explain historical regression. Pointing to
the faults in Marxism, he particularly called into question Marx's view that
capitalism represented a progressive force in human affairs. Finally, he also sees
it as being a way of moving away from the continuing influence of Mackinder.
'The starting-point for almost all discussions of geopolitics is Sir Halford
Mackinder's Heartland Theory [which] remains probably the most well-known
geographical model throughout the world' (Taylor, 1993a: 53). Asserting that it
was its global scale which underlay the Heartland's 'remarkable achievement of
longevity', Taylor asserted that 'Wallerstein's world-economy approach
presents an opportunity for political geographers to return to the global scale
of analysis without paying any homage to Mackinder'. While Mackinder points
towards East–West conflict, Wallerstein 'places the North versus South conflict
at the centre of the stage'. Taylor maintained that 'The change of spatial
orientation is a direct result of the social theories being used: Wallerstein's
approach is deeply embedded in the economic base of the global situation
whereas Mackinder-type approaches only consider the workings of the political
superstructure' (Taylor, 1981: 166). The world-economy approach thus
facilitated a kind of post-Marxist radical progressive world-view sustained by
a post-Mackinder geopolitical world-view. In this way geopolitics was firmly
tied to the world-economy approach and world orders can be regarded as being
'relatively stable structures that define distinct periods of world politics'
(Taylor, 1993a: 44).

In his *magnum opus, Civilisation and Capitalism,* Braudel took issue with
Wallerstein's over-emphasis on economic considerations (Braudel, 1984: 19).
Reviewing the relevance of Wallerstein to 'the real world,' Braudel posed
Rostow's question, 'Is man in society firmly *homo economicus*?' and came back
with Rostow's answer, which was 'an emphatic no' (Rostow, 1971). Braudel
considered that Wallerstein was too rigid in his explanatory framework and

criticised him 'for letting the lines of his model get in the way of observing realities other than the economic order' (Braudel, 1984: 66). Turning to the new interest in cycles, which he called 'the return of Kondratieff', Braudel contended that many different cycles were taking place on different time-scales.[6] The longest and most important of these is the 'secular trend' to which he gave the name *la longue durée* (the long term) (*ibid.*: 76–8). This is an extended period consisting of an upward trend, a period of crisis and then a downward trend (Figure 9.4). During each successive period of *la longue durée* a dominant state arises in the world-economy. Since the thirteenth century in the capitalist world-economy this over-arching role has been successively filled by Venice, the Netherlands, Great Britain and the United States. There have also been a number of other states which have fulfilled key roles at different periods during the process. The stage on which this *longue durée* cycle takes place is the world-economy, which Braudel envisages as being 'the greatest possible vibrating surface.... It is the world-economy which creates uniformity as an arterial system distributes blood throughout a living organism. It is a structure in itself' (*ibid.*: 83). Braudel sees the European world-economy, the 'matrix of capitalism', as 'occupying strategic points and extending its antennae' out from the centre. It has been the 'conquering world-economy', and since the sixteenth century the North Atlantic area has possessed the complex conjuncture of political, economic, technological and cultural factors which has enabled it to maintain its hegemonic position in the world.

Although having its origins in systems analysis, which can be traced back to ideas current in the 1950s and 1960s, the idea of the world-economy and all that it entails for geopolitical thinking is very much a product of the peri- and post-Cold War years. As the Cold War drew towards its conclusion, the continentalist scenario of the political geographers of the immediate post-war period, which reached its most dramatic expression in the Heartland thesis, was vigorously called into question. The immense potential ascribed to the Heartland had not materialised and the spectre of Soviet power was increasingly perceived to be illusory. The collapse of the Soviet Union in 1990 appeared to be conclusive proof of this and consequently demonstrated that the associated continentalist idea had also been a false one. The Cold War image of the maritime world as a weak and scattered periphery around a powerful Soviet world centre, its strength founded on the enormous potential of the Heartland, gave place to that of a West as the centre of the capitalist world-economy and with the United States as its contemporary hegemonic power. The world had been turned inside out and the centre–periphery view now appeared more appropriate than the binary or pluralist one to describe and explain the 'new world order'.

The protagonists of the world-economy approach may have put forward quite different models to describe its functioning but, while the emphases may be different, they share a number of common characteristics. The first of these is that there exists a world system which is coherent and susceptible to rational

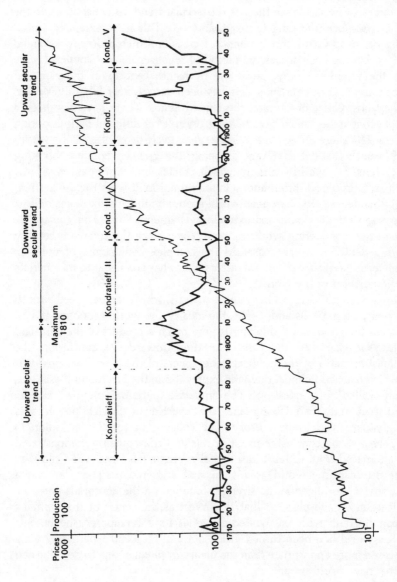

Figure 9.4 Kondratieff cycles and the secular trend. The graph, based in prices in Great Britain from 1700 to 1950, shows both the Kondratieff cycles and the secular trend. The production curve has been added.
Source: Based on Imbert, G. (1959) *Des mouvements de longue durée Kondratieff*

analysis and interpretation. It has a distinct spatial structure which comprises a core, a middle and a periphery. The core cannot be explained in terms of one set of characteristics, such as political or military ones, but has many attributes which together form a multi-faceted and complex whole. In this conjuncture 'world-civilisations and world-economies ... join hands and help each other' (Braudel, 1984: 66). The North Atlantic has been the centre of gravity of the whole system and the place from which it has been controlled. There is a cycle of growth, ascendancy and decline which has produced a succession of hegemonial powers within it. The conflicts associated with cyclic changes are what Dilke termed 'the contest for centreship' (Dilke, 1890: 70).

Does the world-economy theory, then, confute the ideas of the 'blind' political geographers of the past? The question is whether world systems analysis can produce a world-view which is really more in accordance with geopolitical reality in the *longue durée* than any of the others have done. During the 1990s it has come very much to the fore as the latest of a long line of attempts to explain the nature of the human world in geopolitical terms. However, its post-Cold War popularity may relate to a perception of its political correctness together with the fact that it appears to provide the most convincing explanation for the collapse of the Soviet Union. As with the number of legs which, in Orwell's *Animal Farm*, was deemed to be 'good', could it be a case of 'North–South good; East–West bad'? However convincing it may appear to be in the circumstances of the time, one has to beware of generalising too much and using one's generalisations as the basis for a world-view which is designed as much to justify as to explain.

NOTES

1. 'Heart' and 'heartland' are terms which have been used to describe the geographical and cultural centre of a particular state or a nation, for instance the so-called 'Hindu Heartland' in India and the respective 'heartlands' of the United States and Russia. In a more general way it is possible to talk of the 'heart' of England or of Europe. Halford Mackinder used the term 'Heartland' in a very special way to denote the land-locked centre of the largest continent (Chapter 5).
2. Central-place theory was based on the ideas of the German geographer Walter Christaller. It postulated a hierarchy of cities of varying importance, and attempts were made during the Nazi period to apply it to planning in the occupied areas of Eastern Europe. Aside from this its impact on political geography and geopolitics has been slight (Heske, 1994c: 42).
3. By the 'Perpendicular' Marlowe meant the prime meridian of longitude, which was given a number of different locations by the sixteenth-century mapmakers. It signified both centrality and power, and to 'begin' the Perpendicular in the sense used here by Tamburlaine signified the place from which his empire was to be established. It appears to relate to the use of the meridian as the line of demarcation in the division of the world between Spain and Portugal at the Treaty

of Tordesillas in 1494. According to Seaton, the map of the world used by Marlowe was that of Ortelius published in Antwerp in 1570. 'He [Marlowe] was playing a great game of chess with kings and conquerors for pieces, and for chess board the *Theatrum Orbis Terrarum*: a *Kriegspiel*' (Seaton, 1964: 55).

4.   It is interesting to note that a quarter of a century earlier Charles Dilke had taken an altogether different view. He termed it 'another Western theory – that the powers of the future must be "Continental". Germany, or else Russia, is to absorb all Asia and Europe, except Britain'. This he called 'government from the centre' which would be brought about, according to this theory, 'by the necessity under which the nations on the head waters of all streams will find themselves of having the outlets in their hands. Even if it be true that railways are beating rivers, still the railways must also lead seawards to the ports, and the need for their control is still felt by the producers in the centre countries of the continent. The Upper States must everywhere command the Lower, and salt-water despotism find its end' (Dilke, 1890: 71).

5.   The basis of the distinction between world and global powers is made quite clear. To be classified as a world power it needs to possess at least 50 per cent of the total warships, ocean-going capacity or equivalent naval expenditure. A global power need possess only a minimum of 5 per cent of these (Modelski and Thompson, 1988: 44–5).

6.   The Kondratieff cycle is named after the Russian economist who in the 1920s made an important contribution to the study of long-term trade fluctuations. The Austrian economist Joseph Schumpeter subsequently gave the idea greater precision. Braudel explains that there are many different types of movements affecting society, and the combination or conjuncture of these movements provides a truer explanation of the nature of change.

CHAPTER 10

IN ACCORDANCE WITH REALITY?
GEOPOLITICS AS PROCESS

'Geopolitics,' said Robert Walters, 'can provide a map of the world more in accordance with reality' (Walters, 1974: 202). Such 'reality' he contrasted with the distorted maps produced by the injection of political, strategic and ideological predilections into the perceptions of the world. The result of this was a Kafka-like mental map filled with uncertainties, fears and apprehensions. Its overall effect had been to substitute myth for reality and then to confuse the two. He considered that the Heartland had been one of the most influential of contemporary geopolitical myths of this sort. In this 'dreadfully ominous' world scenario, 'the Silent Castle, epitomised by the Kremlin itself, and by the Heartland, loomed overpoweringly in the dark recesses of the mind. It is no wonder that the writings of Kafka seem to reflect the atmosphere of the Cold War' (ibid.: 43). In like fashion, George Ball expressed the opinion that Americans navigated 'by a disturbed chart – like something drawn by medieval cartographers' (Ball, 1968: 7), while Henrikson drew attention to the tendency of American leaders to have 'sketched in the coast of Bohemia' when constructing their mental maps of the world (Henrikson, 1980: 497). What Walters, Henrikson and Ball were saying was that contemporary geopolitical world-views were made up more of myth than reality and in this respect they were no better than the medieval *mappa mundi*. The purpose underlying both was to legitimise systems of belief by giving them a geographical dimension and so providing a chart by which the faithful could navigate. This analogy was pursued by Blaut, who proposed 'an alternative historical atlas of the world since 1492'. He claimed that his theory of underdevelopment 'writes a different geography' and also 'redraws our *mappa mundi*' (Blaut, 1978: 309). The Peters projection (Figure 8.3b), which arose from such ideas of underdevelopment, was just what Blaut had in mind.[1]

The use of maps to sustain and promote beliefs of one sort or another has had such a long history that it is reasonable to ask whether it is at all possible to express some kind of abstract 'reality' in cartographic terms. How is one to be sure that any particular geopolitics is not subject to some form of distortion in Henrikson's sense? While Walters expressed the opinion that it was possible to construct a map which was 'more in accordance with reality', he then went on to cast doubt on this by observing that 'Any system of thought concerning geopolitics cannot exist independently of society . . . It is a matter of faith in the long run' (Walters, 1974: 174). Indeed, he went on to demonstrate that he himself was less interested in a geopolitics which was 'in accordance with reality' *per se* than one which was a more effective tool for the purpose in hand. The 'new projection' which he called for was to be 'a tool towards the shaping of policy' (*ibid.*: 202). It was ultimately not a more real world map which Walters had in mind but yet another *mappa mundi*, and one which would be more effective as a guide for the new faithful. This is a rather different objective from that of seeing things in accordance with reality.

The history of geopolitics had been littered with obstacles to seeing things as they really are. A major one has been that many of those who have been engaged in it have themselves also been active participants in the political scene of their day. Mahan and Mackinder, who were responsible for the first modern geopolitical world-views, did not exist in some kind of political vacuum. Mahan was an admiral actively involved in promoting American sea power while Mackinder was a Member of Parliament and a diplomat concerned with the security of the British Empire. The major concerns of both were with the best interests of their respective countries.

The only effective test of the credibility of any proposition or theory has to be the extent to which it conforms to observed reality. Each of the major world-views has been examined against the totality of the geopolitical scene and, on the basis of the evidence, conclusions have been reached as to its validity. Thus the protagonists of the binary world-view see bipolar confrontation as being the recurring geopolitical theme. The stage, the furniture and the actors may change but the eventual outcome was a confrontation of the Mighty Opposites. As has been seen, the long conflict between the Graeco-Roman world and the Persian Empire has been traced on through many subsequent metamorphoses to emerge in the second half of the twentieth century as the conflict of the superpowers. Its protagonists during the Cold War period then considered that this represented some kind of 'ultimate' metamorphosis into its final global form. Likewise those who propose the polycentric world-view saw some transformation of the nineteenth-century 'balance of power' on to a world scale as being the underlying reality. Whichever of these is taken as representing 'reality', an accompanying trend has been from simplicity towards complexity in geopolitical forms. When the overarching structures of the universal states collapsed, they were replaced by a proliferation of smaller states. Thus, following the breakup of the overall structure of Christendom, Europe became a collection of smaller states out of which a number of significant poles of power eventually disengaged themselves. An uneasy balance of power among them broke down as a result of one power (France) attempting to achieve a position of dominance. By the time of the Napoleonic Wars it was quite possible to detect the emergence of a bipolar world structure, but by the end of the nineteenth century this had given place again to a proliferation of powers existing in an uneasy balance and each engaged in establishing its own imperial Great Sphere. The observation of what is basically the same set of data has produced very different conclusions as to its interpretation. The place and time of the observation appears to have been a major factor in the conclusions reached and the interpretations of reality which have been put upon them.

A fundamental problem in the world-views has been the relationship between the scales of operation. Thus what was taking place within any particular region did not necessarily relate to what was taking place on the global scale. In recent times this problem has been addressed by systems analysis, which has seen the world system as originating in the Western ecumene. The advocates of the world-system approach contend that the world-economy which arose in the North Atlantic area during the sixteenth century expanded into a world-economy of truly global dimensions (Braudel, 1972). It resulted in the consolidation of a world centre which henceforth organised and dominated the rest of the world. In so doing it reduced the other world-economies to marginal status and produced a world for the first time organised along centre–periphery lines.

That world-view which originates in a particular place and time is likely to possess a particular set of characteristics which distinguish it from those of others. Walters called this 'a distinctive global outlook ... which must differ from one point in time to another' (Walters, 1974: 174). This is *mappa mundi* geopolitics and it has two distinctive features: the attempt to simplify a complex reality, and the perception of the nature of this simplified reality in terms of a particular set of ideas. Thus on the basis of what are essentially the same geopolitical criteria, world-views have been produced which differ radically from one another. Despite the essentially diachronic nature of geopolitical analysis, it has been largely on the evidence of actual situations at particular times that the favoured geopolitical conclusions have been reached. The geopolitical scene changes have invariably been accompanied by new macro-geopolitical views which are believed to correspond more closely to the new realities (see Figure 10.1, for example). Together with these global views, attempts have been made to fit regional developments into the larger picture. This suggests no ultimate situation towards which the scheme of things moves, but rather a series of scene changes each of which has its own particular logic and to which an explanatory response is required and given. Such responses have taken the form of geopolitical paradigm shifts seeking to explain and interpret the new realities. They have often complicated rather than simplified the task of reaching the objective of seeing things more in accordance with reality.

The most recent scene change has accompanied the end of the Cold War, following which the old conventional wisdom of bipolarity has given place to the new conventional wisdom of systems analysis. Although both have laid claim to being explanations of some transcending geopolitical reality, their role in practice has been to explain what has taken place and to provide a rationale

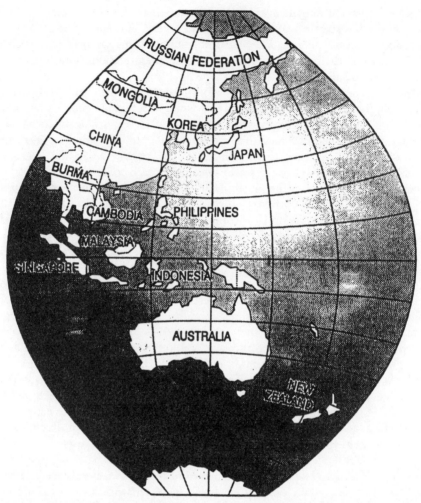

Figure 10.1 Australia's place in the world: the East Asian hemisphere. This Australian map represents an attempt to recast the country's identity, breaking free from its European past and forging a future within the Asia–Pacific region
Source: Based on official Australian sources, 1997

for the changes. The social sciences cupboard has now supplied a world systems theory which has been given a spatial dimension and a geopolitical gloss. In this way it has become the new *mappa mundi* for the 1990s.

In addition to the problem arising from the task of simplifying and providing explanations there is another problem arising from the interposition of a particular set of ideas between the observer and the observed. To Strausz-Hupé this was the attempt to reconcile the dichotomy of the 'actual' and the 'should be' with the objective of being scientific (Strausz-Hupé, 1942: 67). Wallerstein made a similar distinction between the 'scientist-scholar' and the 'apologist-advocate' (Taylor, 1989: 338). It is the problem of distinguishing between the two which has in the past produced a geopolitics which has sought to prove and to advocate in the same breath. It is in the nature of a *mappa mundi* that it seeks less to attain objective truth than to sustain faith, and it is the former rather than the latter which is sacrificed when it has been expedient to do so. Mackinder was motivated to paint his great canvas by what he saw as the need to deliver a spectacular warning to his fellow countrymen of the extreme danger in which they now lay. He clearly hoped that this would jolt them out of their nineteenth-century sense of complacency about British power. The last line of the famous triptych – 'Who rules the World-Island commands the World' – can be seen as being both a deterministic prediction and a stark statement of a worst-case scenario which had at all costs to be prevented. A quarter of a century later Haushofer, heir to Mackinder's world-view, was using the Heartland thesis as the basis of his scenario for a German-dominated world. Haushofer, the geopolitical magician, sought to conjure up a global scenario which did not exist, while Mackinder had painted a scenario which he believed to be all too real but which he sought at all costs to avoid.

The claims made for the world-views, whether they have been conceived of as being schemes, orders, biological organisms, structures or systems, have been that each one represents some kind of ultimate truth about the nature of the geopolitical world. Thus while the binary proposition has allowed for the existence of other situations, the ultimate geopolitical resolution is seen as being into the 'Mighty Opposites', and similarly the advocates of the trinary proposition see the world as being ultimately divided into 'Great Spheres'.

While one must concede that each of the major world-views contains its own set of truths, they are clearly truths which, in each case, are more apparent at certain times than at others. It is as though the world-views are not bespoke but come off the shelf, ready to be fitted to the size and shape – and fashion – required. Thus at times the world has indeed looked as if it is divided into two while at other times the scene change has made things look quite different. As Stephen Jones observed at the height of the Cold War, none of the major global views is perfect and therefore 'We need a series of filters, a composite or an eclectic global view' (Jones, 1955: 505).

One method of cutting through such seeming incompatibility and achieving some of the eclecticism advocated by Jones is to conceive of each of the views as being possible stages in an unfolding geopolitical process rather than as being absolute explanations in their own right. This approach is inherent in the diachronic developmental idea, and in it some kind of synthesis could then lead on to a more holistically based world-view. A problem of a synthetic developmental approach of this sort is the question of which – if any – of them would constitute its end-product. To concede such an end-product would risk giving further justification to one view as being the ultimate explanation of geopolitical phenomena. Since claims of this sort have been made for each of them, they cannot be easily reconciled on an equal footing. This is not to concede that the world-views are so mutually exclusive that they must always remain irreconcilable. The problem lies in linking them together into a meaningful diachronic synthesis which produces something more than the sum of the parts. Is a general theory at all possible?

The intellectual climate of the present day, in which global issues have come to the fore and the global dimension is seen as being essential in addressing them, has made it both possible and necessary to conceive of a geopolitics which is not inextricably bound up with the interests of particular states, but which is directed towards the interests of the world as a whole. A global geopolitics thus fits into wider thinking on a global scale. In view of this it should be possible to produce a geopolitics which is holistic and inclusive in a way in which the geopolitics of the past was limited and exclusive, even when addressing the global dimension. However, it would be as much folly to imagine that prejudices engendered by time and space can be totally expunged as it was in the past to have imagined that such prejudices did not exist, or rather that they existed only in the thinking of the opponents.

The alternative to a general theory derived from the competing world-views themselves is one based on a re-evaluation of the nature of the geopolitical world. The methodology used should also seek to unscramble the 'is' from the 'should be', thus discounting those past *Zeitgeists* which had such a powerful distortive effect on the formulation of concepts and theories. The overall objective is to construct a geopolitics which is 'more in accordance with' (Walters) or 'more attuned to' (Cohen) reality without the caveat that it should necessarily be of use in 'the shaping of policy'. Any practical application of the perception of this reality lies in the realms of advocacy and not of scholarship.

It has been observed that the political units which together constitute the world's geopolitical surface came in all shapes and sizes. They have varied enormously in both time and space from the very large to the very small; the insular to the landlocked; the homogeneous to the diverse; the centrifugal to the centripetal. The one feature which they do have in common is their territoriality. They all exist – or have existed – in geographical space, and their common *raison d'être* is that they represent aspirations to some form of order on the world's surface. In the fulfilment of this aspiration they have frequently grouped together in *ad hoc* fashion in order to establish limited forms of order within particular areas. They constitute the building-blocks of the world, and any form of order which comes into being on a scale higher than their own has to have their collective acquiescence.

The behaviour of states may appear to be as varied as the states themselves but their behaviour patterns resolve themselves into two overall types: the conflictual and the associative. This is the really great divide which separates categories of states and which ultimately determines the nature of the geopolitical world as a whole. It is so basic that it divides states into two distinct categories which are more fundamental than any of the other categorisations which have been applied. Either states have sought to resolve the problems inherent in their mutual existence within a defined geographical space by engaging in conflict with one another or they have attempted to resolve these problems by cooperative means. While states have engaged in both sorts of behaviour, there has been a propensity for certain states invariably to behave in a conflictual manner and for others to behave cooperatively.

Conflictual patterns of behaviour are the result of attempts to solve problems through control (hegemony, domination), and these have taken the form of attempts at territorial expansion or the establishment of territorial spheres of influence. Associative behaviour patterns, on the other hand, are founded on the desire to resolve problems without having recourse to conflict. Thus while the ultimate resolution of a conflict is the zero-sum game of winner and loser, the ultimate of associative behaviour is to agree on solutions from which the benefits are more widely spread. Both are to be found within the overall patterns of relationships and both may be found taking place at the same time. Since they are so completely different from one another they can best be understood geopolitically as being parallel processes. However, the two processes have been far from equal in their impact. It is the conflictual process which has made the greater impact on the nature of the geopolitical world, and the world political map is very much a product of the conflictual process. Conflict has been the norm in inter-state behaviour, and cooperation has been an attempt to put an end to it. The two are therefore referred to here as the Normative and the Alternative Geopolitical Processes.

The Normative Geopolitical Process is the one which results in the domination of one state over the others. Ultimately it has produced that type of state which has been referred to as 'Alexandrine' by Gottmann, 'extensive' by Goblet and *Raumüberwindende* by Haushofer. It has been an enduring theme in the ideas of Ratzel, Semple, Haushofer, Mackinder and others, all of whom have considered it as being as being a necessary adjunct to progress. Its opposite, which Joseph Goebbels referred to scornfully as a *Kleinstaatengerümpel* (rubbish of small states), was considered to be geopolitically degenerate. The argument has been that a virile and dynamic people need more room and must therefore engage in territorial expansion in order to get it; through the possession of space they gain resources and so liberate their potential.

The Normative Process in any ecumene culminates in the achievement of an absolute dominance by one state, and this then becomes the universal state. Resistance to this from within the ecumene is likely to be strongest in the peripheral regions. This resistance is likely to be most successful in the maritime peripheries as a result of the dominant state's relative weakness in this environment and its inability to achieve complete control over it. Such resistance may prove successful in restricting the extent and power of the dominant state and in preventing its full transformation into a universal state. In so doing the maritime periphery will evolve its own power structures, and these may include the emergence of a dominant state within it. This may initially be the centre of an alliance or grouping of smaller states, but a single state is likely to emerge which attains a position of pre-eminence among them. Given the limited nature of the resources available to the maritime periphery to challenge the power of a proto-universal state within the ecumene, it will be forced to look outwards from the ecumene to find the resources which it requires. This brings about a complete change in geographical values, which has the effect of transforming the periphery into the centre of a new geopolitical entity. The pre-eminent maritime state then assumes a new importance as the centre of this geopolitical entity which it has itself brought into existence. The maritime periphery demonstrates a space-bridging capacity, and as a result of the new power which it has acquired, it itself moves into a wider position of pre-eminence. At its most powerful, the maritime periphery has the capacity to produce a state outside the ecumene which possesses resources as great as, if not greater than, those available to the proto-universal state within it. Although so very different in its origins and political character, such a maritime imperial state can develop geopolitical characteristics very similar to those of the proto-universal state itself. The patterns of behaviour of the two are also likely to be in many ways similar and, excluded from the territory of the ecumene, the maritime state may seek to create its own territoriality within other ecumenes. As a result, its relationship to its own ecumene is likely to be a far more detached one than that of the proto-universal state. In addition to this, the fragmentation of its territories may contribute to its premature breakup or at least to an internal weakening. The centripetal structures associated with the proto-universal state are likely to give place to centrifugal ones, and as a result a wider distribution of power develops within it.

Thus the dominant power of the maritime periphery is unlikely to be able to attain a position of such absolute dominance as that of the continental power. Large areas are likely to remain outside its territorial grasp, and within these it relies for its power more on establishing a sphere of influence than on territorial control. In these circumstances, hegemony is a term more appropriate than dominance to describe its position. Finally, the maritime world has proved to be most effective at the creation of wealth and, in these circumstances, the hegemonic state may eventually have greater power at its disposal than does the dominant state. This advantage could be negated both by centrifugal tendencies and by the relative weakness of a maritime state in relation to the ecumene itself. It is not easily able to prevent the buildup of power within the ecumene, a power which, once established, may then challenge its own maritime pre-eminence. The continental dominating state, on the other hand, possesses greater possibilities for sustaining its power within the ecumene, and its powerful centripetal structure delays its eventual fragmentation.

While Stage 1 in the General Geopolitical Process thus consists in the bid by one state to achieve a position of dominance over the ecumene, Stage 2 consists in two large powers, or power groupings, in confrontation with one another (Figure 10.2). One of these draws its strength from the continental interior while the other does so largely from the exterior. This is the situation of two pre-eminent powers, a situation which has come into being periodically from ancient times to the Cold War. In Stage 3 the dominant and hegemonial powers weaken and one or both of them will begin to fragment. Such fragmentation produces a number of smaller states which seek to establish a balance among themselves until such time as the next bid for dominance takes place. This bid could result from the metamorphosis of one of the former great powers, such as Russian Empire into the Soviet Union, which then assumed what are basically the same objectives as those of its predecessor. Alternatively it could result from the emergence on the scene of a completely new state, such as Prussia's transformation into the German Empire, which then challenges the existing powers for a position of dominance.

The propositions underlying the Normative Geopolitical Process can thus be summarised as follows: that there is a process which has normally unfolded in a certain manner. This has been recurrent and has taken a number of different forms. When the final stage is achieved, the process then comes to an end and it will begin all over again only if and when the universal state collapses. The length of time which the whole process takes is variable depending on the circumstances of the particular time and place. It certainly contains what Braudel refers to as the Buddenbrooks syndrome of growth and success followed by decline. The attempts by dominant and hegemonial powers to arrest their decline and fall constitute a feature of the final stage of the process. This 'Buddenbrooks geopolitics' arises from what Barbara Tuchman called 'Humpty Dumpty folly', since it was, she maintained, as futile as attempting to reconstruct a broken egg (Tuchman, 1984). The time which the process takes to fulfil itself from one recurrence to the next can most appropriately be thought of in terms similar to those of Braudel's *la longue durée*. The process begins on the scale of a single ecumene but may then expand spatially. While not entirely absent from the other ecuemenes, it has been most in evidence in the Western ecumene, which, as we have seen, has a different set of geopolitical characteristics from those of the others. Those 'new worlds' into which it has moved have enabled both extensions of territory and extensions of the process to take place. The space–time continuum contains within it the possibility of radically different perceptions of the reality which is to be addressed and understood. The territorial expansion identified by Ratzel and Semple as producing new challenges to national greatness can also have the effect of producing new ideas on the solution of those problems which have in the past involved the search for such 'greatness'.

The Normative Geopolitical Process is most in evidence when the great powers are themselves at their strongest. When they are weaker, the operation of the Normative Process is itself weakened, and it is at such times the Alternative Geopolitical Process is likely to be strongest. This is associated with the attempts by smaller states both to maintain their independence and at the same time to establish an overall order. Because of their limited size and power,

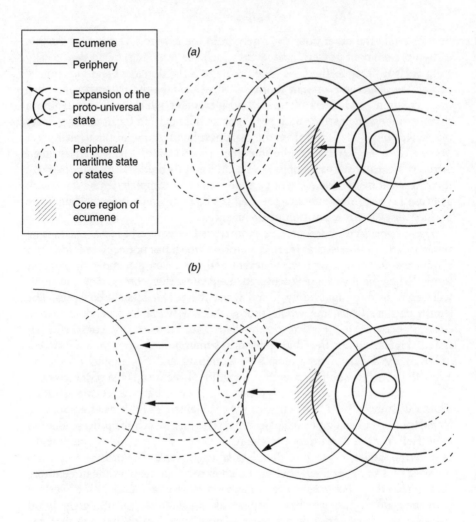

Figure 10.2 The Normative Geopolitical Process: (a) Stage 1: the territorial advance of the proto-universal state (b) Stage 2: the reaction of the maritime periphery

an overarching order which is mutually beneficial is most likely to be brought about by association. The development of associative structures of this sort is most in evidence during the interglacial periods in the international scene. It is during such periods that rigidity is most likely to give place to flexibility and greater possibilities exist for alternatives to control and domination.

The most important examples of the Alternative Process in modern times in the Western ecumene have been the associations of city-states in early modern Europe. They came into being during that gap between the decline of the medieval empires and the rise of the state-nations. Prominent among them was the Hanseatic League of Northern European city-states centring on the North Sea and the Baltic.[2] It flourished during the period between the decline of the Holy Roman Empire and the emergence of powerful territorial states, notably Sweden, Poland and Prussia (Pounds, 1990: 205–6). It, like similar associations elsewhere in Europe, was highly successful in facilitating trade over a wide area and establishing order within it (Rokkan, 1997: 37–58). Similar city-state formations had been characteristic of the European macrocore itself before the modern great powers took it over (Williams, 1985: 112–15). This city-state system centred on the Rhinelands and it functioned at a time when the Rhine was a routeway rather than a barrier for the peoples living around it (Demangeon and Febvre, 1935). The rise of the territorial states was linked to the decline of a system which had proved to be highly successful (Goblet, 1936: 59–68). The main weakness of the city-states was that they were not able to defend themselves against the new territorial states, which were able to incorporate them within their boundaries and divert their wealth into the furtherance of their own objectives. These objectives usually included further territorial expansion, and the wealth of the cities was therefore diverted towards the enhancement of the power of those states which had supplanted them (*ibid.*). They also themselves assumed certain features of the Alternative Process and used these for their own benefit.

Inter-state relationships in Western Europe since 1950 have been more characteristic of the Alternative than the Normative Geopolitical Process. The operation of the latter was brought to a halt by the fall of the great powers of continental Europe during World War II. Until then their efforts had been directed towards securing dominating or hegemonial positions both in the Western ecumene and in the world as a whole. The associative principle has underlain the European Community, which has been the principal heir to the early-twentieth-century ideas involving grouping and union. It is also in many ways the heir to the Hansa and other associations of small states. Its fundamental objective has been the transfer of power from the territorial states and to a supra-state body. The basic thesis lying behind this, as developed by Jean Monnet, is that the capacity of the states to behave in the way in which they had done in the past would in this way be curtailed if not entirely removed (Parker, 1983: 1–17). The underlying idea is of disaggregation from the existing centres and the transfers of power both upwards to the supra-state level and downwards to the sub-state level. The basic idea of subsidiarity contained in the Maastricht Treaty is thus essentially a manifestation of the Alternative Process.

By the 1980s it had become evident that some of the more powerful of the territorial states, erstwhile great powers on the European and world stage, had increasing reservations about the continuation of integration, in other words about allowing the Alternative Process to run its course. In many quarters there has been a clearly enunciated desire to reactivate the General Process in some new form. The idea of a European superstate in a world of superstates certainly accords with thinking of this sort. The territorial expansion of a superstate is a very different thing from the expansion of the 'community' idea, which was very much in the minds of its founding fathers. This may be the modern version of the difference between *Anschluss* and *groupement*.

The Normative Geopolitical Process, based as it is on the assertion of power, has thus generally prevailed over the Alternative Geopolitical Process. The latter has flourished only when the former has been weak. It has had a chance only during the periods of the temporary withdrawal of great-power influence. Otherwise it has survived only in those places such as mountains and maritime fringes which have proved to be relatively inaccessible to the great powers. This Process has been able to continue only until the revived territorial states have rediscovered the capacity for the consolidation of power. Central to this has been securing control over the macrocore, strategically located in relation to the communications network, and with this the possession of the necessary economic power to re-establish control. While typified by Ancel's *Musspreussen*, the earlier attempts by Spain's Philip II and France's Louis XIV to secure the Rhinelands had, when viewed geopolitically, precisely the same objectives.

It has been the objective of the great powers of every age to make the Normative Process prevail over the Alternative Process, and in doing this they have frequently themselves used elements of the Alternative Process in order to facilitate the attainment of their goals. Thus empires have been called nations; territorial expansion has been called national defence; and the imposition of control has become the dissemination of a superior civilisation. The Normative Process masquerading as the Alternative Process has been a recurrent feature of the attempts by great powers in modern times to maintain and enhance their positions.

The processes outlined here represent different ways in which the question of order can be addressed. Either it is by means of control exerted from one centre or it is by means of agreement by many. The achievement of the former entails conflict while the latter entails cooperation. While the Normative Process has generally prevailed, there have been times when this has not been so. It is at these times that it is more possible to discern the existence of the Alternative Process and of the possibilities which it holds for non-conflictual solutions to problems.

NOTES

1. The Peters Projection, invented by Arno Peters of Hamburg, was adopted during the 1980s by Oxfam, United Nations relief agencies and other world organisations as their favoured cartographic image and world-view. It represents arguably the most important advance in popular cartographic imagery since the Mercator projection. It focuses on the inter-tropical world – the 'South' – in much the same way as the Mercator projection, long favoured by the imperial powers and especially by Britain, focused on the 'North'.

2. 'Hansa' is the Old High German for an association. Established in the fourteenth century, the Hansa of cities consisted mainly of trading cities located around the North Sea and the Baltic. Its nominal head was Lübeck, where its deliberating body, the *Hansetag*, met. While it was basically a trading organisation it also had its own defence force. 'Hanseatic League' is strictly speaking tautological, although it is generally used in English.

EPILOGUE:
PURE AND APPLIED – THE FUTURE OF GEOPOLITICS

Twenty years after Kjellén's death, Edvard Thermaenius expressed the opinion that Kjellén 'had created something completely new and original' and that this was 'the true science of the state as a spatial unit' (Haggman, 1988: 12). Sir Peter Medawar defined science as being the art of the soluble, and he saw problem-solving as being its main function (Medawar, 1967). However, there is a fundamental distinction in science between the pure and the applied; between the objective analysis of data and the subsequent application of the results of the analysis. It is this essential distinction which has so often been blurred by those who have sought to use geopolitics, and often political geography as well, in support of a particular agenda. In his *Apologie der deutschen Geopolitik*, written during the last years of this life, Karl Haushofer clarified the distinction between the two and admitted that he had himself often transgressed the boundaries between them (Chapter 3). In many ways Haushofer has been made to carry the responsibility for what was also widely done elsewhere. In this connection, Walsh commented that it was not the general fact of the 'use' of geopolitics which was objectionable but the specific purposes for which the German geopoliticians had used it.

If the contention is made that geopolitics is a science, then geopolitical science must be about the study of an objective 'reality' which exists and is subject to analysis and explanation in much the same way as other objects of scientific study such as the weather or the rotation of the planets. It must also be possible to generalise and to discern repeating patterns since, as Vallaux pointed out, 'there can be no science of the particular' (Vallaux, 1911).

This, of course, poses the central problem that the subject matter of geopolitics is not a natural but a human creation. The spatial objects which are the raw materials of geopolitics, and which have their own structures and combine together to make new ones, are in reality more like other structures in the human world than those natural structures on which they have been built. The subject matter thus lies at the interface between the human and the physical. The question of human free will in a world of structures and systems was addressed by the French possibilists, who maintained that humanity had the ability to choose from the available options. This is totally opposed to that determinism which maintains that there is only one way and that humanity is bound by the structures and systems which it has itself created to follow a particular course of future action. The link between these two positions is the contention that there may be many options, but there is only one which will be successful: there may be many paths through the maze, but there is only one way to extricate oneself from it. While this may be conceded, the question which then arises is what exactly constitutes 'success' in these terms. What is the particular outcome which one would consider as constituting success?

It is clear that the kind of success which was envisaged by those who embarked upon the geopolitical project in the early twentieth century is far from being success as one would understand it today. Since the return of geopolitics in the 1970s, success has been measured by a very different yardstick. In the context of the problems faced by the human race as the twentieth century draws towards its close, the approach has been a holistic one directed towards the world as a whole rather than to the state in particular. As the planetary dimension has loomed ever larger, the state has come to be seen as being ever less relevant. The planet, as Bunge put it, was 'too small for war' but 'big enough for peace'. 'The heavenly planet', as he called it, was within reach, but in order to achieve it 'we must keep our planet human' (Bunge, 1989: 355–7). What Bunge termed 'human space' – rather than national space – is increasingly seen today as being the essential area of operation. The basic question confronting the future of geopolitics is thus the extent to which it can be successfully transposed from the state to the global dimension. This is something which is being addressed in the context of the relationship of geography and international relations in the age of globalisation (Kofman and Youngs, 1996).

It has become evident that since its inception geopolitics has meant many different things to different people. In the 1990s critical geopolitics has made an important contribution to the recognition of this fact. The object of the discourse in critical geopolitics has been to confront the reality of what geopolitics has been, while at the same time pointing to the varied possibilities inherent in its methodology. Geopolitics 'does not have a singular, all-encompassing meaning or identity,' observed Ó Tuathail; it 'is not an immanently meaningful term but a highly ambiguous and unstable concept' (Ó Tuathail, 1994: 259). He attacked the way geopolitics had been used by the Americans during the Cold War in order to justify their own position. 'Following Foucault, we can read this type of geopolitical knowledge production as a form of panopticonism, an institutionalised strategic gaze that examines, normalises and judges states from a central observation point' (ibid.: 261). Seen in this way, geopolitics is about 'advice to the prince', commented Ó Tuathail, as exemplified by Mackinder's airy cherub whispering in the ears of the statesmen at Versailles. This, he observed, is 'an archaic medieval' concept anachronistic in an age less of advisers and princes than of discourses and subjectivities (ibid.: 269).

This view of the geopolitical world is actually a view of the operation of the

Normative Geopolitical Process. The Alternative Geopolitical Process, on the other hand, is founded on the premise that it does not necessarily have to be this way (Chapter 10). The fact that the General Process may be deemed to be 'undesirable' *per se* is a value judgement which is inherent in critical geopolitics. It is a *Realpolitik* which can be countered by an *Idealpolitik* which possesses those features that it lacks. However, the Alternative Process is not a form of *Idealpolitik* of this sort since it has actually existed alongside the Normative Process and, as we have seen, at particular times it has been very much in evidence. The Alternative Process is therefore not an ideal which it is contended could or should exist but a reality which has existed, but it has a totally different ethos from that of the Great Game and the *Kriegspiel*. While Mackinder himself emphasised the central importance of paying attention to 'reality' when examining options, he also called for 'emancipation' from that geopolitical reality which had been the dominating force in the world.

Inherent in critical geopolitics is also the recognition that while there are many meanings there is a common perspective. It may be that 'geopolitical discourse in global politics is understood to be the result of perpetual geo-graphing' (Dodds and Sidaway, 1994: 518), but there is a methodology which has been common to all of them and not just to the grand strategists and game players. Critical geopolitics thus 'opens up rather than closes off' the rethinking and reconstituting of geopolitics (*ibid.*).

While critical geopolitics has analysed and deconstructed one of the particular meanings of geopolitics, the alternative geopolitics seeks to examine the alternatives which exist and have existed. This alternative geopolitical project was inherent in Goblet's idea of turning geopolitics from alchemy to experiment (Goblet, 1936). The possibilities for an experimental geopolitics of the sort which he had in mind appeared to be promising in the League of Nations atmosphere of the 1920s, but in that increasingly nationalistic 'twilight' of the 1930s they were overshadowed by the return of normative geopolitics. With the end of the Cold War, the possibilities for alternative geopolitics have, for a time at least, once more presented themselves.

The different meanings of geopolitics, as Ó Tuathail observed, do not imply ontological distinctness. The meaning originally given to it by its founder accords well both with the subject's scientific credentials and with the project of finding solutions to contemporary problems. In this respect modern geopolitics has returned to first principles. Kjellén identified the central importance of territory in understanding the behaviour of states. Sidaway sees the present as being characterised by ' "hypermobility" and (ultra) rapid response which is – reducing – or at the very least dramatically reconfiguring – the significance of territory' (Sidaway, 1994: 491). Reconfiguring the significance of territory may be the major task which now confronts geopolitics as the millennium approaches. What Semple called 'the solid earth' can still have a central role in giving humanity the necessary points of reference in the age of cyberspace and globalisation.

GLOSSARY OF GEOPOLITICAL TERMS

Note

Many of the terms in this Glossary are known and used in other disciplines. The definitions given here refer specifically to the sense in which they are generally used in geopolitics and political geography. All are terms which are used in this book. A far wider range of geopolitical terminology, together with biographical notes on the major geopoliticians and political geographers, is to be found in the *Dictionary of Geopolitics*, edited by John O'Loughlin (Greenwood Press, 1994). This reference work should be used when fuller information is required.

Terminology which is of non-English origin is identified as follows: French = Fr; German = Ger; Italian = It.

Anschluss (Ger)   Takeover or annexation of one country, or part of a country, by another. The best known example of this was the occupation of Austria by Nazi Germany in 1938 and its incorporation into the Third Reich. The term was also used by certain French political geographers to denote the process of piecemeal takeover which characterised the expansion of Prussia within Germany during the nineteenth century.

Axis   Geometrical and mechanical term for a line through the centre of a construction; adapted politically to mean a link or alliance between two or more states. The metaphor was first used in 1936 by Benito Mussolini to describe the collaboration between fascist Italy and Nazi Germany. This 'Rome–Berlin Axis' was joined subsequently by Japan, and the term 'Axis Powers' was applied to this group of three powers during World War II.

Boden (Ger)   Ground, soil. Geopolitically this has the sense of a geographical area occupied by a particular population group which possesses a common identity. Such an identity includes a number of different attributes, the precise geographical extent of which may vary. This has been very much in evidence in the case of Germany, a fact which can be traced to the indeterminate physical character of the space occupied by that country in the heart of Europe and the problems which have arisen from this (see *Mitteleuropa*). Particular attributes include the *Volksboden* (people or race), *Kulturboden* (culture), *Sprachsboden* (speech) and *Reichsboden* (state). The principal objective of state policy was seen as being the harmonisation of these into a single cohesive national entity. This underlay the adoption of an expansionist foreign policy.

Brandt Report   See Chapter 8, note 7.

Buffer zone   Area lying between the spheres of influence of two or more powers and acting as a cushion between them. The idea was developed by Lord Curzon in relation to the British and Russian spheres in Central Asia in the late nineteenth century, and after World War I in eastern Europe between Germany and Russia. See also *Cordon sanitaire*, Crush zone.

Central Europe   See *Mitteleuropa*.

Centre–periphery analysis   This is based on the idea that every geopolitical formation has a centre which is the principal focus of its wealth and power and the dynamo of its development (see Core region). Balancing this is a periphery which is altogether poorer and dependent on the centre. Between the two is an intermediate zone which possesses some of the characteristics of both. The core and the periphery represent the extreme parts of a mutually interdependent unit insofar as the centre is dependent on the resources (physical and human) of the periphery and the periphery is dependent on the resources (economic, technological and financial) of the centre. In recent times the concept has been extended into the idea of a world organised along centre–periphery lines. In this the global centre is considered as being in the Northern Hemisphere, particularly the North Atlantic area, while the global periphery is in the South and East (see North and South; World-economy).

Cold War   The situation of non-military confrontation between the Western and Communist blocs which existed for nearly half a century following the end of World War II. The growing hostility between the three principal Western powers and their former ally the Soviet Union intensified following the enunciation of the Truman Doctrine in 1947, and did not begin to abate until after the death of Stalin in 1953. However, despite some amelioration in relations, the confrontation persisted and remained the central feature of international relations until the collapse of the Soviet Union followed by the disintegration of the Communist bloc in the early 1990s.

Containment   Strategy adopted by the United States in the 1950s and associated particularly with the ideas of George Kennan. It became an important feature of the strategy of the Cold War (q.v.) and through the building up of military alliances it was hoped to prevent the further territorial expansion of the Soviet Union and of communist ideology. It was underpinned geopolitically by ideas deriving from Halford Mackinder and, in particular, the theory of the Heartland (q.v.).

Cordon sanitaire (Fr)   Originally meaning a line of sentries posted along a boundary to restrict movement so as to prevent the spread of infectious diseases, this term came to signify a zone around the frontiers of a state set up to prevent or discourage its further expansion, or a zone between two states designed to keep them apart. Such a zone usually contains a number of small states which themselves have a vested interest in the maintenance of peace. The classic example of such a *cordon* was in Central and Eastern Europe between the two world wars. It represented an attempt by France and Britain to keep Germany and Russia apart while at the same time using it as a base for the spread of Western influence. During the 1950s the Western powers, concluding that the Soviet Union was an expansionist state, adopted the policy of containment (q.v.) and established a *cordon* in the Middle East, consisting of Turkey, Iran and Pakistan. These were the 'northern tier' of Middle Eastern states and its purpose was to prevent the spread of Soviet influence into the economically vital Persian Gulf and the strategically vulnerable eastern Mediterranean (see Buffer zone; Crush zone).

Core region   The nucleus or central area of a state. It is necessary to distinguish the historic core, from which the state originally developed through territorial expansion, from the modern core which is its present centre of gravity and is likely to contain its major political, economic, financial and cultural centres. The historic and modern cores may coincide territorially, but in many cases they are now quite distinct.

Core–periphery analysis   See centre–periphery analysis.

Critical geopolitics   Contemporary school of geopolitics which aims to confront the reality of what geopolitics has been and to distance contemporary geopolitics from the state-centred approaches. The objective of the discourse is to point to the varied possibilities inherent in the methodology and in so doing to open up the subject for the analysis of contemporary situations and issues.

Crush zone   Used by James Fairgrieve for that 'zone of states' lying around the fringes of the Heartland (q.v.). The most important of these states lie in Eastern Europe, the Near East and the maritime regions of the Far East. According to Fairgrieve 'it has included at various times Finland, Sweden, Norway, Denmark, Holland, Belgium, Luxembourg, Switzerland, Poland, the Balkan States, Persia, Afghanistan, Siam and Korea'.

Domination   In the geopolitical sense this is the achievement of a position of power within a particular state or group of states. At its most absolute it will include economic, political, military and cultural power. The achievement of such power by one state over other states, or over a whole region, produces what is in effect an empire. (See Hegemony.)

Drang nach Osten (Ger)   Drive to the East. The historic German desire for expansion into central and eastern Europe. In the early twentieth century this was widely perceived to be a way of expanding German influence by land through the Balkans and into the Middle East, thus challenging British maritime pre-eminence. During the Nazi period it was linked to *Lebensraum* (q.v.) and entailed the acquisition of large quasi-colonial territories in the Ukraine and southern Russia in which German colonists were to be encouraged to settle. This addressed what was seen as being the problem of overpopulation in Germany itself.

Ecumene   Term coined by Derwent Whittlesey to denote the principal inhabited regions of a country or landmass. It contrasts with those areas which, as a consequence of their remoteness and unfavourable physical conditions, are not able to support more than very limited populations. The word is derived from the Greek *Oikoumene*, which signified the whole of the inhabited world. Arnold Toynbee used the phrase 'the old world *Oikoumene*' to encompass the Mediterranean and Middle Eastern regions. The term 'ecumene' as used in this book is an adaptation of this concept to the modern world scene. The 'western ecumene' is used in preference to the clumsier 'Europe–Mediterranean region'. It stands in distinction to those other 'ecumenes' of the World-island (q.v.): the 'eastern ecumene', centring on China and the Far East; and the 'southern ecumene' consisting of southern Asia.

Entente (Fr)   An understanding or friendly agreement between two or more countries on issues of common interest to them. The most famous example was the Anglo-French *Entente cordiale* of 1904 in which the former imperial rivals reached an understanding on a number of colonial issues. A similar understanding between Great Britain and Russia in 1907 gave rise to the Triple *Entente* of Great Britain, France and Russia. This opposed the Dual Alliance of Germany and Austria–Hungary, and the deterioration in relations between the two groupings led to World War I. (See *Mitteleuropa*.)

Entente cordiale   See Chapter 8, note 7.

Geopolitical equilibrium   Term used by Nicholas Spykman and developed by Saul Cohen to indicate a balance of power among countries or blocs which made for greater international stability. Cohen also used such phrases as 'dynamic balance' and 'isostatic balance of power' to indicate the possibility of periodic changes in power which would lead to a more flexible and less dangerous world.

Geostrategic regions   Term used by Saul Cohen to indicate the overall frameworks of the Western and Communist worlds during the Cold War. Within these huge and diverse geostrategic regions lay more compact and homogeneous areas termed by Cohen 'geopolitical' regions. These were Western Europe, North America, the Soviet Union and its European satellites, and China. Each of these had its own particular agenda within the overall agenda of the wider groupings to which they belonged.

Global powers   Term used by George Modelski to describe those states which at various times had achieved significant, but limited, positions of power in the world but had fallen short of a truly world role. According to Modelski these were France, Spain, Russia/Soviet Union, Germany and Japan. Together they form a category quite distinct from the true world powers (q.v.).

Great Game   See Chapter 7, note 1.

Grossdeutschland (Ger)   'Greater Germany'. Originally conceived of as being the union of all the German peoples, in the later nineteenth century it came to centre on the alliance between the two great Germanic powers, the German and Austro-Hungarian empires, in the Dual Alliance of 1878. The expansion of the Third Reich beginning with the *Anschluss* (q.v.) of 1938 briefly converted the idea into a reality. See *Kleindeutschland.*

Grossraum (Ger)   A large geographical space. In Ratzelian geographical thought, space was considered to be an essential attribute of power. The argument was that a dynamic people required sufficient territory, and the resources which it brought, in order to be able to realise their full potential.

Groupement (Fr)   The association of states by mutual agreement. A concept developed by French political geographers, it became the basic geopolitical idea behind the establishment of the European Union. It stands in contrast to the dominating principle which underlies *Anschluss* (q.v.).

Heartland   Term first used by Halford Mackinder in *Democratic Ideals and Reality* (1919) to denote the then largely inaccessible heart of Asia. It was essentially a modification and extension of the Pivot (q.v.) to the conditions which existed at the end of World War I. Although covering substantially the same area as the latter, it was considerably larger and significantly extended westwards into Europe to include the drainage basins of the Baltic and Black Seas. The Heartland concept has subsequently been scrutinised and modified by succeeding generations of geographers and political scientists. Some of them considered that it exaggerated the power of the centre of Asia, while others thought it did not stress this sufficiently. Among the former, Meinig considerably diminished both its size and its significance, while Fawcett saw it as being the springboard for an even larger Heartland extending across the Middle East and into Africa. Hooson identified it closely with the Soviet Union and used the term 'new Soviet heartland' to indicate the eastward movement of the centre of Soviet power into Asia.

Hegemony/hegemon   Terms used by Gramschi in reference to the nature and dimensions of paramount power. In the geopolitical sense, it refers to the particular state (hegemon) which holds a pre-eminent position in the global system at any given time. In this sense, Immanuel Wallerstein saw the only real world hegemons as having been the Netherlands, Great Britain and the United States. The hegemon is able to exercise wide control over the global system, but this control falls short of the exercise of total power. (See Domination.)

Hérodote   French geographical journal established in 1976 and edited by Yves Lacoste. Subtitled *Revue de géographie et de géopolitique*, it advocated a new geopolitics which would be radically different not only from the old German *Geopolitik* but also from traditional geopolitical thinking in France and the other Western countries. While acknowledging the importance of the work of

Friedrich Ratzel, Lacoste maintained that geopolitics in the sense used in *Hérodote* owes more to thinkers such as Elisée Reclus than to the 'concept hitlérien'. The return of geopolitics to an important place in the examination of world issues owes a great deal to the work of the *Hérodote* school of geographers.

Inner or marginal crescent   Term used by Halford Mackinder for the lands located around the fringes of the Heartland (q.v.). It included continental Europe, the Middle East, southern Asia and most of China. (See Outer or insular crescent; Rimland.)

Iron Curtain   The great fortified line separating the Western from the Soviet spheres during the period of the Cold War (q.v.) which divided Europe into two mutually hostile camps. The term was popularised after it had been used by Winston Churchill in a speech delivered at Fulton, Missouri, in March 1946. However, it had actually been used earlier by Joseph Goebbels, the Nazi Minister of Propaganda, and by Count Schwerin von Krosigk, who, after Hitler's suicide, was a member of the last government of the Third Reich under Admiral Doenitz. Both appear to have foreseen very clearly that, following the defeat of Germany, Europe would be divided into two hostile camps. This prediction was in line with German geopolitical thinking and, in particular, the *Mitteleuropa* strategy (q.v.).

Kleindeutschland (Ger)   'Little Germany'. This came into being after the Franco-Prussian war of 1870–71 as a result of the union of Prussia with the South German states to create the German Empire. It had been Prussia's policy to exclude Austria from this union, since the old hegemonial power of the Holy Roman Empire was considered by the Prussian Chancellor, Otto von Bismarck, to be too much of a threat to unbridled Prussian dominance. Subsequently, a movement began, both in Germany and in Austria, to bring about the union of the two countries. (See *Grossdeutschland*.)

Kondratieff cycle   See Chapter 9, note 6.

Lage   Location. (See *Raum*.)

Land power   The power to control the land and, so, effectively to achieve continental dominance. This is contrasted with sea power (q.v.) which enables a far wider range of influence to be deployed.

Lebensraum (Ger)   Literally 'living space'. A term coined by Friedrich Ratzel to indicate the territory required by a dynamic state to support its growing population. It was subsequently used by the geopoliticians of the Nazi period to justify German territorial expansion and the *Drang nach Osten* (q.v.). (See *Raum*; *Grossraum*.)

Limites naturelles (Fr)   The French concept of natural frontiers. The idea dates from the seventeenth century when it was used to justify the expansion of French territory to the Rhine. At the time of the French Revolution the 'natural' frontiers of the expanded French state were considered to be the Rhine, the Alps and the

Pyrenees. In recent times the whole concept has been criticised by French geographers both on the grounds of its inflexibility and for ignoring the dynamic relationships which exist between humanity and the geographical environment.

Longue durée, la (Fr)   Also known as the 'secular trend', this is a term used by Fernand Braudel to describe the long cycles of economic growth, development and decline which he saw as having been one of the characteristic features of a world-economy (q.v.). Each cycle was associated with a particular state which was the motor for its advance. Braudel identified Venice, the Netherlands, Great Britain and the United States as having had this role at various periods in the Western world-economy.

Macht (Ger)   Power. A concept used by Friedrich Ratzel and analysed in relation to the particular capacities of states. The concepts of *Grossmacht* (great power) and *Weltmacht* (world power) express the extent of such power. The latter is identified with those particular states *(Weltmächter)* which possess the capacity to expand their influence beyond the limits of their own particular regions and so to become global players. This in turn evokes the twin concepts of *Landmacht* (land power) and *Seemacht* (sea power), each making its own particular contribution to the power of the state.

Mainland   Term used by C.B. Fawcett for the combined landmass which Halford Mackinder called the World-island (q.v.).

Mare nostro (It)   Modern Italian adaptation of the ancient Roman imperial idea of the Mediterranean as *Mare Nostrum* (Our Sea). The term was resurrected in the 1920s by the Italian Fascists and came to be associated with their aspiration to achieve a commanding position in the Mediterranean for modern Italy. Such limited regional hegemony as Italy was able to achieve in the eastern Mediterranean in the early 1940s was soon to crumble in the face of overwhelming Anglo-American maritime power.

Midland Ocean   Term used for the North Atlantic Ocean by Halford Mackinder in his 1943 article 'The round world and the winning of the peace'.

Mitteleuropa (Ger)   Central Europe. Although basically a geographical term, it entered the realms of geopolitics as a result of its association with the German foreign policy objective of creating a strong Central Europe which would keep the powers of the powerful European maritime and continental peripheries at bay. This entailed the establishment of a close alliance between Germany and her central European neighbours. In the early twentieth century this strategy centred on the Dual Alliance with Austria–Hungary, but during the Nazi period the objective was transformed into one of securing German dominance over her smaller neighbours. Because of its geographical indeterminacy, *Mitteleuropa* has proved to be a difficult geopolitical concept to identify with any degree of precision. While it is quite clearly delimited to the north and south by the sea and the Alps respectively, in view of the fact that the major physiographic trend of the continent is from west to east, in these directions *Mitteleuropa* tends to merge imperceptibly into the other European macroregions. In spite of this, it has been contended that *Mitteleuropa* has a real unity but that this is based more on human than on physical factors. (See *Boden*.)

Monroe Doctrine   See Chapter 8, note 2.

Natural frontiers   See *Limites naturelles*.

North–South   Concept popularised by the Brandt Report (1980), which identified the great divide which exists between the rich and the poor countries. The rich were seen to be located largely in the northern hemisphere while the poor were to be found mainly in the south, although by no means entirely within the southern hemisphere. This evocative North–South concept has presented the idea of a new global dichotomy, one which is in its own way no less threatening to global stability than was the superpower confrontation of the Cold War.

Outer or insular crescent   Term used by Halford Mackinder for the global archipelago, together with its associated promontories and subcontinents, which swathes the World-island (q.v.). It includes North and South America, Australasia and Southern Africa. Significantly, it also includes the British and Japanese island groups, which were thus seen by Mackinder as being geopolitically detached from their respective continents. (See Inner or marginal crescent.)

Pan-ideen   See Pan-regions.

Pan-regions   Concept associated with German *Geopolitik* in which they were known as the *Pan-ideen*. On a far larger scale than most of the existing states, these regions were thought of as being the world powers of the future. For the most part they consisted of groups of states which were brought together under the dominance of one major power. It was envisaged that a future Far Eastern pan-region would be dominated by Japan and a European pan-region by Germany.

Peters projection   See Chapter 10, note 1.

Pivot   Term used by Halford Mackinder to describe those huge fastnesses of Central Asia which had inland or Arctic drainage. Since it possessed considerable physical resources while being out of reach of maritime power, Mackinder saw the Pivot as being the key geopolitical region in the world of his time. He first used the term in his 1904 article 'The geographical pivot of world history', and later expanded the whole concept into the Heartland (q.v.).

Raum (Ger)   Territory. Attribute fundamental to the Ratzelian concept of the state as a spatial organism. The other fundamental attribute of the state was *Lage*, location. To Ratzel, *Raum* and *Lage* together explained the nature and requirements of the state and dictated the policies which it needed to pursue in order to achieve success. While accepting Ratzel's thesis, Kjellén added a third attribute. Using the terms *Topopolitik* and *Physiopolitik* for territory and location, he added *Morphopolitik*, by which he meant the way in which the morphological characteristics (form) of the state influenced its behaviour. (See also *Lebensraum; Grossraum.*)

Realpolitik (Ger)   Political action based on the realities of the world as it is, rather than on idealistic notions of what it should or could be. In geopolitics, this means policies arising from the imperatives dictated by the nature of the geographical space occupied by the state.

Rimland   Term coined by Nicholas Spykman for those regions located around the maritime fringes of the Heartland (q.v.). This coincided largely with Halford Mackinder's 'inner or marginal crescent' (q.v.), and included peninsular Europe, the Middle East and southern and eastern Asia. Spykman considered these lands, and not the Heartland, to be geopolitically the most significant regions of the world, since they were endowed with the greatest physical and human resources and lay strategically at the junction between the continental and maritime worlds. As a consequence of this, Spykman deemed the Rimland to be the key to the balance of power, and considered it necessary for the United States to project its power into it in order to prevent its domination by a hostile state.

Sea power   The modern geopolitical idea of the importance of sea power owes much to Alfred Thayer Mahan, the American admiral who believed it to be the most important single factor explaining the success of nations and their transformation from regional into world powers. Having in mind his own country in particular, Mahan considered that it was essential for any state aspiring to a global role to build up its naval strength. Halford Mackinder interpreted world history as having been the conflict of land power and sea power, but he saw the latter as being in the more vulnerable position of the two (see Heartland). Ratzel believed that sea power possessed a unique capacity to bridge geographical space and so to be the only type of power able to achieve a truly global reach. They were *Raumüberwindende* (space-conquering), while land powers were *Raumgebundende* (space-bound). The latter were thus confined to their particular regions and could never become truly global.

Third World   A concept which originated in the idea of a 'third' geopolitical area which was not a participant in the global confrontation of the West and the Communist blocs (the First and Second Worlds) during the Cold War (q.v.). Originating in the Bandung Conference of 1955 (see Chapter 8, note 5) it came to be associated politically with the idea of non-alignment and economically with the development of the poorer countries. While, originally, consisting primarily of the countries of South and South-East Asia, with the independence of the former colonies of the European imperial powers in the 1950s and 1960s it was joined by ever more new states, and became in many ways synonymous with the Afro-Asian world. Following the Brandt Report (q.v.), it was increasingly superceded as a socio-economic concept by that of the 'South'. (See North–South.)

Volksboden   See *Boden*.

Weltanschauung (Ger)   A philosophy or outlook on life. In the specifically geopolitical sense, it refers to a complete world-view or spatial philosophy.

Weltmacht (Ger)   World power. Ratzel distinguished between regional powers which were able to secure a position of local regional dominance from true world powers whose influence extended widely and was not bound by the particular geographical region within which they were located. He believed that the attainment of such true world power necessitated the mastery of the sea. (See *Macht*; Sea power.)

World orders   Relatively stable structures which have distinct features and which define particular periods of world history. Thus the period of the Cold War was a distinct 'world order' in this sense. Following the collapse of the Soviet Union, the idea of a post-Cold War 'new world order' was enunciated. From a Western perspective this was based on the pre-eminent position of the West, which was seen as having been the winner in the Cold War. From a non-Western perspective this idea was not acceptable and during the 1990s Western hegemony (q.v.) has been challenged from many quarters.

World powers   Term used by George Modelski and others to describe those powers which at various times have been 'entities uniquely dominant in the global system'. According to Modelski, there have been only four powers which have attained a commanding position within the world system: Portugal, the Netherlands, Great Britain and the United States. The pre-eminence of each of these powers was linked to one of the 'long cycles' in the Western world-economy. World powers are essentially maritime powers, and it has been overwhelming sea power (q.v.) which has enabled them to achieve their positions of pre-eminence. They form a different category from the global powers (q.v.), the pre-eminence of which has been a more limited one. (See *Weltmacht*; world-economy.)

World-economy   An economically autonomous part of the world, within which the economy functions as an integrated whole. Such areas extend across political boundaries and possess their own internal spatial structures and dynamics. Most basic in this is the existence of a centre–periphery structure (q.v.). Fernand Braudel saw the European world-economy as the 'matrix of capitalism' and Immanuel Wallerstein has identified a Western world-economy which is the centre or core of a centre–periphery world (see North–South).

World-island   Term used by Halford Mackinder to describe the combined landmass made up of Europe, Asia and Africa.

World-systems analysis   Deriving from systems analysis, this is the examination of the world as a 'system' which is thus seen as a totality in which all the parts relate to one another and are affected by overall changes. The analysis of the totality is thus essential in order to explain the characteristics of the parts which can in this way be put into the context of the whole.

Zeitschrift für Geopolitik The German journal of geopolitics which appeared from 1924 to 1944. It was the principal forum for *Geopolitik* and its main editor throughout the greater part of this period was Karl Haushofer, the imprint of whose ideas is indelibly marked on it. During the Nazi period it came steadily more under the influence of the Nazi ideology and was increasingly used as an instrument of their expansionist and racialist policies. Haushofer, increasingly disillusioned with the Nazis, fell from favour and the journal ceased publication in 1944. It was revived between 1951 and 1968, during which time it was largely devoted to Cold War (q.v.) issues.

REFERENCES

Abdel-Malek, A. (1977) 'Geopolitics and national movements: an essay on the dialectics of imperialism', in Peet, R. (ed.) *Radical Geography: Alternative Viewpoints on Contemporary Social Issues*. London: Methuen.

Agnew, J. (1993) 'The United States and American hegemony', in Taylor, P.J. (ed.) *Political Geography of the Twentieth Century*. London: Belhaven.

Agnew, J. (ed.) (1997) *Political Geography: A Reader*. London: Arnold.

Amery, L.S. (1939) *The German Colonial Claim*. London: Chambers.

Ancel, J. (1936) *Géopolitique*. Paris: Delagrave.

Ancel, J. (1938) *Géographie des frontières*. Paris: Librairie Gallimard.

Ancel, J. (1947) *Slaves et Germains*. Paris: Armand Colin.

Antonsich, M. (1995) 'La Géopolitique méditerranéenne de l'Italie fasciste', in Coutau-Bergerie, H. (ed.) *La Pensée géopolitique navale*. Paris: Economica.

Arbatov, G. (1971) *The War of Ideas in Contemporary International Relations*. Moscow: Progress Publishers.

Bacon, F. (1924) *Essays Civil and Moral*. Letchworth: Temple Press.

Ball, G.W. (1968) *The Discipline of Power*. London: The Bodley Head.

Bassin, M. (1987) 'Friedrich Ratzel', in Freeman, T.W. (ed.) *Geographers: Biobibliographical Studies*, vol. 11. London: Mansell.

Betts, R.F. (1976) *The False Dawn: European Imperialism in the Nineteenth Century*. Minneapolis: University of Minnesota Press.

Betts, R.F. (1978) *Tricouleur: The French Overseas Empire*. London: Gordon and Cremonesi.

Blaikie, P. (1989) 'The use of natural resources in developing and developed countries', in Johnson, R.J. and Taylor, P.J. (eds). *A World in Crisis? Geographical Perspective*, 2nd edition. Oxford: Basil Blackwell.

Blaut, J.M. (1978) 'The theory of development', in Peet, R. (ed.) *Radical Geography: Alternative Viewpoints on Contemporary Social Issues*. London: Methuen.

Blij, H.J. de (1973) *Systematic Political Geography*, 2nd edition. New York: Wiley.

Bowman, I. (1922) *The New World: Problems in Political Geography*. London: Harrap.

Bowman, I. (1942) 'Geography versus geopolitics'. *Geographical Review* 32.

Bowman, I. (1943) 'Geography versus geopolitics', in Weigert, H.W. and Stefansson, V. (eds) *Compass of the World*. London: Harrap.

Brandt, W. (Chairman) (1980) *North–South: A Programme for Survival*. Report of Independent Commission on International Development Issues. London.

Braudel, F. (1972) *The Mediterranean and the Mediterranean World in the Age of Philip II.* London: Collins Fontana.

Braudel, F. (1984) *Civilisation and Capitalism,* vol. 3: *The Perspective of the World.* London: Collins.

Brecher, M. (1963) *The New States of Asia.* London: Oxford University Press.

Brecher, M. (1968) *India and World Politics: Krishna Menon's View of the World.* London: Oxford University Press.

Brunhes, J. (1947) *La Géographie humaine.* Paris: Presses Universitaires de France.

Brunn, S.D. and Mingst, K.A. (1985) 'Geopolitics', in Pacione, M. (ed.) *Progress in Political Geography.* London: Croom Helm.

Bryce, J. (1902) 'The relations of the advanced and the backward races of mankind'. Romanes Lecture. Oxford: Clarendon Press.

Bullock, A. (1983) *Ernest Bevin: Foreign Secretary 1945–51.* London: Heinemann.

Bunge, W. (1989) 'Our planet is big enough for peace but too small for war', in Johnson R.J. and Taylor P. (eds) *A World in Crisis? Geographical Perspectives,* 2nd edition. Oxford: Basil Blackwell.

Burnett, A. and Taylor, P.J. (eds) (1981) *Political Studies from Spatial Perspectives.* Chichester: Wiley.

Calleo, D. (1978) *The German Problem Reconsidered.* Cambridge: Cambridge University Press.

Carlson, L. (1962) *Geography and World Politics.* Englewood Cliffs, NJ: Prentice-Hall.

Chaturvedi, S. (1996) *The Polar Regions: A Political Geography.* Chichester: Wiley.

Chaunu, P. (1970) *La Civilisation de l'Europe classique.* (Quoted in Braudel, F. (1991) *The Identity of France.* vol. 2. trans. F. Reynolds. London: Fontana/HarperCollins.

Chéradame, A. (1916) *The Pan-German Plot Unmasked.* New York: Charles Scribner's Sons.

Chéradame, A. (1919) *The Essentials of an Enduring Victory.* New York: Charles Scribner's Sons.

Chessin, S. de (1930) *Darkness from the East.* London: Harrap.

Claval, P. (1994) *Géopolitique et Géostrategie.* Paris: Éditions Nathan.

Cobban, A. (1969) *The Nation State and National Self-Determination.* London: Collins.

Cohen, S.B. (1964) *Geography and Politics in a Divided World.* London: Methuen.

Cohen, S.B. (1973) *Geography and Politics in a World Divided,* 2nd edition, New York: Random House.

Cohen, S.B. (1991) 'Global geopolitical change in the post-Cold War era', *Annals of the Association of American Geographers,* 81(4).

Cornish, V. (1923) *The Great Capitals.* London: Methuen.

Cotterell, A. (1993) *East Asia: From Chinese Predominance to the Rise of the Pacific Rim.* London: John Murray.

Crawley, C.W. (1965) 'Modern Greece 1821–1939', in Heurtley, W.A. *et al.* (eds) *A Short History of Greece.* Cambridge: Cambridge University Press.

Cressey, G.B. (1945) *The Basis of Soviet Strength*. New York: Whittlesey House.

Crone, G.R. (1969) *Background to Political Geography*. London: Pitman Publishers.

Curzon, N.S., Lord. (1908) *Frontiers*. Oxford: Clarendon.

Darby, H.C. (1965) 'Turkish Greece', in Heurtley, W. A. *et al.* (eds) *A Short History of Greece*. Cambridge: Cambridge University Press.

Demangeon, A. (1920) *Le Déclin de l'Europe*. Paris: Payot.

Demangeon, A. (1922) 'Géographie militaire et géographie politique, à propos d'ouvrages récents'. *Annales de Géographie*, 31: 191.

Demangeon, A. (1923) *The British Empire*. London: Harrap.

Demangeon, A. (1932) Géographie politique. *Annales de Géographie*, 41: 229.

Demangeon, A. (1939) 'Géographie politique, à propos de l'Allemagne'. *Annales de Géographie*, 48: 272.

Demangeon, A. and Febvre, L. (1935) *Le Rhin: Problèmes d'histoire et d'économie*. Paris: Armand Colin.

Dewdney, J.C. (1971) *A Geography of the Soviet Union*. Oxford: Pergamon Press.

Dikshit, R.D. (ed.) (1997) *Developments in Political Geography: A Century of Progress*. New Delhi: Sage.

Dilke, C.W. (1890) *Greater Britain*. London: Macmillan.

Dobbs-Higginson, M.S. (1994) *Asia Pacific: Its Role in the New World Order*. London: Heinemann.

Dodds, K.J. and Sidaway, J.D. (1994) 'Locating critical geopolitics'. *Society and Space*, 12. 515–24.

Dorpalen, A. (1942) *The World of General Haushofer*. New York: Farrar & Rinehart.

Dukes, P. (1970) *The Emergence of the Superpowers: A Short Comparative History of the USA and the USSR*. London: Macmillan.

East, W.G. and Moodie, A.E. (eds) (1956) *The Changing World*. London: Harrap.

East, W.G. and Prescott, J.R.V. (1975) *Our Fragmented World*. London: Macmillan.

East, W.G. and Spate, O.H.K. (1961) *The Changing Map of Asia: A Political Geography*. London: Methuen.

Edmonds, R. (1991) *The Big Three*. London: Penguin.

Emmanuel, A. (1972) *Unequal Exchange: A Study of the Imperialism of Trade*. New York and London: Monthly Review Press.

Fairgrieve, J. (1915) *Geography and World Power*. London: University of London Press.

Fairgrieve, J. (1932) *Geography and World Power*, 2nd edition. London: University of London Press.

Fawcett, C.B. (1949) 'Marginal and interior lands of the Old World', in Weigert, H.W., Stefansson, V. and Harrison, R.E. (eds) *New Compass of the World*. New York: Macmillan.

Febvre, L. (1932) *A Geographical Introduction to History*. London: Keegan Paul, Trench, Trubner.

Fisher, C.A. (1968) (ed.) *Essays in Political Geography*. London: Methuen.
Fisher, W.B. (1956) 'South-West Asia: external relations', in East, W.G. and Moodie, A.E. (eds) *The Changing World*. London: Harrap.
Gallois, L. (1919) 'La Paix de Versailles: les nouvelles frontières de l'Allemagne', *Annales de Géographie*, 27: 248.
Gauss, A. (1915) *The German Emperor as Shown in His Public Utterances*. London: Heinemann.
Gilbert, E.W. (1965) Introduction to Mackinder, H.J. *The Scope and Methods of Geography* and *The Geographical Pivot of History*. London: Royal Geographical Society.
Glassner, M.I. (1993) *Political Geography*. New York: Wiley.
Goblet, Y.-M. (1936) *The Twilight of Treaties*. London: Bell.
Goblet, Y.-M. (1956) *Political Geography and the World Map*. London: George Philip.
Gooch, J. (1989) 'Maritime command: Mahan and Corbett', in Gray, C.S. and Barnett, R.W. (eds) *Seapower and Strategy*. London: Tri-Service Press.
Gottmann, J. (ed.) (1980) *Centre and Periphery: Spatial Variations in Politics*. London: Sage.
Gray, C.S. and Barnett, R.W. (eds) (1989) *Seapower and Strategy*. London: Tri-Service Press.
Gyorgy, A. (1944) *Geopolitics: The New German Science*. Berkeley: University of California Press.
Haggman, B. (1988) *Rudolf Kjellén: Founder of Geopolitics*. Helsingborg: Centre for Research on Geopolitics. Paper no. 3.
Hall, S.S. (1993) *Mapping the Next Millennium*. New York: Random House.
Hartshorne, R. (1939) The Nature of Geography. *Annals of the Association of American Geographers* 29(3/4).
Harvey, D.G. (1969) *Explanation in Geography*. London: Arnold.
Haushofer, K. (1913) *Dai Nihon: Betrachtungen über Gross-Japans Wehrkraft, Weltstellung und Zukunft*. Berlin: Mittler.
Haushofer, K. (1924) *Geopolitik des Pazifischen Ozeans*. Berlin: Kurt Vowinckel Verlag.
Haushofer, K. (1925) *Politische Erdkunde und Geopolitik*, in *Frei Wege Vergleichender Erdkunde*. Munich and Berlin: Kurt Vowinckel Verlag.
Haushofer, K. (1927) 'Bericht' *Zeitschrift für Geopolitik*, 4.
Haushofer, K. *et al.* (1928) *Bausteine zu Geopolitik*. Berlin: Kurt Vowinckel Verlag.
Haushofer, K. (1929) 'Was ist Geopolitik?' *Haushofer Nachlass* (Haushofer Archive), 834.
Haushofer, K. (1931) *Geopolitik der Panideen*. Berlin: Zentralverlag.
Hennig, R. (1917) 'Der Krieg als Forderer geographischer Bestrebungen'. *Petermanns Mitteilungen*, 12: 361–3.
Henrikson, A.K. (1980) 'The geographical "mental maps" of American foreign policy makers'. *International Political Science Review*, 1.
Hérodote, 2 (1976) 'Elisée Reclus, Hegel et la géographie'.

Hérodote, 22 (1981) 'Elisée Reclus'.

Hérodote, 26 (1982) 'Écologies/ Géographie'.

Heske, H. (1994a) 'Ratzel, Friedrich', in O'Loughlin, J. (ed.) *Dictionary of Geopolitics*. Westport, CT: Greenwood Press.

Heske, H. (1994b) 'Blut und Boden', in O'Loughlin, J. (ed.) *Dictionary of Geopolitics*. Westport, CT: Greenwood Press.

Heske, H. (1994c) 'Christaller, Walter', in O'Loughlin, J. (ed.) *Dictionary of Geopolitics*. Westport, CT: Greenwood Press.

Heske, H. (1994d) 'Haushofer, Karl', in O'Loughlin, J. (ed.) *Dictionary of Geopolitics*. Westport, CT: Greenwood Press.

Heske, H. (1994e) 'Geopolitik', in O'Loughlin, J. (ed.) *Dictionary of Geopolitics*. Westport, CT: Greenwood Press.

Hess, W.R. (1986) *My Father Rudolf Hess*. London: Allen.

Heurtley, W.A. *et al.* (1965) *A Short History of Greece*. Cambridge: Cambridge University Press.

Hitler, A. (1939) *Mein Kampf*. London: Hurst and Blackett.

Holdar, S. (1994) 'Kjellén, Rudolf', in O'Loughlin, J. (ed.) *Dictionary of Geopolitics*. Westport, CT: Greenwood Press.

Hooson, D.J.M. (1964) *A New Soviet Heartland*. Princeton, NJ: Van Nostrand.

Hopkirk, P. (1990) *The Great Game*. Oxford: Oxford University Press.

Hopkirk, P. (1996) *Quest for Kim. In Search of Kipling's Great Game* London: John Murray.

Horrabin, J.F. (1934) *An Atlas of Current Affairs*. London: Gollancz.

Johnson, R.J. and Taylor, P.A. (eds) (1989) *A World in Crisis? Geographical Perspectives*, 2nd edn. Oxford: Basil Blackwell.

Jones, E., Frost, L. and White, C. (1993) *Coming Full Circle*. Boulder, CO: Westview Press.

Jones, S. (1955) 'Global strategic views'. *Geographical Review*, 45(4).

Keegan, J. and Wheatcroft, A. (1986) *Zones of Conflict: An Atlas of Future Wars*. London: Cape.

Kennedy, P. (1988) *The Rise and Fall of the Great Powers*. New York: Random House.

Kjellén, R. (1897) *Fosterlandet och unionen*. Göteborg: Meddelanden från Fosterländska förbundet i Göteborg 5.

Kjellén, R. (1914) *Die Grossmächte der Gegenwart*. Leipzig and Berlin: Hirzel.

Kjellén, R. (1916) *Staten som lifsform*. Published in German in 1917 as *Der Staat als Lebenform*. Leipzig: Hirzel.

Kjellén, R. (1919) 'Varldskrigets politiska problem', in *Statsvetenskaplig Tidskrift*, 4.

Kjellén, R. (1920) *Grundris zu einem System der Politik*. Leipzig: Hirzel.

Kjellén-Björkquist, R. (1970) *Rudolf Kjéllen: En Mänska i tiden kring sekelskiftet*. Stockholm: Verbum.

Kliot, N. and Waterman, S. (1991) *The Political Geography of Conflict and Peace*. London: Belhaven.

Kofman, E. and Youngs, G. (1996) *Globalization: Theory and Practice*. London: Pinter.

Kolarz, W. (1946) *Myths and Realities in Eastern Europe*. London: Lindsay Drummond.

Korinman, M. (1990) *Quand l'Allemagne pensait le monde*. Paris: Fayard.

Kristof, L.K.D. (1968) 'The Russian image of Russia', in Fisher, C.A. (ed.) *Essays in Political Geography*. London: Methuen.

Kropotkin, P. (1893) 'On the teaching of physiography', *Geographical Journal*, 2.

Kwanten, L. (1979) *Imperial Nomads: A History of Central Asia 500–1500*. Leicester: Leicester University Press.

Lacoste, Y. (1976a) Editorial, *Hérodote*, 1.

Lacoste, Y. (1976b) *La Géographie ça sert, d'abord, à faire la guerre*. Paris: Maspero.

Lacoste, Y. (1979) 'Bas Vidal ... viva Vidal', *Hérodote*, 16.

Lacoste, Y. (1994) 'Yves Lacoste', *Historiens et Géographes*, 345.

Lattimore, O. (1943) 'The inland crossroads of Asia', in Weigert, H.W. and Stefansson, V. (eds) *Compass of the World*. London: Harrap.

Lattimore, O. (1948) 'Inner Asian frontiers', in Weigert, H.W., Stefansson, V. and Harrison, R.E. (eds) *New Compass of the World*. New York: Macmillan.

Lattimore, O. (1950) *Pivot of Asia*. Boston: Little, Brown.

Lavisse, E. (1891) *General View of the Political History of Europe*. London: Longmans, Green.

Legg, S. (1970) *The Heartland*. London: Secker & Warburg.

Lemert, B.F. (1948) 'The Middle East states of Iran and Afghanistan', in Pearcy, G.E. and Fifield, R.H. (eds) *World Political Geography*. New York: Crowell.

Ley, D. and Samuels, M.S. (eds) (1978) *Humanistic Geography: Prospects and Problems*. London: Croom Helm.

Lipsky, G.A. (1957) 'The position of the USSR in world affairs', in Pearcy, G.E. *et al.* (eds) *World Political Geography*, 2nd edition. New York: Crowell.

Livingstone, D. (1992) *The Geographical Tradition*. Oxford: Basil Blackwell.

Lyde, L.W. (1915) *Some Frontiers of Tomorrow: An Aspiration for Europe*. London: Black.

Mackinder, H.J. (1887) 'On the scope and methods of geography'. *Proceedings of the Royal Geographical Society*, 9.

Mackinder, H.J. (1902) *Britain and the British Seas*. Oxford: Clarendon Press.

Mackinder, H.J. (1904) 'The geographical pivot of history', *Geographical Journal*, 23.

Mackinder, H.J. (1919) *Democratic Ideals and Reality: A Study in the Politics of Reconstruction*. London: Constable.

Mackinder, H.J. (1943) 'The round world and the winning of the peace'. *Foreign Affairs*, 21(4).

MacLeish, A. (1943) 'The image of victory', in Weigert, H.W. and Stefansson, V. (eds) *Compass of the World*. London: Harrap.

Mahan, A.T. (1890) *The Influence of Sea Power upon History 1660–1783*. London: Sampson Low, Marston.

Mahan, A.T. (1900) *The Problem of Asia*. New York: Little, Brown.

Massie, R.K. (1992) *Dreadnought: Britain, Germany and the Coming of the Great War*. London: Cape.

Maull, O. (1936) *Das Wesen der Geopolitik*. Leipzig: Teubner.

Medawar, P.B. (1967) *The Art of the Soluble*. London: Methuen.

Meinig, D.W. (1956) 'Heartland and rimland in Eurasian history', *Western Political Quarterly*, 9: 553–69.

Minogue, K.R. (1967) *Nationalism*. London: Batsford.

Modelski, G. (1978) 'The long cycle of global politics and the nation state', in *Comparative Studies in Society and History*, 20.

Modelski, G. (1986) *Long Cycles in World Politics*. Seattle: University of Washington Press.

Modelski, G. and Thompson, W.R. (1988) *Seapower in Global Politics, 1494–1993*. London: Macmillan.

Muir, R. (1975) *Modern Political Geography*. London: Macmillan.

Naumann, F. (1915) *Mitteleuropa*. Published in English in 1916 as *Central Europe*. London: King.

Nijman, J. (1994) 'Sprout, Harold and Margaret', in O'Loughlin, J. *Dictionary of Geopolitics*. Westport, CT: Greenwood Press.

Nordau, M. (1993) *Degeneration*. Lincoln, NB and London: University of Nebraska Press.

O'Loughlin, J. (1994a) (ed) *Dictionary of Geopolitics*. Westport, CT: Greenwood Press.

O'Loughlin, J. (1994b) 'Monroe Doctrine', in O'Loughlin, J. *Dictionary of Geopolitics*. Westport, CT: Greenwood Press.

O'Loughlin, J. and Heske, H. (1991) 'From Geopolitik to géopolitique: converting a discipline of war to a discipline of peace', in Kliot, N. and Waterman, S. (eds) *The Political Geography of Conflict and Peace*. New Haven, CT: Belhaven.

O'Loughlin, J. and Nijman, J. (1994) 'Henry Kissinger', in O'Loughlin, J. (ed.) *Dictionary of Geopolitics*. Westport, CT: Greenwood Press.

O'Sullivan, P. (1994) 'Buffer zone', in O'Loughlin, J. (ed.) *Dictionary of Geopolitics*. Wesport, CT: Greenwood Press.

Ó Tuathail, G. (1994) 'Problematising geopolitics: survey, statesmanship and strategy', *Transactions of the Institute of British Geographers*, 19(3): 259–72.

Ó Tuathail, G. (1996) *Critical Geopolitics*. Minneapolis: University of Minnesota Press.

Pacione, M. (1985) *Progress in Political Geography*. London: Croom Helm.

Palmer, A. (1970) *The Lands Between*. London: Weidenfeld & Nicolson.

Parker, G. (1983) *A Political Geography of Community Europe*. London: Butterworths.

Parker, G. (1985) *Western Geopolitical Thought in the Twentieth Century*. London: Croom Helm.

Parker, G. (1987a) 'Demangeon, Albert', in Freeman, T.W. (ed.) *Geographers: Biobibliographical Studies*, vol. 11. London: Mansell.

Parker, G. (1987b) 'Geopolitics', in Bogdanor, V. (ed.) *Encyclopaedia of Political Institutions*. Oxford: Basil Blackwell.

Parker, G. (1987c) 'French geopolitical thought in the interwar years and the emergence of the European idea', *Political Geography Quarterly*, 6(2).

Parker, G. (1988) *The Geopolitics of Domination*. London: Routledge.

Parker, G. (1994a) 'Political geography and geopolitics', in Groom, A.J.R. and Light, M. (eds) *Contemporary International Relations: A Guide to Theory*. London: Pinter.

Parker, G. (1994b) 'Brunhes, Jean', in O'Loughlin, J. (ed.) *Dictionary of Geopolitics*. Westport, CT: Greenwood Press.

Parker, G. (1994c) 'Febvre, Lucien', in O'Loughlin, J. (ed.) *Dictionary of Geopolitics*. Westport, CT: Greenwood Press.

Parker, G. (1994d) 'Lacoste, Yves', in O'Loughlin, J. (ed.) *Dictionary of Geopolitics*. Westport, CT: Greenwood Press.

Parker, G. (1994e) 'Vidal de la Blache, Paul', in O'Loughlin, J. (ed.) *Dictionary of Geopolitics*. Westport, CT: Greenwood Press.

Parker, G. (1994f) '*Cordon sanitaire*', in O'Loughlin, J. (ed.) *Dictionary of Geopolitics*. Westport, CT: Greenwood Press.

Parker, G. (1994g) 'Vallaux, Camille' in O'Loughlin, J. (ed.) *Dictionary of Geopolitics*. Westport, CT: Greenwood Press.

Parker, G. (1996) 'Globalization and geopolitical world orders', in Kofman, E. and Youngs, G. (eds) *Globalization: Theory and Practice*. London: Pinter.

Parker, W.H. (1982) *Mackinder: Geography as an Aid to Statecraft*. Oxford: Clarendon Press.

Partsch, J. (1903) *Central Europe*. London: Heinemann.

Pearcy, G.E. and Fifield, R.H. (eds) (1948) *World Political Geography*. New York: Crowell.

Pearcy, G.E. *et al.* (eds) (1957) *World Political Geography*, 2nd edn. New York: Crowell.

Peet, R. (1977) (ed.) *Radical Geography: Alternative Viewpoints on Contemporary Social Issues*. London: Methuen.

Peterson, V.S. (1996) 'Shifting ground(s): epistemological and territorial remapping in the context of globalization(s)', in Kofman, E. and Youngs, G. (eds) *Globalization: Theory and Practice*. London: Pinter.

Pounds, N.J.G. (1951) 'The origin of the idea of natural frontiers in France'. *Annals of the Association of American Geographers*, 41.

Pounds, N.J.G. (1954) 'France and "les limites naturelles" from the seventeenth to the twentieth centuries'. *Annals of the Association of American Geographers*, 44.

Pounds, N.J.G. (1963) *Political Geography*. New York: McGraw-Hill.

Pounds, N.J.G. (1990) *An Historical Geography of Europe*. Cambridge: Cambridge University Press.

Puleston, W.D. (1939) *Mahan*. New Haven, CT: Yale University Press.

Raffestin, C. (1980) *Pour une géographie du pouvoir*. Paris: Librairies Techniques.

Ratzel, F. (1882) *Anthropogeographie*. Stuttgart: Engelhorn.

Ratzel, F. (1897) *Politische Geographie*. Munich: Oldenbourg.

Ratzel, F. (1900) *Das Meer als Quelle der Völkergrösse*. Leipzig: Oldenbourg.

Renner, G.T. (1942) 'Maps for a new world'. *Collier's Magazine*, 533.

Renner, G.T. (1948a) 'Political geography and its point of view', in Pearcy, G.E. and Fifield. R.H. (eds) *World Political Geography*. New York: Crowell.

Renner, G.T. (1948b) 'The substance and scope of political geography', in Pearcy, G.E. and Fifield, R.H. (eds) *World Political Geography*. New York: Crowell.

Rokkan, S. (1997) 'Territories, centres and peripheries: toward a geoethnic–geoeconomic–geopolitical model of differentiation within Western Europe (1980)', in Agnew, J. (ed.) *Political Geography: A Reader*. London: Arnold.

Rostow, W.W. (1971) *The Stages of Economic Growth: A Non-Communist Manifesto*. London: Cambridge University Press.

Russett, B.M. (1967) *International Regions and the International System: A Study in Political Ecology*. Chicago: Rand McNally.

Russett, B.M. (1974) *Power and Community in World Politics*. San Francisco: Freeman.

Said, E.W. (1993) *Culture and Imperialism*. London: Chatto & Windus.

Schumacher, E.F. (1973) *Small Is Beautiful: Economics as if People Mattered* London: Blond & Briggs.

Seaton, E. (1964) 'Marlowe's map', in Leech, C. (ed.) *Marlowe*. Englewood Cliffs, NJ: Prentice-Hall.

Semple, E. (1911) *Influences of Geographic Environment*. New York: Henry Holt.

Sereny, G. (1995) *Albert Speer: His Battle with Truth*. London: Macmillan.

Sidaway, J. (1994) 'Political geography in the time of cyberspaces: new agendas?', *Geoforum*, 25(4): 487–503.

Smith, N. (1994a) 'Bowman, Isaiah', in O'Loughlin, J. (ed.) *Dictionary of Geopolitics*. Westport, CT: Greenwood Press.

Smith, N. (1994b) 'Renner, George', in O'Loughlin, J. (ed.) *Dictionary of Geopolitics*. Westport, CT: Greenwood Press.

Smith, N. and Nijman, J. (1994) 'Mahan, Alfred Thayer', in O'Loughlin, J. (ed.) *Dictionary of Geopolitics*. Westport, CT: Greenwood Press.

Solch, J. (1933) 'Der Zwite Band von E. de Martonne's Mitteleuropa'. *Geographische Zeitschrift*, 39(4).

Spate, O.H.K. and Learmonth, A.T.A. (1972) *India and Pakistan*. London: Methuen.

Sprout H. (1968) 'Geography: political geography', in *International Encyclopaedia of the Social Sciences*, vol 6.

Spykman, N. (1938) Geography and foreign policy, *American Political Science Review*, 1.

Spykman, N. (1942) *America's Strategy in World Politics: The United States and the Balance of Power*. New York: Harcourt, Brace.

Spykman, N. (1944) *The Geography of the Peace*. New York: Harcourt, Brace.

Stirk, S.D. (1945) 'Myths, types and propaganda', in Gooch, G.P. *et al.* (eds) *The German Mind and Outlook*. London: Chapman & Hall.
Stoakes, G. (1986) *Hitler and the Quest for World Dominion*. Leamington Spa: Berg.
Strausz-Hupé, R. (1942) *Geopolitics: The Struggle for Space and Power*. New York: Putnam.
Sweezy, P.M. (1974) *Modern Capitalism and Other Essays*. New York and London: Monthly Review Press.
Taylor, A.J.P. (1938) *Germany's First Bid for Colonies*. London: Macmillan.
Taylor, P.J. (1981) 'Political geography and the world-economy', in Burnett, A. and Taylor, P.J. (eds) *Political Studies from Spatial Perspectives*. Chichester: Wiley.
Taylor, P.J. (1989) 'The world-systems project' in Johnson, R.J. and Taylor, P.J. (eds) *A World In Crisis? Geographical Perspectives*, 2nd edn. Oxford: Blackwell.
Taylor, P.J. (1993a) *Political Geography: World-Economy, Nation-State and Locality*. London: Longman.
Taylor, P.J. (1993b) (ed.) *Political Geography of the Twentieth Century*. London: Belhaven.
Tinker, H. (1963a) 'The family of continental nations'. London: Liberal Party Publications.
Tinker, H. (1963b) 'Democratic ideals in Asia'. Ramsey Muir Memorial Lecture, Oxford. London: Liberal Party Publications.
Tinker, H. (1989) *South Asia: A Short History*. London: Macmillan.
Tuchman, B. (1966) *The Proud Tower: A Portrait of the World before the War 1890–1914*. London: Hamish Hamilton.
Tuchman, B. (1984) *The March of Folly*. London: Michael Joseph.
Tuthill, R.L. (1948) 'The Soviet Union: a landmass power', in Pearcy, G.E. and Fifield, R.H. (eds) *World Political Geography*. New York: Crowell.
Vallaux, C. (1911) *Le Sol et l'état*. Paris: Doin.
Vidal de la Blache, P. (1898) 'La Géographie politique à propos des écrits de M. Frédéric Ratzel'. *Annales de Géographie*, 7.
Vidal de la Blache, P. (1917) *La France de l'Est*. Paris: Armand Colin.
Vidal de la Blache, P. (1926) *Principles of Human Geography*. London: Constable.
Wallerstein, I. (1984) *The Politics of the World-Economy*. Cambridge: Cambridge University Press.
Walsh, E.A. (1943) 'Geopolitics and International Morals', in Weigert, H.W. and Stefansson, V. (eds) *Compass of the World: A Symposium on Political Geography*. London: George Harrap.
Walsh, E.A. (1946) 'Wahr anstatt falsche Geopolitik für Deutschland'. *Forum Academicum*, no. 5. Schulte-Blumke.
Walsh, E.A. (1951) *Total Empire*. Milwaukee: Bruce.
Walters, R.E. (1974) *The Nuclear Trap*. Harmondsworth: Penguin.
Weigert, H.W. (1941) *German Geopolitics*. Oxford: Oxford University Press.
Weigert, H.W. (1942) *Generals and Geographers: The Twilight of Geopolitics*. New York: Oxford University Press.

Weigert, H.W. (1945) 'Mackinder's Heartland'. *The American Scholar*, 15: 43–54.

Weigert, H.W. and Stefansson V. (1943) *Compass of the World*. London: Harrap.

Weigert, H.W., Stefansson, V. and Harrison, R.E. (1948) *New Compass of the World*. New York: Macmillan.

Weigert, H.W. *et al.* (1957) *Principles of Political Geography*. New York: Appleton-Century-Crofts.

Whittlesey, D. (1939) *The Earth and the State: A Study in Political Geography*. New York: Henry Holt.

Williams, C.H. (1985) 'Minority groups in the modern state', in Pacione, M. (ed.) *Progress in Political Geography*. London: Croom Helm.

Williams, P. (1993) 'Kim and Orientalism', in Williams, P. and Chrisman, L. (eds) *Colonial Discourse and Post-colonial Theory*. New York: Harvester Wheatsheaf.

Willis, F.R. (1971) *Italy Chooses Europe*. London: Oxford University Press.

INDEX